Robert Louis Stevenson (13 November 1850 – 3 December 1894) was a Scottish novelist and travel writer, most noted for Treasure Island, Kidnapped, Strange Case of Dr Jekyll and Mr Hyde, and A Child's Garden of Verses. Born and educated in Edinburgh, Stevenson suffered from serious bronchial trouble for much of his life, but continued to write prolifically and travel widely, in defiance of his poor health. As a young man, he mixed in London literary circles, receiving encouragement from Andrew Lang, Edmund Gosse, Leslie Stephen and W. E. Henley, the last of whom may have provided the model for Long John Silver in Treasure Island. His travels took him to France, America and Australia, before he finally settled in Samoa, where he died. A celebrity in his lifetime, Stevenson attracted a more negative critical response for much of the 20th century, though his reputation has been largely restored. He is currently ranked as the 26th most translated author in the world.(Source: Wikipedia)

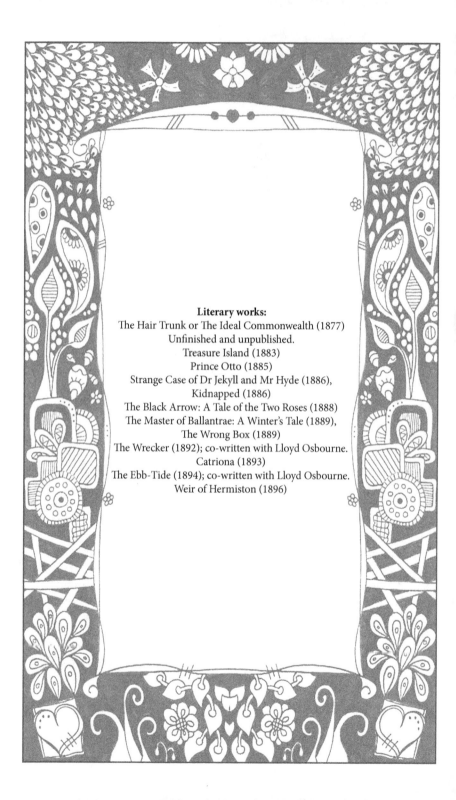

Literary works:
The Hair Trunk or The Ideal Commonwealth (1877)
Unfinished and unpublished.
Treasure Island (1883)
Prince Otto (1885)
Strange Case of Dr Jekyll and Mr Hyde (1886),
Kidnapped (1886)
The Black Arrow: A Tale of the Two Roses (1888)
The Master of Ballantrae: A Winter's Tale (1889),
The Wrong Box (1889)
The Wrecker (1892); co-written with Lloyd Osbourne.
Catriona (1893)
The Ebb-Tide (1894); co-written with Lloyd Osbourne.
Weir of Hermiston (1896)

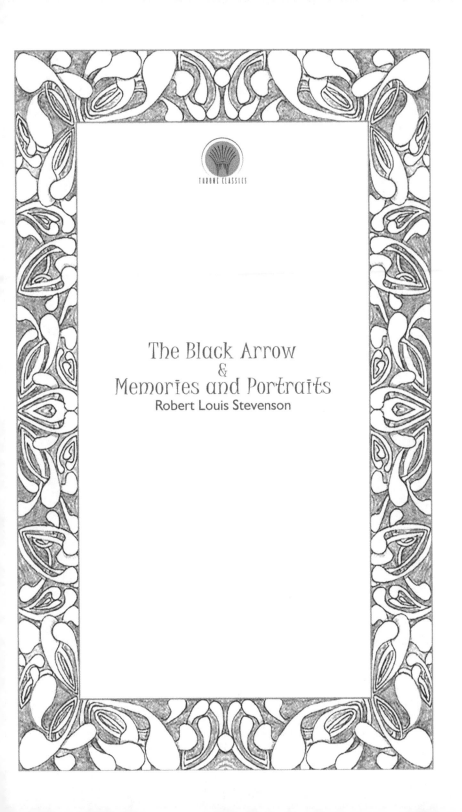

TUDUNE CLASSICS

The Black Arrow
&
Memories and Portraits
Robert Louis Stevenson

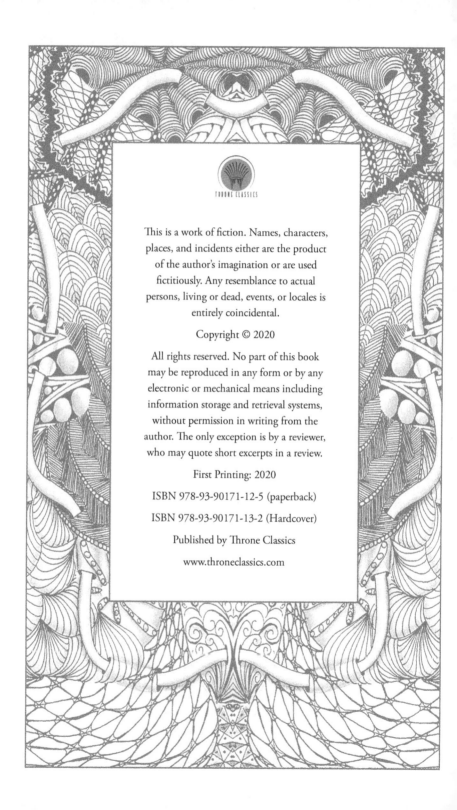

First Printing: 2020

ISBN 978-93-90171-12-5 (paperback)

ISBN 978-93-90171-13-2 (Hardcover)

Published by Throne Classics

www.throneclassics.com

Contents

The Black Arrow
&
Memories and Portraits

THE BLACK ARROW

CRITIC ON THE HEARTH:

No one but myself knows what I have suffered, nor what my books have gained, by your unsleeping watchfulness and admirable pertinacity. And now here is a volume that goes into the world and lacks your imprimatur: a strange thing in our joint lives; and the reason of it stranger still! I have watched with interest, with pain, and at length with amusement, your unavailing attempts to peruse The Black Arrow; and I think I should lack humour indeed, if I let the occasion slip and did not place your name in the fly-leaf of the only book of mine that you have never read—and never will read.

That others may display more constancy is still my hope. The tale was written years ago for a particular audience and (I may say) in rivalry with a particular author; I think I should do well to name him, Mr. Alfred R. Phillips. It was not without its reward at the time. I could not, indeed, displace Mr. Phillips from his well-won priority; but in the eyes of readers who thought less than nothing of Treasure Island, The Black Arrow was supposed to mark a clear advance. Those who read volumes and those who read story papers belong to different worlds. The verdict on Treasure Island was reversed in the other court; I wonder, will it be the same with its successor?

R. L. S.

Saranac Lake, April 8, 1888

PROLOGUE

JOHN AMEND-ALL

On a certain afternoon, in the late springtime, the bell upon Tunstall Moat House was heard ringing at an unaccustomed hour. Far and near, in the forest and in the fields along the river, people began to desert their labours and hurry towards the sound; and in Tunstall hamlet a group of poor countryfolk stood wondering at the summons.

Tunstall hamlet at that period, in the reign of old King Henry VI., wore much the same appearance as it wears to-day. A score or so of houses, heavily framed with oak, stood scattered in a long green valley ascending from the river. At the foot, the road crossed a bridge, and mounting on the other side, disappeared into the fringes of the forest on its way to the Moat House, and further forth to Holywood Abbey. Half-way up the village, the church stood among yews. On every side the slopes were crowned and the view bounded by the green elms and greening oak-trees of the forest.

Hard by the bridge, there was a stone cross upon a knoll, and here the group had collected—half-a-dozen women and one tall fellow in a russet smock—discussing what the bell betided. An express had gone through the hamlet half an hour before, and drunk a pot of ale in the saddle, not daring to dismount for the hurry of his errand; but he had been ignorant himself of what was forward, and only bore sealed letters from Sir Daniel Brackley to Sir Oliver Oates, the parson, who kept the Moat House in the master's absence.

But now there was the noise of a horse; and soon, out of the edge of the wood and over the echoing bridge, there rode up young Master Richard Shelton, Sir Daniel's ward. He, at the least, would know, and they hailed him and begged him to explain. He drew bridle willingly enough—a young fellow not yet eighteen, sun-browned and grey-eyed, in a jacket of deer's leather, with a black velvet collar, a green hood upon his head, and a steel cross-bow at his back. The express, it appeared, had brought great news. A battle was impending. Sir Daniel had sent for every man that could draw a bow or carry a bill to go post-haste to Kettley, under pain of his severe displeasure; but for whom they were to fight, or of where the battle was expected, Dick knew nothing. Sir Oliver would come shortly himself, and Bennet Hatch was arming at that moment, for he it was who should lead the party.

"It is the ruin of this kind land," a woman said. "If the barons live at war, ploughfolk must eat roots."

"Nay," said Dick, "every man that follows shall have sixpence a day, and archers twelve."

"If they live," returned the woman, "that may very well be; but how if they die, my master?"

"They cannot better die than for their natural lord," said Dick.

"No natural lord of mine," said the man in the smock. "I followed the Walsinghams; so we all did down Brierly way, till two years ago, come Candlemas. And now I must side with Brackley! It was the law that did it; call ye that natural? But now, what with Sir Daniel and what with Sir Oliver—that knows more of law than honesty—I have no natural lord but poor King Harry the Sixt, God bless him!—the poor innocent that cannot tell his right hand from his left."

"Ye speak with an ill tongue, friend," answered Dick, "to miscall your good master and my lord the king in the same libel. But King Harry—praised be the saints!—has come again into his right mind, and will have all things peaceably ordained. And as for Sir Daniel, y'are very brave behind his back. But I will be no tale-bearer; and let that suffice."

"I say no harm of you, Master Richard," returned the peasant. "Y'are a lad; but when ye come to a man's inches, ye will find ye have an empty pocket. I say no more: the saints help Sir Daniel's neighbours, and the Blessed Maid protect his wards!"

"Clipsby," said Richard, "you speak what I cannot hear with honour. Sir

Daniel is my good master, and my guardian."

"Come, now, will ye read me a riddle?" returned Clipsby. "On whose side is Sir Daniel?"

"I know not," said Dick, colouring a little; for his guardian had changed sides continually in the troubles of that period, and every change had brought him some increase of fortune.

"Ay," returned Clipsby, "you, nor no man. For, indeed, he is one that goes to bed Lancaster and gets up York."

Just then the bridge rang under horse-shoe iron, and the party turned and saw Bennet Hatch come galloping—a brown-faced, grizzled fellow, heavy of hand and grim of mien, armed with sword and spear, a steel salet on his head, a leather jack upon his body. He was a great man in these parts; Sir Daniel's right hand in peace and war, and at that time, by his master's interest, bailiff of the hundred.

"Clipsby," he shouted, "off to the Moat House, and send all other laggards the same gate. Bowyer will give you jack and salet. We must ride before curfew. Look to it: he that is last at the lych-gate Sir Daniel shall reward. Look to it right well! I know you for a man of naught. Nance," he added, to one of the women, "is old Appleyard up town?"

"I'll warrant you," replied the woman. "In his field, for sure."

So the group dispersed, and while Clipsby walked leisurely over the bridge, Bennet and young Shelton rode up the road together, through the village and past the church.

"Ye will see the old shrew," said Bennet. "He will waste more time grumbling and prating of Harry the Fift than would serve a man to shoe a horse. And all because he has been to the French wars!"

The house to which they were bound was the last in the village, standing alone among lilacs; and beyond it, on three sides, there was open meadow rising towards the borders of the wood.

Hatch dismounted, threw his rein over the fence, and walked down the field, Dick keeping close at his elbow, to where the old soldier was digging, knee-deep in his cabbages, and now and again, in a cracked voice, singing a snatch of song. He was all dressed in leather, only his hood and tippet were of black frieze, and tied with scarlet; his face was like a walnut-shell, both for colour and wrinkles; but his old grey eye was still clear enough, and his sight unabated. Perhaps he was deaf; perhaps he thought it unworthy of an old archer of Agincourt to pay any heed to such disturbances; but neither the surly notes of the alarm bell, nor the near approach of Bennet and the lad, appeared at all to move him; and he continued obstinately digging, and piped up, very thin and shaky:

"Now, dear lady, if thy will be,

I pray you that you will rue on me."

"Nick Appleyard," said Hatch, "Sir Oliver commends him to you, and bids that ye shall come within this hour to the Moat House, there to take command."

The old fellow looked up.

"Save you, my masters!" he said, grinning. "And where goeth Master Hatch?"

"Master Hatch is off to Kettley, with every man that we can horse," returned Bennet. "There is a fight toward, it seems, and my lord stays a reinforcement."

"Ay, verily," returned Appleyard. "And what will ye leave me to garrison withal?"

"I leave you six good men, and Sir Oliver to boot," answered Hatch.

"It'll not hold the place," said Appleyard; "the number sufficeth not. It would take two-score to make it good."

"Why, it's for that we came to you, old shrew!" replied the other. "Who else is there but you that could do aught in such a house with such a garrison?"

"Ay! when the pinch comes, ye remember the old shoe," returned Nick.

"There is not a man of you can back a horse or hold a bill; and as for archery—St. Michael! if old Harry the Fift were back again, he would stand and let ye shoot at him for a farthen a shoot!"

"Nay, Nick, there's some can draw a good bow yet," said Bennet.

"Draw a good bow!" cried Appleyard. "Yes! But who'll shoot me a good shoot? It's there the eye comes in, and the head between your shoulders. Now, what might you call a long shoot, Bennet Hatch?"

"Well," said Bennet, looking about him, "it would be a long shoot from here into the forest."

"Ay, it would be a longish shoot," said the old fellow, turning to look over his shoulder; and then he put up his hand over his eyes, and stood staring.

"Why, what are you looking at?" asked Bennet, with a chuckle. "Do you see Harry the Fift?"

The veteran continued looking up the hill in silence. The sun shone broadly over the shelving meadows; a few white sheep wandered browsing; all was still but the distant jangle of the bell.

"What is it, Appleyard?" asked Dick.

"Why, the birds," said Appleyard.

And, sure enough, over the top of the forest, where it ran down in a tongue among the meadows, and ended in a pair of goodly green elms, about a bowshot from the field where they were standing, a flight of birds was skimming to and fro, in evident disorder.

"What of the birds?" said Bennet.

"Ay!" returned Appleyard, "y'are a wise man to go to war, Master Bennet. Birds are a good sentry; in forest places they be the first line of battle. Look you, now, if we lay here in camp, there might be archers skulking down to get the wind of us; and here would you be, none the wiser!"

"Why, old shrew," said Hatch, "there be no men nearer us than Sir

Daniel's, at Kettley; y'are as safe as in London Tower; and ye raise scares upon a man for a few chaffinches and sparrows!"

"Hear him!" grinned Appleyard. "How many a rogue would give his two crop ears to have a shoot at either of us? St. Michael, man! they hate us like two polecats!"

"Well, sooth it is, they hate Sir Daniel," answered Hatch, a little sobered.

"Ay, they hate Sir Daniel, and they hate every man that serves with him," said Appleyard; "and in the first order of hating, they hate Bennet Hatch and old Nicholas the bow-man. See ye here: if there was a stout fellow yonder in the wood-edge, and you and I stood fair for him—as, by St. George, we stand!—which, think ye, would he choose?"

"You, for a good wager," answered Hatch.

"My surcoat to a leather belt, it would be you!" cried the old archer. "Ye burned Grimstone, Bennet—they'll ne'er forgive you that, my master. And as for me, I'll soon be in a good place, God grant, and out of bow-shoot—ay, and cannon-shoot—of all their malices. I am an old man, and draw fast to homeward, where the bed is ready. But for you, Bennet, y'are to remain behind here at your own peril, and if ye come to my years unhanged, the old true-blue English spirit will be dead."

"Y'are the shrewishest old dolt in Tunstall Forest," returned Hatch, visibly ruffled by these threats. "Get ye to your arms before Sir Oliver come, and leave prating for one good while. An' ye had talked so much with Harry the Fift, his ears would ha' been richer than his pocket."

An arrow sang in the air, like a huge hornet; it struck old Appleyard between the shoulder-blades, and pierced him clean through, and he fell forward on his face among the cabbages. Hatch, with a broken cry, leapt into the air; then, stooping double, he ran for the cover of the house. And in the meanwhile Dick Shelton had dropped behind a lilac, and had his cross-bow bent and shouldered, covering the point of the forest.

Not a leaf stirred. The sheep were patiently browsing; the birds had

18

settled. But there lay the old man, with a cloth-yard arrow standing in his back; and there were Hatch holding to the gable, and Dick crouching and ready behind the lilac bush.

"D'ye see aught?" cried Hatch.

"Not a twig stirs," said Dick.

"I think shame to leave him lying," said Bennet, coming forward once more with hesitating steps and a very pale countenance. "Keep a good eye on the wood, Master Shelton—keep a clear eye on the wood. The saints assoil us! here was a good shoot!"

Bennet raised the old archer on his knee. He was not yet dead; his face worked, and his eyes shut and opened like machinery, and he had a most horrible, ugly look of one in pain.

"Can ye hear, old Nick?" asked Hatch. "Have ye a last wish before ye wend, old brother?"

"Pluck out the shaft, and let me pass, a' Mary's name!" gasped Appleyard. "I be done with Old England. Pluck it out!"

"Master Dick," said Bennet, "come hither, and pull me a good pull upon the arrow. He would fain pass, the poor sinner."

Dick laid down his cross-bow, and pulling hard upon the arrow, drew it forth. A gush of blood followed; the old archer scrambled half upon his feet, called once upon the name of God, and then fell dead. Hatch, upon his knees among the cabbages, prayed fervently for the welfare of the passing spirit. But even as he prayed, it was plain that his mind was still divided, and he kept ever an eye upon the corner of the wood from which the shot had come. When he had done, he got to his feet again, drew off one of his mailed gauntlets, and wiped his pale face, which was all wet with terror.

"Ay," he said, "it'll be my turn next."

"Who hath done this, Bennet?" Richard asked, still holding the arrow in his hand.

"Nay, the saints know," said Hatch. "Here are a good two-score Christian souls that we have hunted out of house and holding, he and I. He has paid his shot, poor shrew, nor will it be long, mayhap, ere I pay mine. Sir Daniel driveth overhard."

"This is a strange shaft," said the lad, looking at the arrow in his hand.

"Ay, by my faith!" cried Bennet. "Black, and black-feathered. Here is an ill-favoured shaft, by my sooth! for black, they say, bodes burial. And here be words written. Wipe the blood away. What read ye?"

"'Appulyaird fro Jon Amend-All,'" read Shelton. "What should this betoken?"

"Nay, I like it not," returned the retainer, shaking his head. "John Amend-All! Here is a rogue's name for those that be up in the world! But why stand we here to make a mark? Take him by the knees, good Master Shelton, while I lift him by the shoulders, and let us lay him in his house. This will be a rare shog to poor Sir Oliver; he will turn paper colour; he will pray like a windmill."

They took up the old archer, and carried him between them into his house, where he had dwelt alone. And there they laid him on the floor, out of regard for the mattress and sought, as best they might, to straighten and compose his limbs.

Appleyard's house was clean and bare. There was a bed, with a blue cover, a cupboard, a great chest, a pair of joint-stools, a hinged table in the chimney-corner, and hung upon the wall the old soldier's armoury of bows and defensive armour. Hatch began to look about him curiously.

"Nick had money," he said. "He may have had three-score pounds put by. I would I could light upon't! When ye lose an old friend, Master Richard, the best consolation is to heir him. See, now, this chest. I would go a mighty wager there is a bushel of gold therein. He had a strong hand to get, and a hard hand to keep withal, had Appleyard the archer. Now may God rest his spirit! Near eighty year he was afoot and about, and ever getting; but now he's on the broad of his back, poor shrew, and no more lacketh; and if his chattels came to a good friend, he would be merrier, methinks, in heaven."

"Come, Hatch," said Dick, "respect his stone-blind eyes. Would ye rob the man before his body? Nay, he would walk!"

Hatch made several signs of the cross; but by this time his natural complexion had returned, and he was not easily to be dashed from any purpose. It would have gone hard with the chest had not the gate sounded, and presently after the door of the house opened and admitted a tall, portly, ruddy, black-eyed man of near fifty, in a surplice and black robe.

"Appleyard—" the newcomer was saying, as he entered; but he stopped dead. "Ave Maria!" he cried. "Saints be our shield! What cheer is this?"

"Cold cheer with Appleyard, sir parson," answered Hatch, with perfect cheerfulness. "Shot at his own door, and alighteth even now at purgatory gates. Ay! there, if tales be true, he shall lack neither coal nor candle."

Sir Oliver groped his way to a joint-stool, and sat down upon it, sick and white.

"This is a judgment! O, a great stroke!" he sobbed, and rattled off a leash of prayers.

Hatch meanwhile reverently doffed his salet and knelt down.

"Ay, Bennet," said the priest, somewhat recovering, "and what may this be? What enemy hath done this?"

"Here, Sir Oliver, is the arrow. See, it is written upon with words," said Dick.

"Nay," cried the priest, "this is a foul hearing! John Amend-All! A right Lollardy word. And black of hue, as for an omen! Sirs, this knave arrow likes me not. But it importeth rather to take counsel. Who should this be? Bethink you, Bennet. Of so many black ill-willers, which should he be that doth so hardily outface us? Simnel? I do much question it. The Walsinghams? Nay, they are not yet so broken; they still think to have the law over us, when times change. There was Simon Malmesbury, too. How think ye, Bennet?"

"What think ye, sir," returned Hatch, "of Ellis Duckworth?"

"Nay, Bennet, never. Nay, not he," said the priest. "There cometh never any rising, Bennet, from below—so all judicious chroniclers concord in their opinion; but rebellion travelleth ever downward from above; and when Dick, Tom, and Harry take them to their bills, look ever narrowly to see what lord is profited thereby. Now, Sir Daniel, having once more joined him to the Queen's party, is in ill odour with the Yorkist lords. Thence, Bennet, comes the blow—by what procuring, I yet seek; but therein lies the nerve of this discomfiture."

"An't please you, Sir Oliver," said Bennet, "the axles are so hot in this country that I have long been smelling fire. So did this poor sinner, Appleyard. And, by your leave, men's spirits are so foully inclined to all of us, that it needs neither York nor Lancaster to spur them on. Hear my plain thoughts: You, that are a clerk, and Sir Daniel, that sails on any wind, ye have taken many men's goods, and beaten and hanged not a few. Y'are called to count for this; in the end, I wot not how, ye have ever the uppermost at law, and ye think all patched. But give me leave, Sir Oliver: the man that ye have dispossessed and beaten is but the angrier, and some day, when the black devil is by, he will up with his bow and clout me a yard of arrow through your inwards."

"Nay, Bennet, y'are in the wrong. Bennet, ye should be glad to be corrected," said Sir Oliver. "Y'are a prater, Bennet, a talker, a babbler; your mouth is wider than your two ears. Mend it, Bennet, mend it."

"Nay, I say no more. Have it as ye list," said the retainer.

The priest now rose from the stool, and from the writing-case that hung about his neck took forth wax and a taper, and a flint and steel. With these he sealed up the chest and the cupboard with Sir Daniel's arms, Hatch looking on disconsolate; and then the whole party proceeded, somewhat timorously, to sally from the house and get to horse.

"'Tis time we were on the road, Sir Oliver," said Hatch, as he held the priest's stirrup while he mounted.

"Ay; but, Bennet, things are changed," returned the parson. "There is now no Appleyard—rest his soul!—to keep the garrison. I shall keep you, Bennet. I must have a good man to rest me on in this day of black arrows. 'The arrow that flieth by day,' saith the evangel; I have no mind of the context; nay, I am a sluggard priest, I am too deep in men's affairs. Well, let us ride forth, Master Hatch. The jackmen should be at the church by now."

So they rode forward down the road, with the wind after them, blowing the tails of the parson's cloak; and behind them, as they went, clouds began to arise and blot out the sinking sun. They had passed three of the scattered houses that make up Tunstall hamlet, when, coming to a turn, they saw the church before them. Ten or a dozen houses clustered immediately round it; but to the back the churchyard was next the meadows. At the lych-gate, near a score of men were gathered, some in the saddle, some standing by their horses' heads. They were variously armed and mounted; some with spears, some with bills, some with bows, and some bestriding plough-horses, still splashed with the mire of the furrow; for these were the very dregs of the country, and all the better men and the fair equipments were already with Sir Daniel in the field.

"We have not done amiss, praised be the cross of Holywood! Sir Daniel will be right well content," observed the priest, inwardly numbering the troop.

"Who goes? Stand! if ye be true!" shouted Bennet.

A man was seen slipping through the churchyard among the yews; and at the sound of this summons he discarded all concealment, and fairly took to his heels for the forest. The men at the gate, who had been hitherto unaware of the stranger's presence, woke and scattered. Those who had dismounted began scrambling into the saddle; the rest rode in pursuit; but they had to make the circuit of the consecrated ground, and it was plain their quarry would escape them. Hatch, roaring an oath, put his horse at the hedge, to head him off; but the beast refused, and sent his rider sprawling in the dust. And though he was up again in a moment, and had caught the bridle, the time had gone by, and the fugitive had gained too great a lead for any hope of capture.

The wisest of all had been Dick Shelton. Instead of starting in a vain pursuit, he had whipped his cross-bow from his back, bent it, and set a quarrel to the string; and now, when the others had desisted, he turned to Bennet and asked if he should shoot.

"Shoot! shoot!" cried the priest, with sanguinary violence.

"Cover him, Master Dick," said Bennet. "Bring me him down like a ripe apple."

The fugitive was now within but a few leaps of safety; but this last part of the meadow ran very steeply up-hill; and the man ran slower in proportion. What with the greyness of the falling night, and the uneven movements of the runner, it was no easy aim; and as Dick levelled his bow, he felt a kind of pity, and a half desire that he might miss. The quarrel sped.

The man stumbled and fell, and a great cheer arose from Hatch and the pursuers. But they were counting their corn before the harvest. The man fell lightly; he was lightly afoot again, turned and waved his cap in a bravado, and was out of sight next moment in the margin of the wood.

"And the plague go with him!" cried Bennet. "He has thieves' heels; he can run, by St. Banbury! But you touched him, Master Shelton; he has stolen your quarrel, may he never have good I grudge him less!"

"Nay, but what made he by the church?" asked Sir Oliver. "I am shrewdly afeared there has been mischief here. Clipsby, good fellow, get ye down from your horse, and search thoroughly among the yews."

Clipsby was gone but a little while ere he returned, carrying a paper.

"This writing was pinned to the church door," he said, handing it to the parson. "I found naught else, sir parson."

"Now, by the power of Mother Church," cried Sir Oliver, "but this runs hard on sacrilege! For the king's good pleasure, or the lord of the manor—well! But that every run-the-hedge in a green jerkin should fasten papers to the chancel door—nay, it runs hard on sacrilege, hard; and men have burned for matters of less weight. But what have we here? The light falls apace. Good Master Richard, y' have young eyes. Read me, I pray, this libel."

Dick Shelton took the paper in his hand and read it aloud. It contained some lines of very rugged doggerel, hardly even rhyming, written in a gross character, and most uncouthly spelt. With the spelling somewhat bettered, this is how they ran:

"I had four blak arrows under my belt,

Four for the greefs that I have felt,

Four for the nomber of ill menne

That have opressid me now and then.

One is gone; one is wele sped;

Old Apulyaird is ded.

One is for Maister Bennet Hatch,

That burned Grimstone, walls and thatch.

One for Sir Oliver Oates,

That cut Sir Harry Shelton's throat.

Sir Daniel, ye shull have the fourt;

We shall think it fair sport.

Ye shull each have your own part,

A blak arrow in each blak heart.

Get ye to your knees for to pray:

Ye are ded theeves, by yea and nay!

"Jon Amend-all

of the Green Wood,

And his jolly fellaweship.

"Item, we have mo arrowes and goode hempen cord for otheres of your following."

"Now, well-a-day for charity and the Christian graces!" cried Sir Oliver, lamentably. "Sirs, this is an ill world, and groweth daily worse. I will swear upon the cross of Holywood I am as innocent of that good knight's hurt, whether in act or purpose, as the babe unchristened. Neither was his throat cut; for therein they are again in error, as there still live credible witnesses to show."

"It boots not, sir parson," said Bennet. "Here is unseasonable talk."

"Nay, Master Bennet, not so. Keep ye in your due place, good Bennet," answered the priest. "I shall make mine innocence appear. I will, upon no consideration, lose my poor life in error. I take all men to witness that I am clear of this matter. I was not even in the Moat House. I was sent of an errand before nine upon the clock——"

"Sir Oliver," said Hatch, interrupting, "since it please you not to stop this sermon, I will take other means. Goffe, sound to horse."

And while the tucket was sounding, Bennet moved close to the bewildered parson, and whispered violently in his ear.

Dick Shelton saw the priest's eye turned upon him for an instant in a startled glance. He had some cause for thought; for this Sir Harry Shelton was his own natural father. But he said never a word, and kept his countenance unmoved.

Hatch and Sir Oliver discussed together for awhile their altered situation; ten men, it was decided between them, should be reserved, not only to garrison the Moat House, but to escort the priest across the wood. In the meantime, as Bennet was to remain behind, the command of the reinforcement was given to Master Shelton. Indeed, there was no choice; the men were loutish fellows, dull and unskilled in war, while Dick was not only popular, but resolute and grave beyond his age. Although his youth had been spent in these rough, country places, the lad had been well taught in letters by Sir Oliver, and Hatch himself had shown him the management of arms and the first principles of command. Bennet had always been kind and helpful; he was one of those who are cruel as the grave to those they call their enemies, but ruggedly faithful and well willing to their friends; and now, while Sir Oliver entered the next house to write, in his swift, exquisite penmanship, a memorandum of the last occurrences to his master, Sir Daniel Brackley, Bennet came up to his pupil to wish him God-speed upon his enterprise.

"Ye must go the long way about, Master Shelton," he said; "round by the bridge, for your life! Keep a sure man fifty paces afore you, to draw shots; and go softly till y'are past the wood. If the rogues fall upon you, ride for't; ye will do naught by standing. And keep ever forward, Master Shelton; turn me not back again, an ye love your life; there is no help in Tunstall, mind ye that. And now, since ye go to the great wars about the king, and I continue to dwell here in extreme jeopardy of my life, and the saints alone can certify if we shall meet again below, I give you my last counsels now at your riding. Keep an eye on Sir Daniel; he is unsure. Put not your trust in the jack-priest; he intendeth not amiss, but doth the will of others; it is a hand-gun for Sir Daniel! Get your good lordship where ye go; make you strong friends; look to it. And think ever a paternoster while on Bennet Hatch. There are worse rogues afoot than Bennet. So, God-speed!"

"And Heaven be with you, Bennet!" returned Dick. "Ye were a good friend to meward, and so I shall say ever."

"And, look ye, master," added Hatch, with a certain embarrassment, "if this Amend-All should get a shaft into me, ye might, mayhap, lay out a gold mark or mayhap a pound for my poor soul; for it is like to go stiff with me in purgatory."

"Ye shall have your will of it, Bennet," answered Dick. "But, what cheer, man! we shall meet again, where ye shall have more need of ale than masses."

"The saints so grant it, Master Dick!" returned the other. "But here comes Sir Oliver. An he were as quick with the long-bow as with the pen, he would be a brave man-at-arms."

Sir Oliver gave Dick a sealed packet, with this superscription: "To my ryght worchypful master. Sir Daniel Brackley, knyght, be thys delyvered in haste."

And Dick, putting it in the bosom of his jacket, gave the word and set forth westward up the village.

BOOK I. THE TWO LADS

CHAPTER I. AT THE SIGN OF THE SUN IN KETTLEY

Sir Daniel and his men lay in and about Kettley that night, warmly quartered and well patrolled. But the Knight of Tunstall was one who never rested from money-getting; and even now, when he was on the brink of an adventure which should make or mar him, he was up an hour after midnight to squeeze poor neighbours. He was one who trafficked greatly in disputed inheritances; it was his way to buy out the most unlikely claimant, and then, by the favour he curried with great lords about the king, procure unjust decisions in his favour; or, if that was too roundabout, to seize the disputed manor by force of arms, and rely on his influence and Sir Oliver's cunning in the law to hold what he had snatched. Kettley was one such place; it had come very lately into his clutches; he still met with opposition from the tenants; and it was to overawe discontent that he had led his troops that way.

By two in the morning, Sir Daniel sat in the inn room, close by the fireside, for it was cold at that hour among the fens of Kettley. By his elbow stood a pottle of spiced ale. He had taken off his visored headpiece, and sat with his bald head and thin, dark visage resting on one hand, wrapped warmly in a sanguine-coloured cloak. At the lower end of the room about a dozen of his men stood sentry over the door or lay asleep on benches; and somewhat nearer hand, a young lad, apparently of twelve or thirteen, was stretched in a mantle on the floor. The host of the Sun stood before the great man.

"Now, mark me, mine host," Sir Daniel said, "follow but mine orders, and I shall be your good lord ever. I must have good men for head boroughs, and I will have Adam-a-More high constable; see to it narrowly. If other men be chosen, it shall avail you nothing; rather it shall be found to your sore cost. For those that have paid rent to Walsingham I shall take good measure—you among the rest, mine host."

"Good knight," said the host, "I will swear upon the cross of Holywood I did but pay to Walsingham upon compulsion. Nay, bully knight, I love not the rogue Walsinghams; they were as poor as thieves, bully knight. Give me a great lord like you. Nay; ask me among the neighbours, I am stout for Brackley."

"It may be," said Sir Daniel, drily. "Ye shall then pay twice."

The innkeeper made a horrid grimace; but this was a piece of bad luck that might readily befall a tenant in these unruly times, and he was perhaps glad to make his peace so easily.

"Bring up yon fellow, Selden!" cried the knight.

And one of his retainers led up a poor, cringing old man, as pale as a candle, and all shaking with the fen fever.

"Sirrah," said Sir Daniel, "your name?"

"An't please your worship," replied the man, "my name is Condall—Condall of Shoreby, at your good worship's pleasure."

"I have heard you ill reported on," returned the knight. "Ye deal in treason, rogue; ye trudge the country leasing; y'are heavily suspicioned of the death of severals. How, fellow, are ye so bold? But I will bring you down."

"Right honourable and my reverend lord," the man cried, "here is some hodge-podge, saving your good presence. I am but a poor private man, and have hurt none."

"The under-sheriff did report of you most vilely," said the knight. "'Seize me,' saith he, 'that Tyndal of Shoreby.'"

"Condall, my good lord; Condall is my poor name," said the unfortunate.

"Condall or Tyndal, it is all one," replied Sir Daniel, coolly. "For, by my sooth, y'are here, and I do mightily suspect your honesty. If ye would save your neck, write me swiftly an obligation for twenty pound."

"For twenty pound, my good lord!" cried Condall. "Here is midsummer madness! My whole estate amounteth not to seventy shillings."

"Condall or Tyndal," returned Sir Daniel, grinning, "I will run my peril of that loss. Write me down twenty, and when I have recovered all I may, I will be good lord to you, and pardon you the rest."

"Alas! my good lord, it may not be; I have no skill to write," said Condall.

"Well-a-day!" returned the knight. "Here, then, is no remedy. Yet I would fain have spared you, Tyndal, had my conscience suffered. Selden, take me this old shrew softly to the nearest elm, and hang me him tenderly by the neck, where I may see him at my riding. Fare ye well, good Master Condall, dear Master Tyndal; y'are post-haste for Paradise; fare ye then well!"

"Nay, my right pleasant lord," replied Condall, forcing an obsequious smile, "an ye be so masterful, as doth right well become you, I will even, with all my poor skill, do your good bidding."

"Friend," quoth Sir Daniel, "ye will now write two-score. Go to! y'are too cunning for a livelihood of seventy shillings. Selden, see him write me this in good form, and have it duly witnessed."

And Sir Daniel, who was a very merry knight, none merrier in England, took a drink of his mulled ale, and lay back, smiling.

Meanwhile, the boy upon the floor began to stir, and presently sat up and looked about him with a scare.

"Hither," said Sir Daniel; and as the other rose at his command and came slowly towards him, he leaned back and laughed outright. "By the rood!" he cried, "a sturdy boy!"

The lad flushed crimson with anger, and darted a look of hate out of his dark eyes. Now that he was on his legs, it was more difficult to make certain of his age. His face looked somewhat older in expression, but it was as smooth as a young child's; and in bone and body he was unusually slender, and somewhat awkward of gait.

"Ye have called me, Sir Daniel," he said. "Was it to laugh at my poor plight?"

"Nay, now, let laugh," said the knight. "Good shrew, let laugh, I pray you. An ye could see yourself, I warrant ye would laugh the first."

"Well," cried the lad, flushing, "ye shall answer this when ye answer for the other. Laugh while yet ye may!"

"Nay, now, good cousin," replied Sir Daniel, with some earnestness, "think not that I mock at you, except in mirth, as between kinsfolk and singular friends. I will make you a marriage of a thousand pounds, go to! and cherish you exceedingly. I took you, indeed, roughly, as the time demanded; but from henceforth I shall ungrudgingly maintain and cheerfully serve you. Ye shall be Mrs. Shelton—Lady Shelton, by my troth! for the lad promiseth bravely. Tut! ye will not shy for honest laughter; it purgeth melancholy. They are no rogues who laugh, good cousin. Good mine host, lay me a meal now for my cousin, Master John. Sit ye down, sweetheart, and eat."

"Nay," said Master John, "I will break no bread. Since ye force me to this sin, I will fast for my soul's interest. But, good mine host, I pray you of courtesy give me a cup of fair water; I shall be much beholden to your courtesy indeed."

"Ye shall have a dispensation, go to!" cried the knight. "Shalt be well shriven, by my faith! Content you, then, and eat."

But the lad was obstinate, drank a cup of water, and, once more wrapping himself closely in his mantle, sat in a far corner, brooding.

In an hour or two, there rose a stir in the village of sentries challenging and the clatter of arms and horses; and then a troop drew up by the inn door, and Richard Shelton, splashed with mud, presented himself upon the threshold.

"Save you, Sir Daniel," he said.

"How! Dickie Shelton!" cried the knight; and at the mention of Dick's name the other lad looked curiously across. "What maketh Bennet Hatch?"

"Please you, sir knight, to take cognisance of this packet from Sir Oliver, wherein are all things fully stated," answered Richard, presenting the priest's letter. "And please you farther, ye were best make all speed to Risingham; for on the way hither we encountered one riding furiously with letters, and by his report, my Lord of Risingham was sore bested, and lacked exceedingly your presence."

"How say you? Sore bested?" returned the knight. "Nay, then, we will make speed sitting down, good Richard. As the world goes in this poor realm of England, he that rides softliest rides surest. Delay, they say, begetteth peril; but it is rather this itch of doing that undoes men; mark it, Dick. But let me see, first, what cattle ye have brought. Selden, a link here at the door!"

And Sir Daniel strode forth into the village street, and, by the red glow of a torch, inspected his new troops. He was an unpopular neighbour and an unpopular master; but as a leader in war he was well beloved by those who rode behind his pennant. His dash, his proved courage, his forethought for the soldiers' comfort, even his rough gibes, were all to the taste of the bold blades in jack and salet.

"Nay, by the rood!" he cried, "what poor dogs are these? Here be some as crooked as a bow, and some as lean as a spear. Friends, ye shall ride in the front of the battle; I can spare you, friends. Mark me this old villain on the piebald! A two-year mutton riding on a hog would look more soldierly! Ha! Clipsby, are ye there, old rat? Y'are a man I could lose with a good heart; ye shall go in front of all, with a bull's eye painted on your jack, to be the better butt for archery; sirrah, ye shall show me the way."

"I will show you any way, Sir Daniel, but the way to change sides," returned Clipsby, sturdily.

Sir Daniel laughed a guffaw.

"Why, well said!" he cried. "Hast a shrewd tongue in thy mouth, go to! I will forgive you for that merry word. Selden, see them fed, both man and brute."

The knight re-entered the inn.

"Now, friend Dick," he said, "fall to. Here is good ale and bacon. Eat, while that I read."

Sir Daniel opened the packet, and as he read his brow darkened. When he had done he sat a little, musing. Then he looked sharply at his ward.

"Dick," said he, "y' have seen this penny rhyme?"

The lad replied in the affirmative.

"It bears your father's name," continued the knight; "and our poor shrew of a parson is, by some mad soul, accused of slaying him."

"He did most eagerly deny it," answered Dick.

"He did?" cried the knight, very sharply. "Heed him not. He has a loose tongue; he babbles like a jack-sparrow. Some day, when I may find the leisure, Dick, I will myself more fully inform you of these matters. There was one Duckworth shrewdly blamed for it; but the times were troubled, and there was no justice to be got."

"It befell at the Moat House?" Dick ventured, with a beating at his heart.

"It befell between the Moat House and Holywood," replied Sir Daniel, calmly; but he shot a covert glance, black with suspicion, at Dick's face. "And now," added the knight, "speed you with your meal; ye shall return to Tunstall with a line from me."

Dick's face fell sorely.

"Prithee, Sir Daniel," he cried, "send one of the villains! I beseech you let me to the battle. I can strike a stroke, I promise you."

"I misdoubt it not," replied Sir Daniel, sitting down to write. "But here, Dick, is no honour to be won. I lie in Kettley till I have sure tidings of the war, and then ride to join me with the conqueror. Cry not on cowardice; it is but wisdom, Dick; for this poor realm so tosseth with rebellion, and the king's name and custody so changeth hands, that no man may be certain of the morrow. Toss-pot and Shuttle-wit run in, but my Lord Good-Counsel sits o' one side, waiting."

With that, Sir Daniel, turning his back to Dick, and quite at the farther end of the long table, began to write his letter, with his mouth on one side, for this business of the Black Arrow stuck sorely in his throat.

Meanwhile, young Shelton was going on heartily enough with his breakfast, when he felt a touch upon his arm, and a very soft voice whispering in his ear.

"Make not a sign, I do beseech you," said the voice, "but of your charity tell me the straight way to Holywood. Beseech you, now, good boy, comfort a poor soul in peril and extreme distress, and set me so far forth upon the way to my repose."

"Take the path by the windmill," answered Dick, in the same tone; "it will bring you to Till Ferry; there inquire again."

And without turning his head, he fell again to eating. But with the tail of his eye he caught a glimpse of the young lad called Master John stealthily creeping from the room.

"Why," thought Dick, "he is as young as I. 'Good boy' doth he call me? An I had known, I should have seen the varlet hanged ere I had told him. Well, if he goes through the fen, I may come up with him and pull his ears."

Half an hour later, Sir Daniel gave Dick the letter, and bade him speed to the Moat House. And, again, some half an hour after Dick's departure, a messenger came, in hot haste, from my Lord of Risingham.

"Sir Daniel," the messenger said, "ye lose great honour, by my sooth! The fight began again this morning ere the dawn, and we have beaten their van and scattered their right wing. Only the main battle standeth fast. An we had your fresh men, we should tilt you them all into the river. What, sir knight! Will ye be the last? It stands not with your good credit."

"Nay," cried the knight, "I was but now upon the march. Selden, sound me the tucket. Sir, I am with you on the instant. It is not two hours since the more part of my command came in, sir messenger. What would ye have? Spurring is good meat, but yet it killed the charger. Bustle, boys!"

By this time the tucket was sounding cheerily in the morning, and from all sides Sir Daniel's men poured into the main street and formed before the inn. They had slept upon their arms, with chargers saddled, and in ten minutes five-score men-at-arms and archers, cleanly equipped and briskly disciplined, stood ranked and ready. The chief part were in Sir Daniel's livery, murrey and blue, which gave the greater show to their array. The best armed rode first; and away out of sight, at the tail of the column, came the sorry reinforcement of the night before. Sir Daniel looked with pride along the line.

"Here be the lads to serve you in a pinch," he said.

"They are pretty men, indeed," replied the messenger. "It but augments my sorrow that ye had not marched the earlier."

"Well," said the knight, "what would ye? The beginning of a feast and the end of a fray, sir messenger"; and he mounted into his saddle. "Why! how now!" he cried. "John! Joanna! Nay, by the sacred rood! where is she? Host, where is that girl?"

"Girl, Sir Daniel?" cried the landlord. "Nay, sir, I saw no girl."

"Boy, then, dotard!" cried the knight. "Could ye not see it was a wench? She in the murrey-coloured mantle—she that broke her fast with water, rogue—where is she?"

"Nay, the saints bless us! Master John, ye called him," said the host. "Well, I thought none evil. He is gone. I saw him—her—I saw her in the stable a good hour agone; 'a was saddling a grey horse."

"Now, by the rood!" cried Sir Daniel, "the wench was worth five hundred pound to me and more."

"Sir knight," observed the messenger, with bitterness, "while that ye are here, roaring for five hundred pounds, the realm of England is elsewhere being lost and won."

"It is well said," replied Sir Daniel. "Selden, fall me out with six cross-bowmen; hunt me her down. I care not what it cost; but, at my returning, let me find her at the Moat House. Be it upon your head. And now, sir messenger, we march."

And the troop broke into a good trot, and Selden and his six men were left behind upon the street of Kettley, with the staring villagers.

CHAPTER II. IN THE FEN

It was near six in the May morning when Dick began to ride down into the fen upon his homeward way. The sky was all blue; the jolly wind blew loud and steady; the windmill sails were spinning; and the willows over all the fen rippling and whitening like a field of corn. He had been all night in the saddle, but his heart was good and his body sound, and he rode right merrily.

The path went down and down into the marsh, till he lost sight of all the neighbouring landmarks but Kettley windmill on the knoll behind him, and the extreme top of Tunstall Forest far before. On either hand there were great fields of blowing reeds and willows, pools of water shaking in the wind, and treacherous bogs, as green as emerald, to tempt and to betray the traveller. The path lay almost straight through the morass. It was already very ancient; its foundation had been laid by Roman soldiery; in the lapse of ages much of it had sunk, and every here and there, for a few hundred yards, it lay submerged below the stagnant waters of the fen.

About a mile from Kettley, Dick came to one such break in the plain line of causeway, where the reeds and willows grew dispersedly like little islands and confused the eye. The gap, besides, was more than usually long; it was a place where any stranger might come readily to mischief; and Dick bethought him, with something like a pang, of the lad whom he had so imperfectly directed. As for himself, one look backward to where the windmill sails were turning black against the blue of heaven—one look forward to the high ground of Tunstall Forest, and he was sufficiently directed and held straight on, the water washing to his horse's knees, as safe as on a highway.

Half-way across, and when he had already sighted the path rising high and dry upon the farther side, he was aware of a great splashing on his right, and saw a grey horse, sunk to its belly in the mud, and still spasmodically struggling. Instantly, as though it had divined the neighbourhood of help, the poor beast began to neigh most piercingly. It rolled, meanwhile, a bloodshot eye, insane with terror; and as it sprawled wallowing in the quag, clouds of stinging insects rose and buzzed about it in the air.

"Alack!" thought Dick, "can the poor lad have perished? There is his horse, for certain—a brave grey! Nay, comrade, if thou criest to me so piteously, I will do all man can to help thee. Shalt not lie there to drown by inches!"

And he made ready his cross-bow, and put a quarrel through the creature's head.

Dick rode on after this act of rugged mercy, somewhat sobered in spirit, and looking closely about him for any sign of his less happy predecessor in the way.

"I would I had dared to tell him further," he thought; "for I fear he has miscarried in the slough."

And just as he was so thinking, a voice cried upon his name from the causeway-side, and, looking over his shoulder, he saw the lad's face peering from a clump of reeds.

"Are ye there?" he said, reining in. "Ye lay so close among the reeds that I had passed you by. I saw your horse bemired, and put him from his agony; which, by my sooth! an ye had been a more merciful rider, ye had done yourself. But come forth out of your hiding. Here be none to trouble you."

"Nay, good boy, I have no arms, nor skill to use them if I had," replied the other, stepping forth upon the pathway.

"Why call me 'boy'?" cried Dick. "Y'are not, I trow, the elder of us twain."

"Good Master Shelton," said the other, "prithee forgive me. I have none the least intention to offend. Rather I would in every way beseech your gentleness and favour, for I am now worse bested than ever, having lost my way, my cloak, and my poor horse. To have a riding-rod and spurs, and never a horse to sit upon! And before all," he added, looking ruefully upon his clothes—"before all, to be so sorrily besmirched!"

"Tut!" cried Dick. "Would ye mind a ducking? Blood of wound or dust of travel—that's a man's adornment."

"Nay, then, I like him better plain," observed the lad. "But, prithee, how shall I do? Prithee, good Master Richard, help me with your good counsel. If I come not safe to Holywood, I am undone."

"Nay," said Dick, dismounting, "I will give more than counsel. Take my horse, and I will run awhile, and when I am weary we shall change again, that so, riding and running, both may go the speedier."

So the change was made, and they went forward as briskly as they durst on the uneven causeway, Dick with his hand upon the other's knee.

"How call ye your name?" asked Dick.

"Call me John Matcham," replied the lad.

"And what make ye to Holywood?" Dick continued.

"I seek sanctuary from a man that would oppress me," was the answer. "The good Abbot of Holywood is a strong pillar to the weak."

"And how came ye with Sir Daniel, Master Matcham?" pursued Dick.

"Nay," cried the other, "by the abuse of force! He hath taken me by violence from my own place; dressed me in these weeds; ridden with me till my heart was sick; gibed me till I could 'a' wept; and when certain of my friends pursued, thinking to have me back, claps me in the rear to stand their shot! I was even grazed in the right foot, and walk but lamely. Nay, there shall come a day between us; he shall smart for all!"

"Would ye shoot at the moon with a hand-gun?" said Dick. "'Tis a valiant knight, and hath a hand of iron. An he guessed I had made or meddled with your flight, it would go sore with me."

"Ay, poor boy," returned the other, "y'are his ward, I know it. By the same token, so am I, or so he saith; or else he hath bought my marriage—I wot not rightly which; but it is some handle to oppress me by."

"Boy again!" said Dick.

"Nay, then, shall I call you girl, good Richard?" asked Matcham.

"Never a girl for me," returned Dick. "I do abjure the crew of them!"

"Ye speak boyishly," said the other. "Ye think more of them than ye pretend."

"Not I," said Dick, stoutly. "They come not in my mind. A plague of them, say I! Give me to hunt and to fight and to feast, and to live with jolly foresters. I never heard of a maid yet that was for any service, save one only; and she, poor shrew, was burned for a witch and the wearing of men's clothes in spite of nature."

Master Matcham crossed himself with fervour, and appeared to pray.

"What make ye?" Dick inquired.

"I pray for her spirit," answered the other, with a somewhat troubled voice.

"For a witch's spirit?" Dick cried. "But pray for her, an ye list; she was the best wench in Europe, was this Joan of Arc. Old Appleyard the archer ran from her, he said, as if she had been Mahoun. Nay, she was a brave wench."

"Well, but, good Master Richard," resumed Matcham, "an ye like maids so little, y'are no true natural man; for God made them twain by intention, and brought true love into the world, to be man's hope and woman's comfort."

"Faugh!" said Dick. "Y'are a milk-sopping baby, so to harp on women. An ye think I be no true man, get down upon the path, and whether at fists, backsword, or bow and arrow, I will prove my manhood on your body."

"Nay, I am no fighter," said Matcham, eagerly. "I mean no tittle of offence. I meant but pleasantry. And if I talk of women, it is because I heard ye were to marry."

"I to marry!" Dick exclaimed. "Well, it is the first I hear of it. And with whom was I to marry?"

"One Joan Sedley," replied Matcham, colouring. "It was Sir Daniel's doing; he hath money to gain upon both sides; and, indeed, I have heard the poor wench bemoaning herself pitifully of the match. It seems she is of your mind, or else distasted to the bridegroom."

"Well! marriage is like death, it comes to all," said Dick, with resignation. "And she bemoaned herself? I pray ye now, see there how shuttle-witted are these girls: to bemoan herself before that she had seen me! Do I bemoan myself? Not I. An I be to marry, I will marry dry-eyed! But if ye know her, prithee, of what favour is she? fair or foul? And is she shrewish or pleasant?"

"Nay, what matters it?" said Matcham. "An y'are to marry, ye can but marry. What matters foul or fair? These be but toys. Y'are no milksop, Master Richard; ye will wed with dry eyes, anyhow."

"It is well said," replied Shelton. "Little I reck."

"Your lady wife is like to have a pleasant lord," said Matcham.

"She shall have the lord Heaven made her for," returned Dick. "I trow there be worse as well as better."

"Ah, the poor wench!" cried the other.

"And why so poor?" asked Dick.

"To wed a man of wood," replied his companion. "O me, for a wooden husband!"

"I think I be a man of wood, indeed," said Dick, "to trudge afoot the while you ride my horse; but it is good wood, I trow."

"Good Dick, forgive me," cried the other. "Nay, y'are the best heart in England; I but laughed. Forgive me now, sweet Dick."

"Nay, no fool words," returned Dick, a little embarrassed by his companion's warmth. "No harm is done. I am not touchy, praise the saints."

And at that moment the wind, which was blowing straight behind them as they went, brought them the rough flourish of Sir Daniel's trumpeter.

"Hark!" said Dick, "the tucket soundeth."

"Ay," said Matcham, "they have found my flight, and now I am unhorsed!" and he became pale as death.

"Nay, what cheer!" returned Dick. "Y' have a long start, and we are near the ferry. And it is I, methinks, that am unhorsed."

"Alack, I shall be taken!" cried the fugitive. "Dick, kind Dick, beseech ye help me but a little!"

"Why, now, what aileth thee?" said Dick. "Methinks I help you very patently. But my heart is sorry for so spiritless a fellow! And see ye here, John Matcham—sith John Matcham is your name—I, Richard Shelton, tide what betideth, come what may, will see you safe in Holywood. The saints so do to me again if I default you. Come, pick me up a good heart, Sir Whiteface. The way betters here; spur me the horse. Go faster! faster! Nay, mind not for me; I can run like a deer."

So, with the horse trotting hard, and Dick running easily alongside, they crossed the remainer of the fen, and came out upon the banks of the river by the ferryman's hut.

CHAPTER III. THE FEN FERRY

The river Till was a wide, sluggish, clayey water, oozing out of fens, and in this part of its course it strained among some score of willow-covered, marshy islets.

It was a dingy stream; but upon this bright, spirited morning everything was become beautiful. The wind and the martens broke it up into innumerable dimples; and the reflection of the sky was scattered over all the surface in crumbs of smiling blue.

A creek ran up to meet the path, and close under the bank the ferryman's hut lay snugly. It was of wattle and clay, and the grass grew green upon the roof.

Dick went to the door and opened it. Within, upon a foul old russet cloak, the ferryman lay stretched and shivering; a great hulk of a man, but lean and shaken by the country fever.

"Hey, Master Shelton," he said, "be ye for the ferry? Ill times, ill times! Look to yourself. There is a fellowship abroad. Ye were better turn round on your two heels and try the bridge."

"Nay; time's in the saddle," answered Dick. "Time will ride, Hugh Ferryman. I am hot in haste."

"A wilful man!" returned the ferryman, rising. "An ye win safe to the Moat House, y' have done lucky; but I say no more." And then catching sight of Matcham, "Who be this?" he asked, as he paused, blinking, on the threshold of his cabin.

"It is my kinsman, Master Matcham," answered Dick.

"Give ye good day, good ferryman," said Matcham, who had dismounted, and now came forward, leading the horse. "Launch me your boat, I prithee; we are sore in haste."

The gaunt ferryman continued staring.

"By the mass!" he cried at length, and laughed with open throat.

Matcham coloured to his neck and winced; and Dick, with an angry countenance, put his hand on the lout's shoulder.

"How now, churl!" he cried. "Fall to thy business, and leave mocking thy betters."

Hugh Ferryman grumblingly undid his boat, and shoved it a little forth into the deep water. Then Dick led in the horse, and Matcham followed.

"Ye be mortal small made, master," said Hugh, with a wide grin; "something o' the wrong model, belike. Nay, Master Shelton, I am for you," he added, getting to his oars. "A cat may look at a king. I did but take a shot of the eye at Master Matcham."

"Sirrah, no more words," said Dick. "Bend me your back."

They were by that time at the mouth of the creek, and the view opened up and down the river. Everywhere it was enclosed with islands. Clay banks were falling in, willows nodding, reeds waving, martens dipping and piping. There was no sign of man in the labyrinth of waters.

"My master," said the ferryman, keeping the boat steady with one oar, "I have a shrew guess that John-a-Fenne is on the island. He bears me a black grudge to all Sir Daniel's. How if I turned me up stream and landed you an arrow-flight above the path? Ye were best not meddle with John Fenne."

"How, then, is he of this company?" asked Dick.

"Nay, mum is the word," said Hugh. "But I would go up water, Dick. How if Master Matcham came by an arrow?" and he laughed again.

"Be it so, Hugh," answered Dick.

"Look ye, then," pursued Hugh. "Sith it shall so be, unsling me your cross-bow—so: now make it ready—good; place me a quarrel. Ay, keep it so, and look upon me grimly."

"What meaneth this?" asked Dick.

"Why, my master, if I steal you across, it must be under force or fear," replied the ferryman; "for else, if John Fenne got wind of it, he were like to prove my most distressful neighbour."

"Do these churls ride so roughly?" Dick inquired. "Do they command Sir Daniel's own ferry?"

"Nay," whispered the ferryman, winking. "Mark me! Sir Daniel shall down. His time is out. He shall down. Mum!" And he bent over his oars.

They pulled a long way up the river, turned the tail of an island, and came softly down a narrow channel next the opposite bank. Then Hugh held water in mid-stream.

"I must land you here among the willows," he said.

"Here is no path but willow swamps and quagmires," answered Dick.

"Master Shelton," replied Hugh, "I dare not take ye nearer down, for your own sake now. He watcheth me the ferry, lying on his bow. All that go by and owe Sir Daniel good-will, he shooteth down like rabbits. I heard him swear it by the rood. An I had not known you of old days—ay, and from so high upward—I would 'a' let you go on; but for old days' remembrance, and because ye had this toy with you that's not fit for wounds or warfare, I did risk my two poor ears to have you over whole. Content you; I can no more, on my salvation!"

Hugh was still speaking, lying on his oars, when there came a great shout from among the willows on the island, and sounds followed as of a strong man breasting roughly through the wood.

"A murrain!" cried Hugh. "He was on the upper island all the while!" He pulled straight for shore. "Threat me with your bow, good Dick; threat me with it plain," he added. "I have tried to save your skins, save you mine!"

The boat ran into a tough thicket of willows with a crash. Matcham, pale, but steady and alert, at a sign from Dick, ran along the thwarts and leaped ashore; Dick, taking the horse by the bridle, sought to follow, but what with the animal's bulk, and what with the closeness of the thicket, both stuck fast. The horse neighed and trampled; and the boat, which was swinging in an eddy, came on and off and pitched with violence.

"It may not be, Hugh; here is no landing," cried Dick; but he still struggled valiantly with the obstinate thicket and the startled animal.

A tall man appeared upon the shore of the island, a long-bow in his hand. Dick saw him for an instant, with the corner of his eye, bending the bow with a great effort, his face crimson with hurry.

"Who goes?" he shouted. "Hugh, who goes?"

"'Tis Master Shelton, John," replied the ferryman.

"Stand, Dick Shelton!" bawled the man upon the island. "Ye shall have no hurt, upon the rood! Stand! Back out, Hugh Ferryman."

Dick cried a taunting answer.

"Nay, then, ye shall go afoot," returned the man; and he let drive an arrow.

The horse, struck by the shaft, lashed out in agony and terror; the boat capsized, and the next moment all were struggling in the eddies of the river.

When Dick came up, he was within a yard of the bank; and before his eyes were clear, his hand had closed on something firm and strong that instantly began to drag him forward. It was the riding-rod, that Matcham, crawling forth upon an overhanging willow, had opportunely thrust into his grasp.

"By the mass!" cried Dick, as he was helped ashore, "that makes a life I owe you. I swim like a cannon-ball." And he turned instantly towards the island.

Midway over, Hugh Ferryman was swimming with his upturned boat, while John-a-Fenne, furious at the ill-fortune of his shot, bawled to him to hurry.

"Come, Jack," said Shelton, "run for it! Ere Hugh can hale his barge across, or the pair of 'em can get it righted, we may be out of cry."

And adding example to his words, he began to run, dodging among the willows, and in marshy places leaping from tussock to tussock. He had no time to look for his direction; all he could do was to turn his back upon the river, and put all his heart to running.

Presently, however, the ground began to rise, which showed him he was still in the right way, and soon after they came forth upon a slope of solid turf, where elms began to mingle with the willows.

But here Matcham, who had been dragging far into the rear, threw himself fairly down.

"Leave me, Dick!" he cried, pantingly; "I can no more."

Dick turned, and came back to where his companion lay.

"Nay, Jack, leave thee!" he cried. "That were a knave's trick, to be sure, when ye risked a shot and a ducking, ay, and a drowning too, to save my life. Drowning, in sooth; for why I did not pull you in along with me, the saints alone can tell!"

"Nay," said Matcham, "I would 'a' saved us both, good Dick, for I can swim."

"Can ye so?" cried Dick, with open eyes. It was the one manly accomplishment of which he was himself incapable. In the order of the things that he admired, next to having killed a man in single fight came swimming. "Well," he said, "here is a lesson to despise no man. I promised to care for you as far as Holywood, and, by the rood, Jack, y'are more capable to care for me."

"Well, Dick, we're friends now," said Matcham

"Nay, I never was unfriends," answered Dick. "Y'are a brave lad in your way, albeit something of a milksop, too. I never met your like before this day. But, prithee, fetch back your breath, and let us on. Here is no place for chatter."

"My foot hurts shrewdly," said Matcham.

"Nay, I had forgot your foot," returned Dick. "Well, we must go the gentlier. I would I knew rightly where we were. I have clean lost the path; yet that may be for the better, too. An they watch the ferry, they watch the path, belike, as well. I would Sir Daniel were back with two-score men; he would sweep me these rascals as the wind sweeps leaves. Come, Jack, lean ye on my shoulder, ye poor shrew. Nay, y'are not tall enough. What age are ye, for a wager?—twelve?"

"Nay, I am sixteen," said Matcham.

"Y'are poorly grown to height, then," answered Dick. "But take my hand. We shall go softly, never fear. I owe you a life; I am a good repayer, Jack, of good or evil."

They began to go forward up the slope.

"We must hit the road, early or late," continued Dick; "and then for a fresh start. By the mass! but y' 'ave a rickety hand, Jack. If I had a hand like that, I would think shame. I tell you," he went on, with a sudden chuckle, "I swear by the mass I believe Hugh Ferryman took you for a maid."

"Nay, never!" cried the other, colouring high.

"A' did, though, for a wager!" Dick exclaimed. "Small blame to him. Ye look liker maid than man; and I tell you more—y'are a strange-looking rogue for a boy; but for a hussy, Jack, ye would be right fair—ye would. Ye would be well favoured for a wench."

"Well," said Matcham, "ye know right well that I am none."

"Nay, I know that; I do but jest," said Dick. "Ye'll be a man before your mother, Jack. What cheer, my bully! Ye shall strike shrewd strokes. Now, which, I marvel, of you or me, shall be first knighted, Jack? for knighted I shall be, or die for't. 'Sir Richard Shelton, Knight': it soundeth bravely. But 'Sir John Matcham' soundeth not amiss."

"Prithee, Dick, stop till I drink," said the other, pausing where a little clear spring welled out of the slope into a gravelled basin no bigger than a pocket. "And O, Dick, if I might come by anything to eat!—my very heart aches with hunger."

"Why, fool, did ye not eat at Kettley?" asked Dick.

"I had made a vow—it was a sin I had been led into," stammered Matcham; "but now, if it were but dry bread, I would eat it greedily."

"Sit ye, then, and eat," said Dick, "while that I scout a little forward for the road." And he took a wallet from his girdle, wherein were bread and pieces of dry bacon, and, while Matcham fell heartily to, struck farther forth among the trees.

A little beyond there was a dip in the ground, where a streamlet soaked among dead leaves; and beyond that, again, the trees were better grown and stood wider, and oak and beech began to take the place of willow and elm. The continued tossing and pouring of the wind among the leaves sufficiently concealed the sounds of his footsteps on the mast; it was for the ear what a moonless night is to the eye; but for all that Dick went cautiously, slipping from one big trunk to another, and looking sharply about him as he went. Suddenly a doe passed like a shadow through the underwood in front of him, and he paused, disgusted at the chance. This part of the wood had been certainly deserted, but now that the poor deer had run, she was like a messenger he should have sent before him to announce his coming; and instead of pushing farther, he turned him to the nearest well-grown tree, and rapidly began to climb.

Luck had served him well. The oak on which he had mounted was one of the tallest in that quarter of the wood, and easily out-topped its neighbours by a fathom and a half; and when Dick had clambered into the topmost fork and clung there, swinging dizzily in the great wind, he saw behind him the whole fenny plain as far as Kettley, and the Till wandering among woody islets, and in front of him, the white line of highroad winding through the forest. The boat had been righted—it was even now midway on the ferry. Beyond that there was no sign of man, nor aught moving but the wind. He was about to descend, when, taking a last view, his eye lit upon a string of moving points about the middle of the fen. Plainly a small troop was threading the causeway, and that at a good pace; and this gave him some concern as he shinned vigorously down the trunk and returned across the wood for his companion.

CHAPTER IV. A GREENWOOD COMPANY

Matcham was well rested and revived; and the two lads, winged by what Dick had seen, hurried through the remainder of the outwood, crossed the road in safety, and began to mount into the high ground of Tunstall Forest. The trees grew more and more in groves, with healthy places in between, sandy, gorsy, and dotted with old yews. The ground became more and more uneven, full of pits and hillocks. And with every step of the ascent the wind still blew the shriller, and the trees bent before the gusts like fishing-rods.

They had just entered one of the clearings, when Dick suddenly clapped down upon his face among the brambles, and began to crawl slowly backward towards the shelter of the grove. Matcham, in great bewilderment, for he could see no reason for this flight, still imitated his companion's course; and it was not until they had gained the harbour of a thicket that he turned and begged him to explain.

For all reply, Dick pointed with his finger.

At the far end of the clearing, a fir grew high above the neighbouring wood, and planted its black shock of foliage clear against the sky. For about fifty feet above the ground the trunk grew straight and solid like a column. At that level, it split into two massive boughs; and in the fork, like a mastheaded seaman, there stood a man in a green tabard, spying far and wide. The sun glistened upon his hair; with one hand he shaded his eyes to look abroad, and he kept slowly rolling his head from side to side, with the regularity of a machine.

The lads exchanged glances.

"Let us try to the left," said Dick. "We had near fallen foully, Jack."

Ten minutes afterwards they struck into a beaten path.

"Here is a piece of forest that I know not," Dick remarked. "Where goeth me this track?"

"Let us even try," said Matcham.

A few yards farther, the path came to the top of a ridge and began to go down abruptly into a cup-shaped hollow. At the foot, out of a thick wood of flowering hawthorn, two or three roofless gables, blackened as if by fire, and a single tall chimney marked the ruins of a house.

"What may this be?" whispered Matcham.

"Nay, by the mass, I know not," answered Dick. "I am all at sea. Let us go warily."

With beating hearts, they descended through the hawthorns. Here and there, they passed signs of recent cultivation; fruit trees and pot herbs ran wild among the thicket; a sun-dial had fallen in the grass; it seemed they were treading what once had been a garden. Yet a little farther and they came forth before the ruins of the house.

It had been a pleasant mansion and a strong. A dry ditch was dug deep about it; but it was now choked with masonry, and bridged by a fallen rafter. The two farther walls still stood, the sun shining through their empty windows; but the remainder of the building had collapsed, and now lay in a great cairn of ruin, grimed with fire. Already in the interior a few plants were springing green among the chinks.

"Now I bethink me," whispered Dick, "this must be Grimstone. It was a hold of one Simon Malmesbury; Sir Daniel was his bane! 'Twas Bennet Hatch that burned it, now five years agone. In sooth, 'twas pity, for it was a fair house."

Down in the hollow, where no wind blew, it was both warm and still; and Matcham, laying one hand upon Dick's arm, held up a warning finger.

"Hist!" he said.

Then came a strange sound, breaking on the quiet. It was twice repeated ere they recognised its nature. It was the sound of a big man clearing his throat; and just then a hoarse, untuneful voice broke into singing.

"Then up and spake the master, the king of the outlaws:

'What make ye here, my merry men, among the greenwood shaws?'

And Gamelyn made answer—he looked never adown:

'O, they must need to walk in wood that may not walk in town!'"

The singer paused, a faint clink of iron followed, and then silence.

The two lads stood looking at each other. Whoever he might be, their invisible neighbour was just beyond the ruin. And suddenly the colour came into Matcham's face, and next moment he had crossed the fallen rafter, and was climbing cautiously on the huge pile of lumber that filled the interior of the roofless house. Dick would have withheld him, had he been in time; as it was, he was fain to follow.

Right in the corner of the ruin, two rafters had fallen crosswise, and protected a clear space no larger than a pew in church. Into this the lads silently lowered themselves. There they were perfectly concealed, and through an arrow-loophole commanded a view upon the farther side.

Peering through this, they were struck stiff with terror at their predicament. To retreat was impossible; they scarce dared to breathe. Upon the very margin of the ditch, not thirty feet from where they crouched, an iron caldron bubbled and steamed above a glowing fire; and close by, in an attitude of listening, as though he had caught some sound of their clambering among the ruins, a tall, red-faced, battered-looking man stood poised, an iron spoon in his right hand, a horn and a formidable dagger at his belt. Plainly this was the singer; plainly he had been stirring the caldron, when some incautious step among the lumber had fallen upon his ear. A little farther off, another man lay slumbering, rolled in a brown cloak, with a butterfly hovering above his face. All this was in a clearing white with daisies; and at the extreme verge, a bow, a sheaf of arrows, and part of a deer's carcase hung upon a flowering hawthorn.

Presently the fellow relaxed from his attitude of attention, raised the spoon to his mouth, tasted its contents, nodded, and then fell again to stirring and singing.

"'O, they must need to walk in wood that may not walk in town,'" he croaked, taking up his song where he had left it.

"O, sir, we walk not here at all an evil thing to do.

But if we meet with the good king's deer to shoot a shaft into."

Still as he sang, he took from time to time another spoonful of the broth, blew upon it, and tasted it, with all the airs of an experienced cook. At length, apparently, he judged the mess was ready; for taking the horn from his girdle, he blew three modulated calls.

The other fellow awoke, rolled over, brushed away the butterfly, and looked about him.

"How now, brother?" he said. "Dinner?"

"Ay, sot," replied the cook, "dinner it is, and a dry dinner, too, with neither ale nor bread. But there is little pleasure in the greenwood now; time was when a good fellow could live here like a mitred abbot, set aside the rain and the white frosts; he had his heart's desire both of ale and wine. But now are men's spirits dead; and this John Amend-All, save us and guard us! but a stuffed booby to scare crows withal."

"Nay," returned the other, "y'are too set on meat and drinking, Lawless. Bide ye a bit; the good time cometh."

"Look ye," returned the cook, "I have even waited for this good time sith that I was so high. I have been a Grey Friar; I have been a king's archer; I have been a shipman, and sailed the salt seas; and I have been in greenwood before this, forsooth! and shot the king's deer. What cometh of it? Naught! I were better to have bided in the cloister. John Abbot availeth more than John Amend-All. By 'r Lady! here they come."

One after another, tall, likely fellows began to stroll into the lawn. Each as he came produced a knife and a horn cup, helped himself from the caldron, and sat down upon the grass to eat. They were very variously equipped and armed; some in rusty smocks, and with nothing but a knife and an old bow; others in the height of forest gallantry, all in Lincoln green, both hood and jerkin, with dainty peacock arrows in their belts, a horn upon a baldrick, and a sword and dagger at their sides. They came in the silence of hunger, and scarce growled a salutation, but fell instantly to meat.

There were, perhaps, a score of them already gathered, when a sound of suppressed cheering arose close by among the hawthorns, and immediately after five or six woodmen carrying a stretcher debouched upon the lawn. A tall, lusty fellow, somewhat grizzled, and as brown as a smoked ham, walked before them with an air of some authority, his bow at his back, a bright boar-spear in his hand.

"Lads!" he cried, "good fellows all, and my right merry friends, y' have sung this while on a dry whistle and lived at little ease. But what said I ever? Abide Fortune constantly; she turneth, turneth swift. And lo! here is her little firstling—even that good creature, ale!"

There was a murmur of applause as the bearers set down the stretcher and displayed a goodly cask.

"And now haste ye, boys," the man continued. "There is work toward. A handful of archers are but now come to the ferry; murrey and blue is their wear; they are our butts —they shall all taste arrows—no man of them shall struggle through this wood. For, lads, we are here some fifty strong, each man of us most foully wronged; for some they have lost lands, and some friends; and some they have been outlawed—all oppressed! Who, then, hath done this evil? Sir Daniel, by the rood! Shall he then profit? shall he sit snug in our houses? shall he till our fields? shall he suck the bone he robbed us of? I trow not. He getteth him strength at law; he gaineth cases; nay, there is one case he shall not gain—I have a writ here at my belt that, please the saints, shall conquer him."

Lawless the cook was by this time already at his second horn of ale. He raised it, as if to pledge the speaker.

"Master Ellis," he said, "y'are for vengeance—well it becometh you!—but your poor brother o' the greenwood, that had never lands to lose nor friends to think upon, looketh rather, for his poor part, to the profit of the thing. He had liever a gold noble and a pottle of canary wine than all the vengeances in purgatory."

"Lawless," replied the other, "to reach the Moat House, Sir Daniel must pass the forest. We shall make that passage dearer, pardy, than any battle. Then, when he hath got to earth with such ragged handful as escapeth us—all his great friends fallen and fled away, and none to give him aid—we shall beleaguer that old fox about, and great shall be the fall of him. 'Tis a fat buck; he will make a dinner for us all."

"Ay," returned Lawless, "I have eaten many of these dinners beforehand; but the cooking of them is hot work, good Master Ellis. And meanwhile what do we? We make black arrows, we write rhymes, and we drink fair cold water, that discomfortable drink."

"Y'are untrue, Will Lawless. Ye still smell of the Grey Friars' buttery; greed is your undoing," answered Ellis. "We took twenty pounds from Appleyard. We took seven marks from the messenger last night. A day ago we had fifty from the merchant."

"And to-day," said one of the men, "I stopped a fat pardoner riding apace for Holywood. Here is his purse."

Ellis counted the contents.

"Five-score shillings!" he grumbled. "Fool, he had more in his sandal, or stitched into his tippet. Y'are but a child, Tom Cuckow; ye have lost the fish."

But, for all that, Ellis pocketed the purse with nonchalance. He stood leaning on his boar-spear, and looked round upon the rest. They, in various attitudes, took greedily of the venison pottage, and liberally washed it down with ale. This was a good day; they were in luck; but business pressed, and they were speedy in their eating. The first-comers had by this time even despatched their dinner. Some lay down upon the grass and fell instantly asleep, like boa-constrictors; others talked together, or overhauled their weapons; and one, whose humour was particularly gay, holding forth an ale-horn, began to sing:

"Here is no law in good green shaw,

Here is no lack of meat;

'Tis merry and quiet, with deer for our diet,

In summer, when all is sweet.

"Come winter again, with wind and rain—

Come winter, with snow and sleet,

Get home to your places, with hoods on your faces,

And sit by the fire and eat."

All this while the two lads had listened and lain close; only Richard had unslung his cross-bow, and held ready in one hand the windac, or grappling-iron that he used to bend it. Otherwise they had not dared to stir; and this scene of forest life had gone on before their eyes like a scene upon a theatre. But now there came a strange interruption. The tall chimney which overtopped the remainder of the ruins rose right above their hiding-place. There came a whistle in the air, and then a sounding smack, and the fragments of a broken arrow fell about their ears. Some one from the upper quarters of the wood, perhaps the very sentinel they saw posted in the fir, had shot an arrow at the chimney-top.

Matcham could not restrain a little cry, which he instantly stifled, and even Dick started with surprise, and dropped the windac from his fingers. But to the fellows on the lawn, this shaft was an expected signal. They were all afoot together, tightening their belts, testing their bow-strings, loosening sword and dagger in the sheath. Ellis held up his hand; his face had suddenly assumed a look of savage energy; the white of his eyes shone in his sun-brown face.

"Lads," he said, "ye know your places. Let not one man's soul escape you. Appleyard was a whet before a meal; but now we go to table. I have three men whom I will bitterly avenge—Harry Shelton, Simon Malmesbury, and"—striking his broad bosom—"and Ellis Duckworth, by the mass!"

Another man came, red with hurry, through the thorns.

"'Tis not Sir Daniel!" he panted. "They are but seven. Is the arrow gone?"

"It struck but now," replied Ellis.

"A murrain!" cried the messenger. "Methought I heard it whistle. And I go dinnerless!"

In the space of a minute, some running, some walking sharply, according as their stations were nearer or farther away, the men of the Black Arrow had all disappeared from the neighbourhood of the ruined house; and the caldron, and the fire, which was now burning low, and the dead deer's carcase on the hawthorn, remained alone to testify they had been there.

CHAPTER V. "BLOODY AS THE HUNTER"

The lads lay quiet till the last footstep had melted on the wind. Then they arose, and with many an ache, for they were weary with constraint, clambered through the ruins, and recrossed the ditch upon the rafter. Matcham had picked up the windac and went first, Dick following stiffly, with his crossbow on his arm.

"And now," said Matcham, "forth to Holywood."

"To Holywood!" cried Dick, "when good fellows stand shot? Not I! I would see you hanged first, Jack!"

"Ye would leave me, would ye?" Matcham asked.

"Ay, by my sooth!" returned Dick. "An I be not in time to warn these lads, I will go die with them. What! would ye have me leave my own men that I have lived among? I trow not! Give me my windac."

But there was nothing further from Matcham's mind.

"Dick," he said, "ye sware before the saints that ye would see me safe to Holywood. Would ye be forsworn? Would you desert me—a perjurer?"

"Nay, I sware for the best," returned Dick. "I meant it too; but now! But look ye, Jack, turn again with me. Let me but warn these men, and, if needs must, stand shot with them; then shall all be clear, and I will on again to Holywood and purge mine oath."

"Ye but deride me," answered Matcham. "These men ye go to succour are the same that hunt me to my ruin."

Dick scratched his head.

"I cannot help it, Jack," he said. "Here is no remedy. What would ye? Ye run no great peril, man; and these are in the way of death. Death!" he added. "Think of it! What a murrain do ye keep me here for? Give me the windac. St. George! shall they all die?"

"Richard Shelton," said Matcham, looking him squarely in the face, "would ye, then, join party with Sir Daniel? Have ye not ears? Heard ye not this Ellis, what he said? or have ye no heart for your own kindly blood and the father that men slew? 'Harry Shelton,' he said; and Sir Harry Shelton was your father, as the sun shines in heaven."

"What would ye?" Dick cried again. "Would ye have me credit thieves?"

"Nay, I have heard it before now," returned Matcham. "The fame goeth currently, it was Sir Daniel slew him. He slew him under oath; in his own house he shed the innocent blood. Heaven wearies for the avenging on't; and you—the man's son—ye go about to comfort and defend the murderer!"

"Jack," cried the lad, "I know not. It may be; what know I? But, see here: This man hath bred me up and fostered me, and his men I have hunted with and played among; and to leave them in the hour of peril—O, man, if I did that, I were stark dead to honour! Nay, Jack, ye would not ask it; ye would not wish me to be base."

"But your father, Dick?" said Matcham, somewhat wavering. "Your father? and your oath to me? Ye took the saints to witness."

"My father?" cried Shelton. "Nay, he would have me go! If Sir Daniel slew him, when the hour comes this hand shall slay Sir Daniel; but neither him nor his will I desert in peril. And for mine oath, good Jack, ye shall absolve me of it here. For the lives' sake of many men that hurt you not, and for mine honour, ye shall set me free."

"I, Dick? Never!" returned Matcham. "An ye leave me, y'are forsworn, and so I shall declare it."

"My blood heats," said Dick. "Give me the windac! Give it me!"

"I'll not," said Matcham. "I'll save you in your teeth."

"Not?" cried Dick. "I'll make you!"

"Try it," said the other.

They stood, looking in each other's eyes, each ready for a spring. Then

Dick leaped; and though Matcham turned instantly and fled, in two bounds he was overtaken, the windac was twisted from his grasp, he was thrown roughly to the ground, and Dick stood across him, flushed and menacing, with doubled fist. Matcham lay where he had fallen, with his face in the grass, not thinking of resistance.

Dick bent his bow.

"I'll teach you!" he cried, fiercely. "Oath or no oath, ye may go hang for me!"

And he turned and began to run. Matcham was on his feet at once, and began running after him.

"What d'ye want?" cried Dick, stopping. "What make ye after me? Stand off!"

"I will follow an I please," said Matcham. "This wood is free to me."

"Stand back, by 'r Lady!" returned Dick, raising his bow.

"Ah, y'are a brave boy!" retorted Matcham. "Shoot!"

Dick lowered his weapon in some confusion.

"See here," he said. "Y' have done me ill enough. Go, then. Go your way in fair wise; or, whether I will or not, I must even drive you to it."

"Well," said Matcham, doggedly, "y'are the stronger. Do your worst. I shall not leave to follow thee, Dick, unless thou makest me," he added.

Dick was almost beside himself. It went against his heart to beat a creature so defenceless; and, for the life of him, he knew no other way to rid himself of this unwelcome and, as he began to think, perhaps untrue companion.

"Y'are mad, I think," he cried. "Fool-fellow, I am hasting to your foes; as fast as foot can carry me, go I thither."

"I care not, Dick," replied the lad. "If y'are bound to die, Dick, I'll die too. I would liever go with you to prison than to go free without you."

"Well," returned the other, "I may stand no longer prating. Follow me, if ye must; but if ye play me false, it shall but little advance you, mark ye that. Shalt have a quarrel in thine inwards, boy."

So saying, Dick took once more to his heels, keeping in the margin of the thicket and looking briskly about him as he went. At a good pace he rattled out of the dell, and came again into the more open quarters of the wood. To the left a little eminence appeared, spotted with golden gorse, and crowned with a black tuft of firs.

"I shall see from there," he thought, and struck for it across a heathy clearing.

He had gone but a few yards, when Matcham touched him on the arm, and pointed. To the eastward of the summit there was a dip, and, as it were, a valley passing to the other side; the heath was not yet out; all the ground was rusty, like an unscoured buckler, and dotted sparingly with yews; and there, one following another, Dick saw half a score green jerkins mounting the ascent, and marching at their head, conspicuous by his boar-spear, Ellis Duckworth in person. One after another gained the top, showed for a moment against the sky, and then dipped upon the farther side, until the last was gone.

Dick looked at Matcham with a kindlier eye.

"So y'are to be true to me, Jack?" he asked. "I thought ye were of the other party."

Matcham began to sob.

"What cheer!" cried Dick. "Now the saints behold us! would ye snivel for a word?"

"Ye hurt me," sobbed Matcham. "Ye hurt me when ye threw me down. Y'are a coward to abuse your strength."

"Nay, that is fool's talk," said Dick, roughly. "Y' had no title to my windac, Master John. I would 'a' done right to have well basted you. If ye go with me, ye must obey me; and so, come."

Matcham had half a thought to stay behind; but, seeing that Dick continued to scour full-tilt towards the eminence and not so much as looked across his shoulder, he soon thought better of that, and began to run in turn. But the ground was very difficult and steep; Dick had already a long start, and had, at any rate, the lighter heels, and he had long since come to the summit, crawled forward through the firs, and ensconced himself in a thick tuft of gorse, before Matcham, panting like a deer, rejoined him, and lay down in silence by his side.

Below, in the bottom of a considerable valley, the short cut from Tunstall hamlet wound downwards to the ferry. It was well beaten, and the eye followed it easily from point to point. Here it was bordered by open glades; there the forest closed upon it; every hundred yards it ran beside an ambush. Far down the path, the sun shone on seven steel salets, and from time to time, as the trees opened, Selden and his men could be seen riding briskly, still bent upon Sir Daniel's mission. The wind had somewhat fallen, but still tussled merrily with the trees, and, perhaps, had Appleyard been there, he would have drawn a warning from the troubled conduct of the birds.

"Now, mark," Dick whispered. "They be already well advanced into the wood; their safety lieth rather in continuing forward. But see ye where this wide glade runneth down before us, and in the midst of it, these two-score trees make like an island? There were their safety. An they but come sound as far as that, I will make shift to warn them. But my heart misgiveth me; they are but seven against so many, and they but carry cross-bows. The long-bow, Jack, will have the uppermost ever."

Meanwhile, Selden and his men still wound up the path, ignorant of their danger, and momently drew nearer hand. Once, indeed, they paused, drew into a group, and seemed to point and listen. But it was something from far away across the plain that had arrested their attention—a hollow growl of cannon that came, from time to time, upon the wind, and told of the great battle. It was worth a thought, to be sure; for if the voice of the big guns were thus become audible in Tunstall Forest, the fight must have rolled ever eastward, and the day, by consequence, gone sore against Sir Daniel and the lords of the dark rose.

But presently the little troop began again to move forward, and came next to a very open, heathy portion of the way, where but a single tongue of forest ran down to join the road. They were but just abreast of this, when an arrow shone flying. One of the men threw up his arms, his horse reared, and both fell and struggled together in a mass. Even from where the boys lay they could hear the rumour of the men's voices crying out; they could see the startled horses prancing, and, presently, as the troop began to recover from their first surprise, one fellow beginning to dismount. A second arrow from somewhat farther off glanced in a wide arch; a second rider bit the dust. The man who was dismounting lost hold upon the rein, and his horse fled galloping, and dragged him by the foot along the road, bumping from stone to stone, and battered by the fleeing hoofs. The four who still kept the saddle instantly broke and scattered; one wheeled and rode, shrieking, towards the ferry; the other three, with loose rein and flying raiment, came galloping up the road from Tunstall. From every clump they passed an arrow sped. Soon a horse fell, but the rider found his feet and continued to pursue his comrades till a second shot despatched him. Another man fell; then another horse; out of the whole troop there was but one fellow left, and he on foot; only, in different directions, the noise of the galloping of three riderless horses was dying fast into the distance.

All this time not one of the assailants had for a moment shown himself. Here and there along the path, horse or man rolled, undespatched, in his agony; but no merciful enemy broke cover to put them from their pain.

The solitary survivor stood bewildered in the road beside his fallen charger. He had come the length of that broad glade, with the island of timber, pointed out by Dick. He was not, perhaps, five hundred yards from where the boys lay hidden; and they could see him plainly, looking to and fro in deadly expectation. But nothing came; and the man began to pluck up his courage, and suddenly unslung and bent his bow. At the same time, by something in his action, Dick recognised Selden.

At this offer of resistance, from all about him in the covert of the woods there went up the sound of laughter. A score of men, at least, for this was the very thickest of the ambush, joined in this cruel and untimely mirth. Then an arrow glanced over Selden's shoulder; and he leaped and ran a little back.

Another dart struck quivering at his heel. He made for the cover. A third shaft leaped out right in his face, and fell short in front of him. And then the laughter was repeated loudly, rising and re-echoing from different thickets.

It was plain that his assailants were but baiting him, as men, in those days, baited the poor bull, or as the cat still trifles with the mouse. The skirmish was well over; farther down the road, a fellow in green was already calmly gathering the arrows; and now, in the evil pleasure of their hearts, they gave themselves the spectacle of their poor fellow-sinner in his torture.

Selden began to understand; he uttered a roar of anger, shouldered his cross-bow, and sent a quarrel at a venture into the wood. Chance favoured him, for a slight cry responded. Then, throwing down his weapon, Selden began to run before him up the glade, and almost in a straight line for Dick and Matcham.

The companions of the Black Arrow now began to shoot in earnest. But they were properly served; their chance had past; most of them had now to shoot against the sun; and Selden, as he ran, bounded from side to side to baffle and deceive their aim. Best of all, by turning up the glade he had defeated their preparations; there were no marksmen posted higher up than the one whom he had just killed or wounded; and the confusion of the foresters' counsels soon became apparent. A whistle sounded thrice, and then again twice. It was repeated from another quarter. The woods on either side became full of the sound of people bursting through the underwood; and a bewildered deer ran out into the open, stood for a second on three feet, with nose in air, and then plunged again into the thicket.

Selden still ran, bounding; ever and again an arrow followed him, but still would miss. It began to appear as if he might escape. Dick had his bow armed, ready to support him; even Matcham, forgetful of his interest, took sides at heart for the poor fugitive, and both lads glowed and trembled in the ardour of their hearts.

He was within fifty yards of them, when an arrow struck him and he fell. He was up again, indeed, upon the instant; but now he ran staggering, and, like a blind man, turned aside from his direction.

Dick leaped to his feet and waved to him.

"Here!" he cried. "This way! here is help! Nay, run, fellow—run!"

But just then a second arrow struck Selden in the shoulder, between the plates of his brigandine, and, piercing through his jack, brought him, like a stone, to earth.

"O, the poor heart!" cried Matcham, with clasped hands.

And Dick stood petrified upon the hill, a mark for archery.

Ten to one he had speedily been shot—for the foresters were furious with themselves, and taken unawares by Dick's appearance in the rear of their position—but instantly, out of a quarter of the wood surprisingly near to the two lads, a stentorian voice arose, the voice of Ellis Duckworth.

"Hold!" it roared. "Shoot not! Take him alive! It is young Shelton—Harry's son."

And immediately after a shrill whistle sounded several times, and was again taken up and repeated farther off. The whistle, it appeared, was John Amend-All's battle trumpet, by which he published his directions.

"Ah, foul fortune!" cried Dick. "We are undone. Swiftly, Jack, come swiftly!"

And the pair turned and ran back through the open pine clump that covered the summit of the hill.

CHAPTER VI. TO THE DAY'S END

It was, indeed, high time for them to run. On every side the company of the Black Arrow was making for the hill. Some, being better runners, or having open ground to run upon, had far outstripped the others, and were already close upon the goal; some, following valleys, had spread out to right and left, and outflanked the lads on either side.

Dick plunged into the nearest cover. It was a tall grove of oaks, firm underfoot and clear of underbrush, and as it lay down-hill, they made good speed. There followed next a piece of open, which Dick avoided, holding to his left. Two minutes after, and the same obstacle arising, the lads followed the same course. Thus it followed that, while the lads, bending continually to the left, drew nearer and nearer to the highroad and the river which they had crossed an hour or two before, the great bulk of their pursuers were leaning to the other hand, and running towards Tunstall.

The lads paused to breathe. There was no sound of pursuit. Dick put his ear to the ground, and still there was nothing; but the wind, to be sure, still made a turmoil in the trees, and it was hard to make certain.

"On again," said Dick; and, tired as they were, and Matcham limping with his injured foot, they pulled themselves together, and once more pelted down the hill.

Three minutes later, they were breasting through a low thicket of evergreen. High overhead, the tall trees made a continuous roof of foliage. It was a pillared grove, as high as a cathedral, and except for the hollies among which the lads were struggling, open and smoothly swarded.

On the other side, pushing through the last fringe of evergreen, they blundered forth again into the open twilight of the grove.

"Stand!" cried a voice.

And there, between the huge stems, not fifty feet before them, they beheld a stout fellow in green, sore blown with running, who instantly drew an arrow to the head and covered them. Matcham stopped with a cry; but Dick, without a pause, ran straight upon the forester, drawing his dagger as he went. The other, whether he was startled by the daring of the onslaught, or whether he was hampered by his orders, did not shoot; he stood wavering; and before he had time to come to himself, Dick bounded at his throat, and sent him sprawling backward on the turf. The arrow went one way and the bow another with a sounding twang. The disarmed forester grappled his assailant; but the dagger shone and descended twice. Then came a couple of groans, and then Dick rose to his feet again, and the man lay motionless, stabbed to the heart.

"On!" said Dick; and he once more pelted forward, Matcham trailing in the rear. To say truth, they made but poor speed of it by now, labouring dismally as they ran, and catching for their breath like fish. Matcham had a cruel stitch, and his head swam; and as for Dick, his knees were like lead. But they kept up the form of running with undiminished courage.

Presently they came to the end of the grove. It stopped abruptly; and there, a few yards before them, was the highroad from Risingham to Shoreby, lying, at this point, between two even walls of forest.

At the sight Dick paused; and as soon as he stopped running, he became aware of a confused noise, which rapidly grew louder. It was at first like the rush of a very high gust of wind, but soon it became more definite, and resolved itself into the galloping of horses; and then, in a flash, a whole company of men-at-arms came driving round the corner, swept before the lads, and were gone again upon the instant. They rode as for their lives, in complete disorder; some of them were wounded; riderless horses galloped at their side with bloody saddles. They were plainly fugitives from the great battle.

The noise of their passage had scarce begun to die away towards Shoreby, before fresh hoofs came echoing in their wake, and another deserter clattered down the road; this time a single rider and, by his splendid armour, a man of high degree. Close after him there followed several baggage-waggons, fleeing at an ungainly canter, the drivers flailing at the horses as if for life. These must have run early in the day; but their cowardice was not to save them. For just before they came abreast of where the lads stood wondering, a man in hacked armour, and seemingly beside himself with fury, overtook the waggons, and with the truncheon of a sword, began to cut the drivers down. Some leaped from their places and plunged into the wood; the others he sabred as they sat, cursing them the while for cowards in a voice that was scarce human.

All this time the noise in the distance had continued to increase; the rumble of carts, the clatter of horses, the cries of men, a great, confused rumour, came swelling on the wind; and it was plain that the rout of a whole army was pouring, like an inundation, down the road.

Dick stood sombre. He had meant to follow the highway till the turn for Holywood, and now he had to change his plan. But above all, he had recognised the colours of Earl Risingham, and he knew that the battle had gone finally against the rose of Lancaster. Had Sir Daniel joined, and was he now a fugitive and ruined? or had he deserted to the side of York, and was he forfeit to honour? It was an ugly choice.

"Come," he said, sternly; and, turning on his heel, he began to walk forward through the grove, with Matcham limping in his rear.

For some time they continued to thread the forest in silence. It was now growing late; the sun was setting in the plain beyond Kettley; the tree-tops overhead glowed golden; but the shadows had begun to grow darker and the chill of the night to fall.

"If there were anything to eat!" cried Dick, suddenly, pausing as he spoke.

Matcham sat down and began to weep.

"Ye can weep for your own supper, but when it was to save men's lives, your heart was hard enough," said Dick, contemptuously. "Y' 'ave seven deaths upon your conscience, Master John; I'll ne'er forgive you that."

"Conscience!" cried Matcham, looking fiercely up. "Mine! And ye have the man's red blood upon your dagger! And wherefore did ye slay him, the poor soul? He drew his arrow, but he let not fly; he held you in his hand, and spared you! 'Tis as brave to kill a kitten, as a man that not defends himself."

Dick was struck dumb.

"I slew him fair. I ran me in upon his bow," he cried.

"It was a coward blow," returned Matcham. "Y'are but a lout and bully, Master Dick; ye but abuse advantages; let there come a stronger, we will see you truckle at his boot! Ye care not for vengeance, neither—for your father's death that goes unpaid, and his poor ghost that clamoureth for justice. But if there come but a poor creature in your hands that lacketh skill and strength, and would befriend you, down she shall go!"

Dick was too furious to observe that "she."

"Marry!" he cried, "and here is news! Of any two the one will still be stronger. The better man throweth the worse, and the worse is well served. Ye deserve a belting, Master Matcham, for your ill-guidance and unthankfulness to meward; and what ye deserve ye shall have."

And Dick, who, even in his angriest temper, still preserved the appearance of composure, began to unbuckle his belt.

"Here shall be your supper," he said, grimly.

Matcham had stopped his tears; he was as white as a sheet, but he looked Dick steadily in the face, and never moved. Dick took a step, swinging the belt. Then he paused, embarrassed by the large eyes and the thin, weary face of his companion. His courage began to subside.

"Say ye were in the wrong, then," he said, lamely.

"Nay," said Matcham, "I was in the right. Come, cruel! I be lame; I be weary; I resist not; I ne'er did thee hurt; come, beat me—coward!"

Dick raised the belt at this last provocation; but Matcham winced and drew himself together with so cruel an apprehension, that his heart failed him yet again. The strap fell by his side, and he stood irresolute, feeling like a fool.

"A plague upon thee, shrew!" he said. "An ye be so feeble of hand, ye should keep the closer guard upon your tongue. But I'll be hanged before I beat you!" and he put on his belt again. "Beat you I will not," he continued; "but forgive you?—never. I knew ye not; ye were my master's enemy; I lent you my horse; my dinner ye have eaten; y' 'ave called me a man o' wood, a coward, and a bully. Nay, by the mass! the measure is filled, and runneth over. 'Tis a great thing to be weak, I trow: ye can do your worst, yet shall none punish you; ye may steal a man's weapons in the hour of need, yet may the man not take his own again;—y' are weak, forsooth! Nay, then, if one cometh charging at you with a lance, and crieth he is weak, ye must let him pierce your body through! Tut! fool words!"

"And yet ye beat me not," returned Matcham.

"Let be," said Dick—"let be. I will instruct you. Y' 'ave been ill-nurtured, methinks, and yet ye have the makings of some good, and, beyond all question, saved me from the river. Nay, I had forgotten it; I am as thankless as thyself. But, come, let us on. An we be for Holywood this night, ay, or to-morrow early, we had best set forward speedily."

But though Dick had talked himself back into his usual good-humour, Matcham had forgiven him nothing. His violence, the recollection of the forester whom he had slain—above all, the vision of the upraised belt, were things not easily to be forgotten.

"I will thank you, for the form's sake," said Matcham. "But, in sooth, good Master Shelton, I had liever find my way alone. Here is a wide wood; prithee, let each choose his path; I owe you a dinner and a lesson. Fare ye well!"

"Nay," cried Dick, "if that be your tune, so be it, and a plague be with you!"

Each turned aside, and they began walking off severally, with no thought of the direction, intent solely on their quarrel. But Dick had not gone ten paces ere his name was called, and Matcham came running after.

"Dick," he said, "it were unmannerly to part so coldly. Here is my hand,

and my heart with it. For all that wherein you have so excellently served and helped me—not for the form, but from the heart, I thank you. Fare ye right well."

"Well, lad," returned Dick, taking the hand which was offered him, "good speed to you, if speed you may. But I misdoubt it shrewdly. Y'are too disputatious."

So then they separated for the second time; and presently it was Dick who was running after Matcham.

"Here," he said, "take my cross-bow; shalt not go unarmed."

"A cross-bow!" said Matcham. "Nay, boy, I have neither the strength to bend nor yet the skill to aim with it. It were no help to me, good boy. But yet I thank you."

The night had now fallen, and under the trees they could no longer read each other's face.

"I will go some little way with you," said Dick. "The night is dark. I would fain leave you on a path, at least. My mind misgiveth me, y'are likely to be lost."

Without any more words, he began to walk forward, and the other once more followed him. The blackness grew thicker and thicker. Only here and there, in open places, they saw the sky, dotted with small stars. In the distance, the noise of the rout of the Lancastrian army still continued to be faintly audible; but with every step they left it farther in the rear.

At the end of half an hour of silent progress they came forth upon a broad patch of heathy open. It glimmered in the light of the stars, shaggy with fern and islanded with clumps of yew. And here they paused and looked upon each other.

"Y'are weary?" Dick said.

"Nay, I am so weary," answered Matcham, "that methinks I could lie down and die."

"I hear the chiding of a river," returned Dick. "Let us go so far forth, for I am sore athirst."

The ground sloped down gently; and, sure enough, in the bottom, they found a little murmuring river, running among willows. Here they threw themselves down together by the brink; and putting their mouths to the level of a starry pool, they drank their fill.

"Dick," said Matcham, "it may not be. I can no more."

"I saw a pit as we came down," said Dick. "Let us lie down therein and sleep."

"Nay, but with all my heart!" cried Matcham.

The pit was sandy and dry; a shock of brambles hung upon one hedge, and made a partial shelter; and there the two lads lay down, keeping close together for the sake of warmth, their quarrel all forgotten. And soon sleep fell upon them like a cloud, and under the dew and stars they rested peacefully.

CHAPTER VII. THE HOODED FACE

They awoke in the grey of the morning; the birds were not yet in full song, but twittered here and there among the woods; the sun was not yet up, but the eastern sky was barred with solemn colours. Half starved and over-weary as they were, they lay without moving, sunk in a delightful lassitude. And as they thus lay, the clang of a bell fell suddenly upon their ears.

"A bell!" said Dick, sitting up. "Can we be, then, so near to Holywood?"

A little after, the bell clanged again, but this time somewhat nearer hand; and from that time forth, and still drawing nearer and nearer, it continued to sound brokenly abroad in the silence of the morning.

"Nay, what should this betoken?" said Dick, who was now broad awake.

"It is some one walking," returned Matcham, "and the bell tolleth ever as he moves."

"I see that well," said Dick. "But wherefore? What maketh he in Tunstall Woods? Jack," he added, "laugh at me an ye will, but I like not the hollow sound of it."

"Nay," said Matcham, with a shiver, "it hath a doleful note. An the day were not come——"

But just then the bell, quickening its pace, began to ring thick and hurried, and then it gave a single hammering jangle, and was silent for a space.

"It is as though the bearer had run for a paternoster while, and then leaped the river," Dick observed.

"And now beginneth he again to pace soberly forward," added Matcham.

"Nay," returned Dick—"nay, not so soberly, Jack. 'Tis a man that walketh you right speedily. 'Tis a man in some fear of his life, or about some hurried business. See ye not how swift the beating draweth near?"

"It is now close by," said Matcham.

They were now on the edge of the pit; and as the pit itself was on a certain eminence, they commanded a view over the greater proportion of the clearing, up to the thick woods that closed it in.

The daylight, which was very clear and grey, showed them a riband of white foot-path wandering among the gorse. It passed some hundred yards from the pit, and ran the whole length of the clearing, east and west. By the line of its course, Dick judged it should lead more or less directly to the Moat House.

Upon this path, stepping forth from the margin of the wood, a white figure now appeared. It paused a little, and seemed to look about; and then, at a slow pace, and bent almost double, it began to draw near across the heath. At every step the bell clanked. Face, it had none; a white hood, not even pierced with eye-holes, veiled the head; and as the creature moved, it seemed to feel its way with the tapping of a stick. Fear fell upon the lads, as cold as death.

"A leper!" said Dick, hoarsely.

"His touch is death," said Matcham. "Let us run."

"Not so," returned Dick. "See ye not?—he is stone blind. He guideth him with a staff. Let us lie still; the wind bloweth towards the path, and he will go by and hurt us not. Alas, poor soul, and we should rather pity him!"

"I will pity him when he is by," replied Matcham.

The blind leper was now about half-way towards them, and just then the sun rose and shone full on his veiled face. He had been a tall man before he was bowed by his disgusting sickness, and even now he walked with a vigorous step. The dismal beating of his bell, the pattering of the stick, the eyeless screen before his countenance, and the knowledge that he was not only doomed to death and suffering, but shut out for ever from the touch of his fellow-men, filled the lads' bosoms with dismay; and at every step that brought him nearer, their courage and strength seemed to desert them.

As he came about level with the pit, he paused, and turned his face full upon the lads.

"Mary be my shield! He sees us!" said Matcham, faintly.

"Hush!" whispered Dick. "He doth but hearken. He is blind, fool!"

The leper looked or listened, whichever he was really doing, for some seconds. Then he began to move on again, but presently paused once more, and again turned and seemed to gaze upon the lads. Even Dick became dead-white and closed his eyes, as if by the mere sight he might become infected. But soon the bell sounded, and this time, without any further hesitation, the leper crossed the remainder of the little heath and disappeared into the covert of the woods.

"He saw us," said Matcham. "I could swear it!"

"Tut!" returned Dick, recovering some sparks of courage. "He but heard us. He was in fear, poor soul! An ye were blind, and walked in a perpetual night, ye would start yourself, if ever a twig rustled or a bird cried 'Peep.'"

"Dick, good Dick, he saw us," repeated Matcham. "When a man hearkeneth, he doth not as this man; he doth otherwise, Dick. This was seeing; it was not hearing. He means foully. Hark, else, if his bell be not stopped!"

Such was the case. The bell rang no longer.

"Nay," said Dick, "I like not that. Nay," he cried again, "I like that little. What may this betoken? Let us go, by the mass!"

"He hath gone east," added Matcham. "Good Dick, let us go westward straight; I shall not breathe till I have my back turned upon that leper."

"Jack, y'are too cowardly," replied Dick. "We shall go fair for Holywood, or as fair, at least, as I can guide you, and that will be due north."

They were afoot at once, passed the stream upon some stepping-stones, and began to mount on the other side, which was steeper, towards the margin of the wood. The ground became very uneven, full of knolls and hollows; trees grew scattered or in clumps; it became difficult to choose a path, and the lads somewhat wandered. They were weary, besides, with yesterday's exertions and the lack of food, and they moved but heavily and dragged their feet among the sand.

Presently, coming to the top of a knoll, they were aware of the leper, some hundred feet in front of them, crossing the line of their march by a hollow. His bell was silent, his staff no longer tapped the ground, and he went before him with the swift and assured footsteps of a man who sees. Next moment he had disappeared into a little thicket.

The lads, at the first glimpse, had crouched behind a tuft of gorse; there they lay, horror-struck.

"Certain, he pursueth us," said Dick—"certain! He held the clapper of his bell in one hand, saw ye? that it should not sound. Now may the saints aid and guide us, for I have no strength to combat pestilence!"

"What maketh he?" cried Matcham. "What doth he want? Who ever heard the like, that a leper, out of mere malice, should pursue unfortunates? Hath he not his bell to that very end, that people may avoid him? Dick, there is below this something deeper."

"Nay, I care not," moaned Dick; "the strength is gone out of me; my legs are like water. The saints be mine assistance!"

"Would ye lie there idle?" cried Matcham. "Let us back into the open. We have the better chance; he cannot steal upon us unawares."

"Not I," said Dick. "My time is come, and peradventure he may pass us by."

"Bend me, then, your bow!" cried the other. "What! will ye be a man?"

Dick crossed himself. "Would ye have me shoot upon a leper?" he cried. "The hand would fail me. Nay, now," he added—"nay, now, let be! With sound men I will fight, but not with ghosts and lepers. Which this is I wot not. One or other, Heaven be our protection!"

"Now," said Matcham, "if this be man's courage, what a poor thing is man! But sith ye will do naught, let us lie close."

Then came a single, broken jangle on the bell.

"He hath missed his hold upon the clapper," whispered Matcham. "Saints! how near he is!"

But Dick answered never a word; his teeth were near chattering.

Soon they saw a piece of the white robe between some bushes; then the leper's head was thrust forth from behind a trunk, and he seemed narrowly to scan the neighbourhood before he once again withdrew. To their stretched senses, the whole bush appeared alive with rustlings and the creak of twigs; and they heard the beating of each other's heart.

Suddenly, with a cry, the leper sprang into the open close by, and ran straight upon the lads. They, shrieking aloud, separated and began to run different ways. But their horrible enemy fastened upon Matcham, ran him swiftly down, and had him almost instantly a prisoner. The lad gave one scream that echoed high and far over the forest, he had one spasm of struggling, and then all his limbs relaxed, and he fell limp into his captor's arms.

Dick heard the cry and turned. He saw Matcham fall; and on the instant his spirit and his strength revived. With a cry of pity and anger, he unslung and bent his arblast. But ere he had time to shoot, the leper held up his hand.

"Hold your shot, Dickon!" cried a familiar voice. "Hold your shot, mad wag! Know ye not a friend?"

And then laying down Matcham on the turf, he undid the hood from off his face, and disclosed the features of Sir Daniel Brackley.

"Sir Daniel!" cried Dick.

"Ay, by the mass, Sir Daniel!" returned the knight. "Would ye shoot upon your guardian, rogue? But here is this——" And there he broke off, and pointing to Matcham, asked: "How call ye him, Dick?"

"Nay," said Dick, "I call him Master Matcham. Know ye him not? He said ye knew him!"

"Ay," replied Sir Daniel, "I know the lad"; and he chuckled. "But he has fainted; and, by my sooth, he might have had less to faint for! Hey, Dick? Did I put the fear of death upon you?"

"Indeed, Sir Daniel, ye did that," said Dick, and sighed again at the mere recollection. "Nay, sir, saving your respect, I had as lief 'a' met the devil in person; and to speak truth, I am yet all a-quake. But what made ye, sir, in such a guise?"

Sir Daniel's brow grew suddenly black with anger.

"What made I?" he said. "Ye do well to mind me of it! What? I skulked for my poor life in my own wood of Tunstall, Dick. We were ill sped at the battle; we but got there to be swept among the rout. Where be all my good men-at-arms? Dick, by the mass, I know not! We were swept down; the shot fell thick among us; I have not seen one man in my own colours since I saw three fall. For myself, I came sound to Shoreby, and being mindful of the Black Arrow, got me this gown and bell, and came softly by the path for the Moat House. There is no disguise to be compared with it; the jingle of this bell would scare me the stoutest outlaw in the forest; they would all turn pale to hear it. At length I came by you and Matcham. I could see but evilly through this same hood, and was not sure of you, being chiefly, and for many a good cause, astonished at the finding you together. Moreover, in the open, where I had to go slowly and tap with my staff, I feared to disclose myself. But see," he added, "this poor shrew begins a little to revive. A little good canary will comfort me the heart of it."

The knight, from under his long dress, produced a stout bottle, and began to rub the temples and wet the lips of the patient, who returned gradually to consciousness, and began to roll dim eyes from one to another.

"What cheer, Jack!" said Dick. "It was no leper, after all; it was Sir Daniel! See!"

"Swallow me a good draught of this," said the knight. "This will give you manhood. Thereafter, I will give you both a meal, and we shall all three on to Tunstall. For, Dick," he continued, laying forth bread and meat upon the grass, "I will avow to you, in all good conscience, it irks me sorely to be safe between four walls. Not since I backed a horse have I been pressed so hard; peril of life, jeopardy of land and livelihood, and to sum up, all these losels in the wood to hunt me down. But I be not yet shent. Some of my lads will pick me their way home. Hatch hath ten fellows; Selden, he had six. Nay, we shall soon be strong again; and if I can but buy my peace with my right fortunate and undeserving Lord of York, why, Dick, we'll be a man again and go a-horseback!"

And so saying, the knight filled himself a horn of canary, and pledged his ward in dumb show.

"Selden," Dick faltered—"Selden—" And he paused again.

Sir Daniel put down the wine untasted.

"How!" he cried, in a changed voice. "Selden? Speak! What of Selden?"

Dick stammered forth the tale of the ambush and the massacre.

The knight heard in silence; but as he listened, his countenance became convulsed with rage and grief.

"Now here," he cried, "on my right hand, I swear to avenge it! If that I fail, if that I spill not ten men's souls for each, may this hand wither from my body! I broke this Duckworth like a rush; I beggared him to his door; I burned the thatch above his head; I drove him from this country; and now, cometh he back to beard me? Nay, but, Duckworth, this time it shall go bitter hard!"

He was silent for some time, his face working.

"Eat!" he cried, suddenly. "And you here," he added to Matcham, "swear me an oath to follow straight to the Moat House."

"I will pledge mine honour," replied Matcham.

"What make I with your honour?" cried the knight. "Swear me upon your mother's welfare!"

Matcham gave the required oath; and Sir Daniel readjusted the hood over his face, and prepared his bell and staff. To see him once more in that appalling travesty somewhat revived the horror of his two companions. But the knight was soon upon his feet.

"Eat with despatch," he said, "and follow me yarely to mine house."

And with that he set forth again into the woods; and presently after the bell began to sound, numbering his steps, and the two lads sat by their untasted meal, and heard it die slowly away up-hill into the distance.

"And so ye go to Tunstall?" Dick inquired.

"Yea, verily," said Matcham, "when needs must! I am braver behind Sir Daniel's back than to his face."

They ate hastily, and set forth along the path through the airy upper levels of the forest, where great beeches stood apart among green lawns, and the birds and squirrels made merry on the boughs. Two hours later, they began to descend upon the other side, and already, among the tree-tops, saw before them the red walls and roofs of Tunstall House.

"Here," said Matcham, pausing, "ye shall take your leave of your friend Jack, whom y'are to see no more. Come, Dick, forgive him what he did amiss, as he, for his part, cheerfully and lovingly forgiveth you."

"And wherefore so?" asked Dick. "An we both go to Tunstall, I shall see you yet again, I trow, and that right often."

"Ye'll never again see poor Jack Matcham," replied the other, "that was so fearful and burthensome, and yet plucked you from the river; ye'll not see him more, Dick, by mine honour!" He held his arms open, and the lads embraced and kissed. "And, Dick," continued Matcham, "my spirit bodeth ill. Y'are now to see a new Sir Daniel; for heretofore hath all prospered in his hands exceedingly, and fortune followed him; but now, methinks, when his fate hath come upon him, and he runs the adventure of his life, he will prove but a foul lord to both of us. He may be brave in battle, but he hath the liar's eye; there is fear in his eye, Dick, and fear is as cruel as the wolf! We go down into that house, St. Mary guide us forth again!"

And so they continued their descent in silence, and came out at last before Sir Daniel's forest stronghold, where it stood, low and shady, flanked with round towers and stained with moss and lichen, in the lilied waters of the moat. Even as they appeared, the doors were opened, the bridge lowered, and Sir Daniel himself, with Hatch and the parson at his side, stood ready to receive them.

BOOK II. THE MOAT HOUSE

CHAPTER I. DICK ASKS QUESTIONS

The Moat House stood not far from the rough forest road. Externally, it was a compact rectangle of red stone, flanked at each corner by a round tower, pierced for archery and battlemented at the top. Within, it enclosed a narrow court. The moat was perhaps twelve feet wide, crossed by a single drawbridge. It was supplied with water by a trench, leading to a forest pool and commanded, through its whole length, from the battlements of the two southern towers. Except that one or two tall and thick trees had been suffered to remain within half a bowshot of the walls, the house was in a good posture for defence.

In the court, Dick found a part of the garrison, busy with preparations for defence, and gloomily discussing the chances of a siege. Some were making arrows, some sharpening swords that had long been disused; but even as they worked, they shook their heads.

Twelve of Sir Daniel's party had escaped the battle, run the gauntlet through the wood, and come alive to the Moat House. But out of this dozen, three had been gravely wounded: two at Risingham in the disorder of the rout, one by John Amend-All's marksmen as he crossed the forest.

This raised the force of the garrison, counting Hatch, Sir Daniel, and young Shelton, to twenty-two effective men. And more might be continually expected to arrive. The danger lay not therefore in the lack of men.

It was the terror of the Black Arrow that oppressed the spirits of the garrison. For their open foes of the party of York, in these most changing times, they felt but a far-away concern. "The world," as people said in those days, "might change again" before harm came. But for their neighbours in the wood, they trembled. It was not Sir Daniel alone who was a mark for hatred.

His men, conscious of impunity, had carried themselves cruelly through all the country. Harsh commands had been harshly executed; and of the little band that now sat talking in the court, there was not one but had been guilty of some act of oppression or barbarity. And now, by the fortune of war, Sir Daniel had become powerless to protect his instruments; now, by the issue of some hours of battle, at which many of them had not been present, they had all become punishable traitors to the State, outside the buckler of the law, a shrunken company in a poor fortress that was hardly tenable, and exposed upon all sides to the just resentment of their victims. Nor had there been lacking grisly advertisements of what they might expect.

At different periods of the evening and the night, no fewer than seven riderless horses had come neighing in terror to the gate. Two were from Selden's troop; five belonged to men who had ridden with Sir Daniel to the field. Lastly, a little before dawn, a spearman had come staggering to the moat side, pierced by three arrows; even as they carried him in, his spirit had departed; but by the words that he uttered in his agony, he must have been the last survivor of a considerable company of men.

Hatch himself showed, under his sun-brown, the pallor of anxiety; and when he had taken Dick aside and learned the fate of Selden, he fell on a stone bench and fairly wept. The others, from where they sat on stools or doorsteps in the sunny angle of the court, looked at him with wonder and alarm, but none ventured to inquire the cause of his emotion.

"Nay, Master Shelton," said Hatch, at last—"nay, but what said I? We shall all go. Selden was a man of his hands; he was like a brother to me. Well, he has gone second; well, we shall all follow! For what said their knave rhyme?—'A black arrow in each black heart.' Was it not so it went? Appleyard, Selden, Smith, old Humphrey gone; and there lieth poor John Carter, crying, poor sinner, for the priest."

Dick gave ear. Out of a low window, hard by where they were talking, groans and murmurs came to his ear.

"Lieth he there?" he asked.

"Ay, in the second porter's chamber," answered Hatch. "We could not bear him further, soul and body were so bitterly at odds. At every step we lifted him, he thought to wend. But now, methinks, it is the soul that suffereth. Ever for the priest he crieth, and Sir Oliver, I wot not why, still cometh not. 'Twill be a long shrift; but poor Appleyard and poor Selden, they had none."

Dick stooped to the window and looked in. The little cell was low and dark, but he could make out the wounded soldier lying moaning on his pallet.

"Carter, poor friend, how goeth it?" he asked.

"Master Shelton," returned the man, in an excited whisper, "for the dear light of heaven, bring the priest. Alack, I am sped; I am brought very low down; my hurt is to the death. Ye may do me no more service; this shall be the last. Now, for my poor soul's interest, and as a loyal gentleman, bestir you; for I have that matter on my conscience that shall drag me deep."

He groaned, and Dick heard the grating of his teeth, whether in pain or terror.

Just then Sir Daniel appeared upon the threshold of the hall. He had a letter in one hand.

"Lads," he said, "we have had a shog, we have had a tumble; wherefore, then, deny it? Rather it imputeth to get speedily again to saddle. This old Harry the Sixt has had the undermost. Wash we, then, our hands of him. I have a good friend that rideth next the duke, the Lord of Wensleydale. Well, I have writ a letter to my friend, praying his good lordship, and offering large satisfaction for the past and reasonable surety for the future. Doubt not but he will lend a favourable ear. A prayer without gifts is like a song without music: I surfeit him with promises, boys—I spare not to promise. What, then, is lacking? Nay, a great thing—wherefore should I deceive you?—a great thing and a difficult: a messenger to bear it. The woods—y'are not ignorant of that—lie thick with our ill-willers. Haste is most needful; but without sleight and caution all is naught. Which, then, of this company will take me this letter, bear me it to my Lord of Wensleydale, and bring me the answer back?"

One man instantly arose.

"I will, an't like you," said he. "I will even risk my carcase."

"Nay, Dicky Bowyer, not so," returned the knight. "It likes me not. Y'are sly indeed, but not speedy. Ye were a laggard ever."

"An't be so, Sir Daniel, here am I," cried another.

"The saints forfend!" said the knight. "Y'are speedy, but not sly. Ye would blunder me head-foremost into John Amend-All's camp. I thank you both for your good courage; but, in sooth, it may not be."

Then Hatch offered himself, and he also was refused.

"I want you here, good Bennet; y'are my right hand, indeed," returned the knight; and then several coming forward in a group, Sir Daniel at length selected one and gave him the letter.

"Now," he said, "upon your good speed and better discretion we do all depend. Bring me a good answer back, and before three weeks, I will have purged my forest of these vagabonds that brave us to our faces. But mark it well, Throgmorton: the matter is not easy. Ye must steal forth under night, and go like a fox; and how ye are to cross Till I know not, neither by the bridge nor ferry."

"I can swim," returned Throgmorton. "I will come soundly, fear not."

"Well, friend, get ye to the buttery," replied Sir Daniel. "Ye shall swim first of all in nut-brown ale." And with that he turned back into the hall.

"Sir Daniel hath a wise tongue," said Hatch, aside, to Dick. "See, now, where many a lesser man had glossed the matter over, he speaketh it out plainly to his company. Here is a danger, 'a saith, and here difficulty; and jesteth in the very saying. Nay, by St. Barbary, he is a born captain! Not a man but he is some deal heartened up! See how they fall again to work."

This praise of Sir Daniel put a thought in the lad's head.

"Bennet," he said, "how came my father by his end?"

"Ask me not that," replied Hatch. "I had no hand nor knowledge in it; furthermore, I will even be silent, Master Dick. For look you, in a man's own business there he may speak; but of hearsay matters and of common talk, not so. Ask me Sir Oliver—ay, or Carter, if ye will; not me."

And Hatch set off to make the rounds, leaving Dick in a muse.

"Wherefore would he not tell me?" thought the lad. "And wherefore named he Carter? Carter—nay, then Carter had a hand in it, perchance."

He entered the house, and passing some little way along a flagged and vaulted passage, came to the door of the cell where the hurt man lay groaning. At his entrance Carter started eagerly.

"Have ye brought the priest?" he cried.

"Not yet awhile," returned Dick. "Y' 'ave a word to tell me first. How came my father, Harry Shelton, by his death?"

The man's face altered instantly.

"I know not," he replied, doggedly.

"Nay, ye know well," returned Dick. "Seek not to put me by."

"I tell you I know not," repeated Carter.

"Then," said Dick, "ye shall die unshriven. Here am I, and here shall stay. There shall no priest come near you, rest assured. For of what avail is penitence, an ye have no mind to right those wrongs ye had a hand in? and without penitence, confession is but mockery."

"Ye say what ye mean not, Master Dick," said Carter, composedly. "It is ill threatening the dying, and becometh you (to speak truth) little. And for as little as it commends you, it shall serve you less. Stay, an ye please. Ye will condemn my soul—ye shall learn nothing! There is my last word to you." And the wounded man turned upon the other side.

Now, Dick, to say truth, had spoken hastily, and was ashamed of his threat. But he made one more effort.

"Carter," he said, "mistake me not. I know ye were but an instrument in the hands of others; a churl must obey his lord; I would not bear heavily on such an one. But I begin to learn upon many sides that this great duty lieth on my youth and ignorance, to avenge my father. Prithee, then, good Carter, set aside the memory of my threatenings, and in pure good-will and honest penitence give me a word of help."

The wounded man lay silent; nor, say what Dick pleased, could he extract another word from him.

"Well," said Dick, "I will go call the priest to you as ye desired; for howsoever ye be in fault to me or mine, I would not be willingly in fault to any, least of all to one upon the last change."

Again the old soldier heard him without speech or motion; even his groans he had suppressed; and as Dick turned and left the room, he was filled with admiration for that rugged fortitude.

"And yet," he thought, "of what use is courage without wit? Had his hands been clean, he would have spoken; his silence did confess the secret louder than words. Nay, upon all sides, proof floweth on me. Sir Daniel, he or his men, hath done this thing."

Dick paused in the stone passage with a heavy heart. At that hour, in the ebb of Sir Daniel's fortune, when he was beleaguered by the archers of the Black Arrow and proscribed by the victorious Yorkists, was Dick, also, to turn upon the man who had nourished and taught him, who had severely punished, indeed, but yet unwearyingly protected his youth? The necessity, if it should prove to be one, was cruel.

"Pray Heaven he be innocent!" he said.

And then steps sounded on the flagging, and Sir Oliver came gravely towards the lad.

"One seeketh you earnestly," said Dick.

"I am upon the way, good Richard," said the priest. "It is this poor Carter. Alack, he is beyond cure."

"And yet his soul is sicker than his body," answered Dick.

"Have ye seen him?" asked Sir Oliver, with a manifest start.

"I do but come from him," replied Dick.

"What said he? what said he?" snapped the priest, with extraordinary eagerness.

"He but cried for you the more piteously, Sir Oliver. It were well done to go the faster, for his hurt is grievous," returned the lad.

"I am straight for him," was the reply. "Well, we have all our sins. We must all come to our latter day, good Richard."

"Ay, sir; and it were well if we all came fairly," answered Dick.

The priest dropped his eyes, and with an inaudible benediction hurried on.

"He, too!" thought Dick—"he, that taught me in piety! Nay, then, what a world is this, if all that care for me be blood-guilty of my father's death? Vengeance! Alas! what a sore fate is mine, if I must be avenged upon my friends!"

The thought put Matcham in his head. He smiled at the remembrance of his strange companion, and then wondered where he was. Ever since they had come together to the doors of the Moat House the younger lad had disappeared, and Dick began to weary for a word with him.

About an hour after, mass being somewhat hastily run through by Sir Oliver, the company gathered in the hall for dinner. It was a long, low apartment, strewn with green rushes, and the walls hung with arras in a design of savage men and questioning bloodhounds; here and there hung spears and bows and bucklers; a fire blazed in the big chimney; there were arras-covered benches round the wall, and in the midst the table, fairly spread, awaited the arrival of the diners. Neither Sir Daniel nor his lady made their appearance. Sir Oliver himself was absent, and here again there was no word of Matcham. Dick began to grow alarmed, to recall his companion's melancholy forebodings, and to wonder to himself if any foul play had befallen him in that house.

After dinner he found Goody Hatch, who was hurrying to my Lady

Brackley.

"Goody," he said, "where is Master Matcham, I prithee? I saw ye go in with him when we arrived."

The old woman laughed aloud.

"Ah, Master Dick," she said, "y' have a famous bright eye in your head, to be sure!" and laughed again.

"Nay, but where is he, indeed?" persisted Dick.

"Ye will never see him more," she returned—"never. It is sure."

"An I do not," returned the lad, "I will know the reason why. He came not hither of his full free will; such as I am, I am his best protector, and I will see him justly used. There be too many mysteries; I do begin to weary of the game!"

But as Dick was speaking, a heavy hand fell on his shoulder. It was Bennet Hatch that had come unperceived behind him. With a jerk of his thumb, the retainer dismissed his wife.

"Friend Dick," he said, as soon as they were alone, "are ye a moon-struck natural? An ye leave not certain things in peace, ye were better in the salt sea than here in Tunstall Moat House. Y' have questioned me; y' have baited Carter; y' have frighted the jack-priest with hints. Bear ye more wisely, fool; and even now, when Sir Daniel calleth you, show me a smooth face for the love of wisdom. Y'are to be sharply questioned. Look to your answers."

"Hatch," returned Dick, "in all this I smell a guilty conscience."

"An ye go not the wiser, ye will soon smell blood," replied Bennet. "I do but warn you. And here cometh one to call you."

And indeed, at that very moment, a messenger came across the court to summon Dick into the presence of Sir Daniel.

CHAPTER II. THE TWO OATHS

Sir Daniel was in the hall; there he paced angrily before the fire, awaiting Dick's arrival. None was by except Sir Oliver, and he sat discreetly backward, thumbing and muttering over his breviary.

"Y' have sent for me, Sir Daniel?" said young Shelton.

"I have sent for you, indeed," replied the knight. "For what cometh to mine ears? Have I been to you so heavy a guardian that ye make haste to credit ill of me? Or sith that ye see me, for the nonce, some worsted, do ye think to quit my party? By the mass, your father was not so! Those he was near, those he stood by, come wind or weather. But you, Dick, y'are a fair-day friend, it seemeth, and now seek to clear yourself of your allegiance."

"An't please you, Sir Daniel, not so," returned Dick, firmly. "I am grateful and faithful, where gratitude and faith are due. And before more is said, I thank you, and I thank Sir Oliver; y' have great claims upon me both—none can have more; I were a hound if I forgot them."

"It is well," said Sir Daniel; and then, rising into anger: "Gratitude and faith are words, Dick Shelton," he continued; "but I look to deeds. In this hour of my peril, when my name is attainted, when my lands are forfeit, when this wood is full of men that hunger and thirst for my destruction, what doth gratitude? what doth faith? I have but a little company remaining; is it grateful or faithful to poison me their hearts with your insidious whisperings? Save me from such gratitude! But, come, now, what is it ye wish? Speak; we are here to answer. If ye have aught against me, stand forth and say it."

"Sir," replied Dick, "my father fell when I was yet a child. It hath come to mine ears that he was foully done by. It hath come to mine ears—for I will not dissemble—that ye had a hand in his undoing. And in all verity, I shall not be at peace in mine own mind, nor very clear to help you, till I have certain resolution of these doubts."

Sir Daniel sat down in a deep settle. He took his chin in his hand and looked at Dick fixedly.

"And ye think I would be guardian to the man's son that I had murdered?" he asked.

"Nay," said Dick, "pardon me if I answer churlishly; but indeed ye know right well a wardship is most profitable. All these years have ye not enjoyed my revenues, and led my men? Have ye not still my marriage? I wot not what it may be worth—it is worth something. Pardon me again; but if ye were base enough to slay a man under trust, here were, perhaps, reasons enough to move you to the lesser baseness."

"When I was a lad of your years," returned Sir Daniel, sternly, "my mind had not so turned upon suspicions. And Sir Oliver here," he added, "why should he, a priest, be guilty of this act?"

"Nay, Sir Daniel," said Dick, "but where the master biddeth there will the dog go. It is well known this priest is but your instrument. I speak very freely; the time is not for courtesies. Even as I speak, so would I be answered. And answer get I none! Ye but put more questions. I rede ye be ware, Sir Daniel; for in this way ye will but nourish and not satisfy my doubts."

"I will answer you fairly, Master Richard," said the knight. "Were I to pretend ye have not stirred my wrath, I were no honest man. But I will be just even in anger. Come to me with these words when y'are grown and come to man's estate, and I am no longer your guardian, and so helpless to resent them. Come to me then, and I will answer you as ye merit, with a buffet in the mouth. Till then ye have two courses: either swallow me down these insults, keep a silent tongue, and fight in the meanwhile for the man that fed and fought for your infancy; or else—the door standeth open, the woods are full of mine enemies—go."

The spirit with which these words were uttered, the looks with which they were accompanied, staggered Dick; and yet he could not but observe that he had got no answer.

"I desire nothing more earnestly, Sir Daniel, than to believe you," he replied. "Assure me ye are free from this."

"Will ye take my word of honour, Dick?" inquired the knight.

"That would I," answered the lad.

"I give it you," returned Sir Daniel. "Upon my word of honour, upon the eternal welfare of my spirit, and as I shall answer for my deeds hereafter, I had no hand nor portion in your father's death."

He extended his hand, and Dick took it eagerly. Neither of them observed the priest, who, at the pronunciation of that solemn and false oath, had half arisen from his seat in an agony of horror and remorse.

"Ah," cried Dick, "ye must find it in your great-heartedness to pardon me! I was a churl, indeed, to doubt of you. But ye have my hand upon it; I will doubt no more."

"Nay, Dick," replied Sir Daniel, "y'are forgiven. Ye know not the world and its calumnious nature."

"I was the more to blame," added Dick, "in that the rogues pointed, not directly at yourself, but at Sir Oliver."

As he spoke, he turned towards the priest, and paused in the middle of the last word. This tall, ruddy, corpulent, high-stepping man had fallen, you might say, to pieces; his colour was gone, his limbs were relaxed, his lips stammered prayers; and now, when Dick's eyes were fixed upon him suddenly, he cried out aloud, like some wild animal, and buried his face in his hands.

Sir Daniel was by him in two strides, and shook him fiercely by the shoulder. At the same moment Dick's suspicions reawakened.

"Nay," he said, "Sir Oliver may swear also. 'Twas him they accused."

"He shall swear," said the knight.

Sir Oliver speechlessly waved his arms.

"Ay, by the mass! but ye shall swear," cried Sir Daniel, beside himself with fury. "Here, upon this book, ye shall swear," he continued, picking up the breviary, which had fallen to the ground. "What! Ye make me doubt you!

Swear, I say; swear!"

But the priest was still incapable of speech. His terror of Sir Daniel, his terror of perjury, risen to about an equal height, strangled him.

And just then, through the high, stained-glass window of the hall, a black arrow crashed, and struck, and stuck quivering, in the midst of the long table.

Sir Oliver, with a loud scream, fell fainting on the rushes; while the knight, followed by Dick, dashed into the court and up the nearest corkscrew stair to the battlements. The sentries were all on the alert. The sun shone quietly on green lawns dotted with trees, and on the wooded hills of the forest which enclosed the view. There was no sign of a besieger.

"Whence came that shot?" asked the knight.

"From yonder clump, Sir Daniel," returned a sentinel.

The knight stood a little, musing. Then he turned to Dick. "Dick," he said, "keep me an eye upon these men; I leave you in charge here. As for the priest, he shall clear himself, or I will know the reason why. I do almost begin to share in your suspicions. He shall swear, trust me, or we shall prove him guilty."

Dick answered somewhat coldly, and the knight, giving him a piercing glance, hurriedly returned to the hall. His first glance was for the arrow. It was the first of these missiles he had seen, and as he turned it to and fro, the dark hue of it touched him with some fear. Again there was some writing: one word—"Earthed."

"Ay," he broke out, "they know I am home, then. Earthed! Ay, but there is not a dog among them fit to dig me out."

Sir Oliver had come to himself, and now scrambled to his feet.

"Alack, Sir Daniel!" he moaned, "y' 'ave sworn a dread oath; y'are doomed to the end of time."

"Ay," returned the knight, "I have sworn an oath, indeed, thou chucklehead; but thyself shalt swear a greater. It shall be on the blessed cross of Holywood. Look to it; get the words ready. It shall be sworn to-night."

"Now, may Heaven lighten you!" replied the priest; "may Heaven incline your heart from this iniquity!"

"Look you, my good father," said Sir Daniel, "if y'are for piety, I say no more; ye begin late, that is all. But if y'are in any sense bent upon wisdom, hear me. This lad beginneth to irk me like a wasp. I have a need for him, for I would sell his marriage. But I tell you, in all plainness, if that he continue to weary me, he shall go join his father. I give orders now to change him to the chamber above the chapel. If that ye can swear your innocency with a good, solid oath and an assured countenance, it is well; the lad will be at peace a little, and I will spare him. If that ye stammer or blench, or anyways boggle at the swearing, he will not believe you; and by the mass, he shall die. There is for your thinking on."

"The chamber above the chapel!" gasped the priest.

"That same," replied the knight. "So if ye desire to save him, save him; and if ye desire not, prithee, go to, and let me be at peace! For an I had been a hasty man, I would already have put my sword through you, for your intolerable cowardice and folly. Have ye chosen? Say!"

"I have chosen," said the priest. "Heaven pardon me, I will do evil for good. I will swear for the lad's sake."

"So is it best!" said Sir Daniel. "Send for him, then, speedily. Ye shall see him alone. Yet I shall have an eye on you. I shall be here in the panel room."

The knight raised the arras and let it fall again behind him. There was the sound of a spring opening; then followed the creaking of trod stairs.

Sir Oliver, left alone, cast a timorous glance upward at the arras-covered wall, and crossed himself with every appearance of terror and contrition.

"Nay, if he is in the chapel room," the priest murmured, "were it at my soul's cost, I must save him."

Three minutes later, Dick, who had been summoned by another messenger, found Sir Oliver standing by the hall table, resolute and pale.

"Richard Shelton," he said, "ye have required an oath from me. I might complain, I might deny you; but my heart is moved towards you for the past, and I will even content you as ye choose. By the true cross of Holywood, I did not slay your father."

"Sir Oliver," returned Dick, "when first we read John Amend-All's paper, I was convinced of so much. But suffer me to put two questions. Ye did not slay him; granted. But had ye no hand in it?"

"None," said Sir Oliver. And at the same time he began to contort his face, and signal with his mouth and eyebrows, like one who desired to convey a warning, yet dared not utter a sound.

Dick regarded him in wonder; then he turned and looked all about him at the empty hall.

"What make ye?" he inquired.

"Why, naught," returned the priest, hastily smoothing his countenance. "I make naught; I do but suffer; I am sick. I—I—prithee, Dick, I must begone. On the true cross of Holywood, I am clean innocent alike of violence or treachery. Content ye, good lad. Farewell!"

And he made his escape from the apartment with unusual alacrity.

Dick remained rooted to the spot, his eyes wandering about the room, his face a changing picture of various emotions, wonder, doubt, suspicion, and amusement. Gradually, as his mind grew clearer, suspicion took the upper hand, and was succeeded by certainty of the worst. He raised his head, and, as he did so, violently started. High upon the wall there was the figure of a savage hunter woven in the tapestry. With one hand he held a horn to his mouth; in the other he brandished a stout spear. His face was dark, for he was meant to represent an African.

Now, here was what had startled Richard Shelton. The sun had moved away from the hall windows, and at the same time the fire had blazed up high on the wide hearth, and shed a changeful glow upon the roof and hangings. In this light the figure of the black hunter had winked at him with a white eyelid.

He continued staring at the eye. The light shone upon it like a gem; it was liquid, it was alive. Again the white eyelid closed upon it for a fraction of a second, and the next moment it was gone.

There could be no mistake. The live eye that had been watching him through a hole in the tapestry was gone. The firelight no longer shone on a reflecting surface.

And instantly Dick awoke to the terrors of his position. Hatch's warning, the mute signals of the priest, this eye that had observed him from the wall, ran together in his mind. He saw he had been put upon his trial, that he had once more betrayed his suspicions, and that, short of some miracle, he was lost.

"If I cannot get me forth out of this house," he thought, "I am dead man! And this poor Matcham, too—to what a cockatrice's nest have I not led him!"

He was still so thinking, when there came one in haste, to bid him help in changing his arms, his clothing, and his two or three books, to a new chamber.

"A new chamber?" he repeated. "Wherefore so? What chamber?"

"'Tis one above the chapel," answered the messenger.

"It hath stood long empty," said Dick, musing. "What manner of room is it?"

"Nay, a brave room," returned the man. "But yet"—lowering his voice—"they call it haunted."

"Haunted?" repeated Dick, with a chill. "I have not heard of it. Nay, then, and by whom?"

The messenger looked about him; and then, in a low whisper, "By the sacrist of St. John's," he said. "They had him there to sleep one night, and in the morning—whew!—he was gone. The devil had taken him, they said; the more betoken, he had drunk late the night before."

Dick followed the man with black forebodings.

CHAPTER III. THE ROOM OVER THE CHAPEL

From the battlements nothing further was observed. The sun journeyed westward, and at last went down; but, to the eyes of all these eager sentinels, no living thing appeared in the neighbourhood of Tunstall House.

When the night was at length fairly come, Throgmorton was led to a room overlooking an angle of the moat. Thence he was lowered with every precaution; the ripple of his swimming was audible for a brief period; then a black figure was observed to land by the branches of a willow and crawl away among the grass. For some half-hour Sir Daniel and Hatch stood eagerly giving ear; but all remained quiet. The messenger had got away in safety.

Sir Daniel's brow grew clearer. He turned to Hatch.

"Bennet," he said, "this John Amend-All is no more than a man, ye see. He sleepeth. We will make a good end of him, go to!"

All the afternoon and evening, Dick had been ordered hither and thither, one command following another, till he was bewildered with the number and the hurry of commissions. All that time he had seen no more of Sir Oliver, and nothing of Matcham; and yet both the priest and the young lad ran continually in his mind. It was now his chief purpose to escape from Tunstall Moat House as speedily as might be; and yet, before he went, he desired a word with both of these.

At length, with a lamp in one hand, he mounted to his new apartment. It was large, low, and somewhat dark. The window looked upon the moat, and although it was so high up, it was heavily barred. The bed was luxurious, with one pillow of down and one of lavender, and a red coverlet worked in a pattern of roses. All about the walls were cupboards, locked and padlocked, and concealed from view by hangings of dark-coloured arras. Dick made the round, lifting the arras, sounding the panels, seeking vainly to open the cupboards. He assured himself that the door was strong and the bolt solid; then he set down his lamp upon a bracket, and once more looked all around.

For what reason had he been given this chamber? It was larger and finer than his own. Could it conceal a snare? Was there a secret entrance? Was it, indeed, haunted? His blood ran a little chilly in his veins.

Immediately over him the heavy foot of a sentry trod the leads. Below him, he knew, was the arched roof of the chapel; and next to the chapel was the hall. Certainly there was a secret passage in the hall; the eye that had watched him from the arras gave him proof of that. Was it not more than probable that the passage extended to the chapel, and, if so, that it had an opening in his room?

To sleep in such a place, he felt, would be foolhardy. He made his weapons ready, and took his position in a corner of the room behind the door. If ill was intended, he would sell his life dear.

The sound of many feet, the challenge, and the password sounded overhead along the battlements; the watch was being changed.

And just then there came a scratching at the door of the chamber; it grew a little louder; then a whisper:

"Dick, Dick, it is I!"

Dick ran to the door, drew the bolt, and admitted Matcham. He was very pale, and carried a lamp in one hand and a drawn dagger in the other.

"Shut me the door," he whispered. "Swift, Dick! This house is full of spies; I hear their feet follow me in the corridors; I hear them breathe behind the arras."

"Well, content you," returned Dick, "it is closed. We are safe for this while, if there be safety anywhere within these walls. But my heart is glad to see you. By the mass, lad, I thought ye were sped! Where hid ye?"

"It matters not," returned Matcham. "Since we be met, it matters not. But, Dick, are your eyes open? Have they told you of to-morrow's doings?"

"Not they," replied Dick. "What make they to-morrow?"

"To-morrow, or to-night, I know not," said the other, "but one time or other, Dick, they do intend upon your life. I had the proof of it; I have heard them whisper; nay, they as good as told me."

"Ay," returned Dick, "is it so? I had thought as much."

And he told him the day's occurrences at length.

When it was done, Matcham arose and began, in turn, to examine the apartment.

"No," he said, "there is no entrance visible. Yet 'tis a pure certainty there is one. Dick, I will stay by you. An y'are to die, I will die with you. And I can help—look! I have stolen a dagger—I will do my best! And meanwhile, an ye know of any issue, any sally-port we could get opened, or any window that we might descend by, I will most joyfully face any jeopardy to flee with you."

"Jack," said Dick, "by the mass, Jack, y'are the best soul, and the truest, and the bravest in all England! Give me your hand, Jack."

And he grasped the other's hand in silence.

"I will tell you," he resumed. "There is a window, out of which the messenger descended; the rope should still be in the chamber. 'Tis a hope."

"Hist!" said Matcham.

Both gave ear. There was a sound below the floor; then it paused, and then began again.

"Some one walketh in the room below," whispered Matcham.

"Nay," returned Dick, "there is no room below; we are above the chapel. It is my murderer in the secret passage. Well, let him come; it shall go hard with him"; and he ground his teeth.

"Blow me the lights out," said the other. "Perchance he will betray himself."

They blew out both the lamps and lay still as death. The footfalls underneath were very soft, but they were clearly audible. Several times they came and went; and then there was a loud jar of a key turning in a lock, followed by a considerable silence.

Presently the steps began again, and then, all of a sudden, a chink of light appeared in the planking of the room in a far corner. It widened; a trap-door was being opened, letting in a gush of light. They could see the strong hand pushing it up; and Dick raised his cross-bow, waiting for the head to follow.

But now there came an interruption. From a distant corner of the Moat House shouts began to be heard, and first one voice, and then several, crying aloud upon a name. This noise had plainly disconcerted the murderer, for the trap-door was silently lowered to its place, and the steps hurriedly returned, passed once more close below the lads, and died away in the distance.

Here was a moment's respite. Dick breathed deep, and then, and not till then, he gave ear to the disturbance which had interrupted the attack, and which was now rather increasing than diminishing. All about the Moat House feet were running, doors were opening and slamming, and still the voice of Sir Daniel towered above all this bustle, shouting for "Joanna."

"Joanna!" repeated Dick. "Why, who the murrain should this be? Here is no Joanna, nor ever hath been. What meaneth it?"

Matcham was silent. He seemed to have drawn further away. But only a little faint starlight entered by the window, and at the far end of the apartment, where the pair were, the darkness was complete.

"Jack," said Dick, "I wot not where ye were all day. Saw ye this Joanna?"

"Nay," returned Matcham, "I saw her not."

"Nor heard tell of her?" he pursued.

The steps drew nearer. Sir Daniel was still roaring the name of Joanna from the courtyard.

"Did ye hear of her?" repeated Dick.

"I heard of her," said Matcham.

"How your voice twitters! What aileth you?" said Dick. "'Tis a most excellent good fortune, this Joanna; it will take their minds from us."

"Dick," cried Matcham, "I am lost; we are both lost. Let us flee if there be yet time. They will not rest till they have found me. Or, see! let me go forth; when they have found me, ye may flee. Let me forth, Dick—good Dick, let me away!"

She was groping for the bolt, when Dick at last comprehended.

"By the mass!" he cried, "y'are no Jack; y'are Joanna Sedley; y'are the maid that would not marry me!"

The girl paused, and stood silent and motionless. Dick, too, was silent for a little; then he spoke again.

"Joanna," he said, "y' 'ave saved my life, and I have saved yours; and we have seen blood flow, and been friends and enemies—ay, and I took my belt to thrash you; and all that time I thought ye were a boy. But now death has me, and my time's out, and before I die I must say this: Y'are the best maid and the bravest under heaven, and, if only I could live, I would marry you blithely; and, live or die, I love you."

She answered nothing.

"Come," he said, "speak up, Jack. Come, be a good maid, and say ye love me!"

"Why, Dick," she cried, "would I be here?"

"Well, see ye here," continued Dick, "an we but escape whole we'll marry; and an we're to die, we die, and there's an end on't. But now that I think, how found ye my chamber?"

"I asked it of Dame Hatch," she answered.

"Well, the dame's staunch," he answered; "she'll not tell upon you. We have time before us."

And just then, as if to contradict his words, feet came down the corridor, and a fist beat roughly on the door.

"Here!" cried a voice. "Open, Master Dick; open!"

Dick neither moved nor answered.

"It is all over," said the girl; and she put her arms about Dick's neck.

One after another, men came trooping to the door. Then Sir Daniel arrived himself, and there was a sudden cessation of the noise.

"Dick," cried the knight, "be not an ass. The Seven Sleepers had been awake ere now. We know she is within there. Open, then, the door, man."

Dick was again silent.

"Down with it," said Sir Daniel. And immediately his followers fell savagely upon the door with foot and fist. Solid as it was, and strongly bolted, it would soon have given way; but once more fortune interfered. Over the thunder-storm of blows the cry of a sentinel was heard; it was followed by another; shouts ran along the battlements, shouts answered out of the wood. In the first moment of alarm it sounded as if the foresters were carrying the Moat House by assault. And Sir Daniel and his men, desisting instantly from their attack upon Dick's chamber, hurried to defend the walls.

"Now," cried Dick, "we are saved."

He seized the great old bedstead with both hands, and bent himself in vain to move it.

"Help me, Jack. For your life's sake, help me stoutly!" he cried.

Between them, with a huge effort, they dragged the big frame of oak across the room, and thrust it endwise to the chamber door.

"Ye do but make things worse," said Joanna, sadly. "He will then enter by the trap."

"Not so," replied Dick. "He durst not tell his secret to so many. It is by the trap that we shall flee. Hark! The attack is over. Nay, it was none!"

It had, indeed, been no attack; it was the arrival of another party of stragglers from the defeat of Risingham that had disturbed Sir Daniel. They had run the gauntlet under cover of the darkness; they had been admitted by the great gate; and now, with a great stamping of hoofs and jingle of accoutrements and arms, they were dismounting in the court.

"He will return anon," said Dick. "To the trap!"

He lighted a lamp, and they went together into the corner of the room. The open chink through which some light still glittered was easily discovered, and, taking a stout sword from his small armoury, Dick thrust it deep into the seam, and weighed strenuously on the hilt. The trap moved, gaped a little, and at length came widely open. Seizing it with their hands, the two young folk threw it back. It disclosed a few steps descending, and at the foot of them, where the would-be murderer had left it, a burning lamp.

"Now," said Dick, "go first and take the lamp. I will follow to close the trap."

So they descended one after the other, and as Dick lowered the trap, the blows began once again to thunder on the panels of the door.

CHAPTER IV. THE PASSAGE

The passage in which Dick and Joanna now found themselves was narrow, dirty, and short. At the other end of it, a door stood partly open; the same door, without doubt, that they had heard the man unlocking. Heavy cobwebs hung from the roof; and the paved flooring echoed hollow under the lightest tread.

Beyond the door there were two branches, at right angles. Dick chose one of them at random, and the pair hurried, with echoing footsteps, along the hollow of the chapel roof. The top of the arched ceiling rose like a whale's back in the dim glimmer of the lamp. Here and there were spy-holes, concealed, on the other side, by the carving of the cornice; and looking down through one of these, Dick saw the paved floor of the chapel—the altar, with its burning tapers—and stretched before it on the steps, the figure of Sir Oliver praying with uplifted hands.

At the other end, they descended a few steps. The passage grew narrower; the wall upon one hand was now of wood; the noise of people talking, and a faint flickering of lights, came through the interstices; and presently they came to a round hole about the size of a man's eye, and Dick, looking down through it, beheld the interior of the hall, and some half-a-dozen men sitting, in their jacks, about the table, drinking deep and demolishing a venison pie. These were certainly some of the late arrivals.

"Here is no help," said Dick. "Let us try back."

"Nay," said Joanna; "maybe the passage goeth farther."

And she pushed on. But a few yards farther the passage ended at the top of a short flight of steps; and it became plain that, as long as the soldiers occupied the hall, escape was impossible upon that side.

They retraced their steps with all imaginable speed, and set forward to explore the other branch. It was exceedingly narrow, scarce wide enough for a large man; and it led them continually up and down by little breakneck stairs, until even Dick had lost all notion of his whereabouts.

At length it grew both narrower and lower; the stairs continued to descend; the walls on either hand became damp and slimy to the touch; and far in front of them they heard the squeaking and scuttling of the rats.

"We must be in the dungeons," Dick remarked.

"And still there is no outlet," added Joanna.

"Nay, but an outlet there must be!" Dick answered.

Presently, sure enough, they came to a sharp angle, and then the passage ended in a flight of steps. On the top of that there was a solid flag of stone by way of trap, and to this they both set their backs. It was immovable.

"Some one holdeth it," suggested Joanna.

"Not so," said Dick; "for were a man strong as ten, he must still yield a little. But this resisteth like dead rock. There is a weight upon the trap. Here is no issue; and, by my sooth, good Jack, we are here as fairly prisoners as though the gyves were on our ankle bones. Sit ye then down, and let us talk. After awhile we shall return, when perchance they shall be less carefully upon their guard; and, who knoweth? we may break out and stand a chance. But, in my poor opinion, we are as good as shent."

"Dick!" she cried, "alas the day that ever ye should have seen me! For like a most unhappy and unthankful maid, it is I have led you hither."

"What cheer!" returned Dick. "It was all written, and that which is written, willy nilly, cometh still to pass. But tell me a little what manner of a maid ye are, and how ye came into Sir Daniel's hands; that will do better than to bemoan yourself, whether for your sake or mine."

"I am an orphan, like yourself, of father and mother," said Joanna; "and for my great misfortune, Dick, and hitherto for yours, I am a rich marriage. My Lord Foxham had me to ward; yet it appears Sir Daniel bought the marriage of me from the king, and a right dear price he paid for it. So here was I, poor babe, with two great and rich men fighting which should marry me, and I still at nurse! Well, then the world changed, and there was a new chancellor, and Sir Daniel bought the warding of me over the Lord Foxham's head. And then the world changed again, and Lord Foxham bought my marriage over Sir Daniel's; and from then to now it went on ill betwixt the two of them. But still Lord Foxham kept me in his hands, and was a good lord to me. And at last I was to be married—or sold, if ye like it better. Five hundred pounds Lord Foxham was to get for me. Hamley was the groom's name, and to-morrow, Dick, of all days in the year, was I to be betrothed. Had it not come to Sir Daniel, I had been wedded, sure—and never seen thee, Dick—dear Dick!"

And here she took his hand, and kissed it, with the prettiest grace; and Dick drew her hand to him and did the like.

"Well," she went on, "Sir Daniel took me unawares in the garden, and made me dress in these men's clothes, which is a deadly sin for a woman; and, besides, they fit me not. He rode with me to Kettley, as ye saw, telling me I was to marry you; but I, in my heart, made sure I would marry Hamley in his teeth."

"Ay!" cried Dick, "and so ye loved this Hamley!"

"Nay," replied Joanna, "not I. I did but hate Sir Daniel. And then, Dick, ye helped me, and ye were right kind, and very bold, and my heart turned towards you in mine own despite; and now, if we can in any way compass it, I would marry you with right good-will. And if, by cruel destiny, it may not be, still ye'll be dear to me. While my heart beats, it'll be true to you."

"And I," said Dick, "that never cared a straw for any manner of woman until now, I took to you when I thought ye were a boy. I had a pity to you, and knew not why. When I would have belted you, the hand failed me. But when ye owned ye were a maid, Jack—for still I will call you Jack—I made sure ye were the maid for me. Hark!" he said, breaking off—"one cometh."

And indeed a heavy tread was now audible in the echoing passage, and the rats again fled in armies.

Dick reconnoitred his position. The sudden turn gave him a post of vantage. He could thus shoot in safety from the cover of the wall. But it was plain the light was too near him, and, running some way forward, he set down the lamp in the middle of the passage, and then returned to watch.

Presently, at the far end of the passage, Bennet hove in sight. He seemed to be alone, and he carried in his hand a burning torch, which made him the better mark.

"Stand, Bennet!" cried Dick. "Another step, and y'are dead."

"So here ye are," returned Hatch, peering forward into the darkness. "I see you not. Aha! y' 'ave done wisely, Dick; y' 'ave put your lamp before you. By my sooth, but, though it was done to shoot my own knave body, I do rejoice to see ye profit of my lessons! And now, what make ye? what seek ye here? Why would ye shoot upon an old, kind friend? And have ye the young gentlewoman there?"

"Nay, Bennet, it is I should question and you answer," replied Dick. "Why am I in this jeopardy of my life? Why do men come privily to slay me in my bed? Why am I now fleeing in mine own guardian's strong house, and from the friends that I have lived among and never injured?"

"Master Dick, Master Dick," said Bennet, "what told I you? Y'are brave, but the most uncrafty lad that I can think upon!"

"Well," returned Dick, "I see ye know all, and that I am doomed indeed. It is well. Here, where I am, I stay. Let Sir Daniel get me out if he be able!"

Hatch was silent for a space.

"Hark ye," he began, "I return to Sir Daniel, to tell him where ye are, and how posted; for, in truth, it was to that end he sent me. But you, if ye are no fool, had best be gone ere I return."

"Be gone!" repeated Dick. "I would be gone already, an I wist how. I cannot move the trap."

"Put me your hand into the corner, and see what ye find there," replied Bennet. "Throgmorton's rope is still in the brown chamber. Fare ye well."

And Hatch, turning upon his heel, disappeared again into the windings of the passage.

Dick instantly returned for his lamp, and proceeded to act upon the hint. At one corner of the trap there was a deep cavity in the wall. Pushing his arm into the aperture, Dick found an iron bar, which he thrust vigorously upwards. There followed a snapping noise, and the slab of stone instantly started in its bed.

They were free of the passage. A little exercise of strength easily raised the trap; and they came forth into a vaulted chamber, opening on one hand upon the court, where one or two fellows, with bare arms, were rubbing down the horses of the last arrivals. A torch or two, each stuck in an iron ring against the wall, changefully lit up the scene.

CHAPTER V. HOW DICK CHANGED SIDES

Dick, blowing out his lamp lest it should attract attention, led the way up-stairs and along the corridor. In the brown chamber the rope had been made fast to the frame of an exceeding heavy and ancient bed. It had not been detached, and Dick, taking the coil to the window, began to lower it slowly and cautiously into the darkness of the night. Joan stood by; but as the rope lengthened, and still Dick continued to pay it out, extreme fear began to conquer her resolution.

"Dick," she said, "is it so deep? I may not essay it. I should infallibly fall, good Dick."

It was just at the delicate moment of the operations that she spoke. Dick started; the remainder of the coil slipped from his grasp, and the end fell with a splash into the moat. Instantly, from the battlement above, the voice of a sentinel cried, "Who goes?"

"A murrain!" cried Dick. "We are paid now! Down with you—take the rope."

"I cannot," she cried, recoiling.

"An ye cannot, no more can I," said Shelton. "How can I swim the moat without you? Do you desert me, then?"

"Dick," she gasped, "I cannot. The strength is gone from me."

"By the mass, then, we are all shent!" he shouted, stamping with his foot; and then, hearing steps, he ran to the room door and sought to close it.

Before he could shoot the bolt, strong arms were thrusting it back upon him from the other side. He struggled for a second; then, feeling himself overpowered, ran back to the window. The girl had fallen against the wall in the embrasure of the window; she was more than half insensible; and when he tried to raise her in his arms, her body was limp and unresponsive.

At the same moment the men who had forced the door against him laid hold upon him. The first he poniarded at a blow, and the others falling back for a second in some disorder, he profited by the chance, bestrode the window-sill, seized the cord in both hands, and let his body slip.

The cord was knotted, which made it the easier to descend; but so furious was Dick's hurry, and so small his experience of such gymnastics, that he span round and round in mid-air like a criminal upon a gibbet, and now beat his head, and now bruised his hands, against the rugged stonework of the wall. The air roared in his ears; he saw the stars overhead, and the reflected stars below him in the moat, whirling like dead leaves before the tempest. And then he lost hold, and fell, and soused head over ears into the icy water.

When he came to the surface his hand encountered the rope, which, newly lightened of his weight, was swinging wildly to and fro. There was a red glow overhead, and looking up, he saw, by the light of several torches and a cresset full of burning coals, the battlements lined with faces. He saw the men's eyes turning hither and thither in quest of him; but he was too far below, the light reached him not, and they looked in vain.

And now he perceived that the rope was considerably too long, and he began to struggle as well as he could towards the other side of the moat, still keeping his head above water. In this way he got much more than half-way over; indeed the bank was almost within reach, before the rope began to draw him back by its own weight. Taking his courage in both hands, he left go and made a leap for the trailing sprays of willow that had already, that same evening, helped Sir Daniel's messenger to land. He went down, rose again, sank a second time, and then his hand caught a branch, and with the speed of thought he had dragged himself into the thick of the tree and clung there, dripping and panting, and still half uncertain of his escape.

But all this had not been done without a considerable splashing, which had so far indicated his position to the men along the battlements. Arrows and quarrels fell thick around him in the darkness, thick like driving hail; and suddenly a torch was thrown down—flared through the air in its swift passage—stuck for a moment on the edge of the bank, where it burned high

112

and lit up its whole surroundings like a bonfire—and then, in a good hour for Dick, slipped off, plumped into the moat, and was instantly extinguished.

It had served its purpose. The marksmen had had time to see the willow, and Dick ensconced among its boughs; and though the lad instantly sprang higher up the bank, and ran for his life, he was yet not quick enough to escape a shot. An arrow struck him in the shoulder, another grazed his head.

The pain of his wounds lent him wings; and he had no sooner got upon the level than he took to his heels and ran straight before him in the dark, without a thought for the direction of his flight.

For a few steps missiles followed him, but these soon ceased; and when at length he came to a halt and looked behind, he was already a good way from the Moat House, though he could still see the torches moving to and fro along its battlements.

He leaned against a tree, streaming with blood and water, bruised, wounded, alone, and unarmed. For all that, he had saved his life for that bout; and though Joanna remained behind in the power of Sir Daniel, he neither blamed himself for an accident that it had been beyond his power to prevent, nor did he augur any fatal consequences to the girl herself. Sir Daniel was cruel, but he was not likely to be cruel to a young gentlewoman who had other protectors, willing and able to bring him to account. It was more probable he would make haste to marry her to some friend of his own.

"Well," thought Dick, "between then and now I will find me the means to bring that traitor under; for I think, by the mass, that I be now absolved from any gratitude or obligation; and when war is open, there is a fair chance for all."

In the meanwhile, here he was in a sore plight.

For some little way farther he struggled forward through the forest; but what with the pain of his wounds, the darkness of the night, and the extreme uneasiness and confusion of his mind, he soon became equally unable to guide himself or to continue to push through the close undergrowth, and he was fain at length to sit down and lean his back against a tree.

When he awoke from something betwixt sleep and swooning, the grey of the morning had begun to take the place of night. A little chilly breeze was bustling among the trees, and as he still sat staring before him, only half awake, he became aware of something dark that swung to and fro among the branches, some hundred yards in front of him. The progressive brightening of the day and the return of his own senses at last enabled him to recognise the object. It was a man hanging from the bough of a tall oak. His head had fallen forward on his breast; but at every stronger puff of wind his body span round and round, and his legs and arms tossed, like some ridiculous plaything.

Dick clambered to his feet, and, staggering and leaning on the tree-trunks as he went, drew near to this grim object.

The bough was perhaps twenty feet above the ground, and the poor fellow had been drawn up so high by his executioners that his boots swung clear above Dick's reach; and as his hood had been drawn over his face, it was impossible to recognise the man.

Dick looked about him right and left; and at last he perceived that the other end of the cord had been made fast to the trunk of a little hawthorn which grew, thick with blossom, under the lofty arcade of the oak. With his dagger, which alone remained to him of all his arms, young Shelton severed the rope, and instantly, with a dead thump, the corpse fell in a heap upon the ground.

Dick raised the hood; it was Throgmorton, Sir Daniel's messenger. He had not gone far upon his errand. A paper, which had apparently escaped the notice of the men of the Black Arrow, stuck from the bosom of his doublet, and Dick, pulling it forth, found it was Sir Daniel's letter to Lord Wensleydale.

"Come," thought he, "if the world changes yet again, I may have here the wherewithal to shame Sir Daniel—nay, and perchance to bring him to the block."

And he put the paper in his own bosom, said a prayer over the dead man, and set forth again through the woods.

His fatigue and weakness increased; his ears sang, his steps faltered, his mind at intervals failed him, so low had he been brought by loss of blood. Doubtless he made many deviations from his true path, but at last he came out upon the highroad, not very far from Tunstall hamlet.

A rough voice bid him stand.

"Stand?" repeated Dick. "By the mass, but I am nearer falling."

And he suited the action to the word, and fell all his length upon the road.

Two men came forth out of the thicket, each in green forest jerkin, each with long-bow and quiver and short sword.

"Why, Lawless," said the younger of the two, "it is young Shelton."

"Ay, this will be as good as bread to John Amend-All," returned the other. "Though, faith, he hath been to the wars. Here is a tear in his scalp that must 'a' cost him many a good ounce of blood."

"And here," added Greensheve, "is a hole in his shoulder that must have pricked him well. Who hath done this, think ye? If it be one of ours, he may all to prayer; Ellis will give him a short shrift and a long rope."

"Up with the cub," said Lawless. "Clap him on my back."

And then, when Dick had been hoisted to his shoulders, and he had taken the lad's arms about his neck, and got a firm hold of him, the ex-Grey Friar added:

"Keep ye the post, brother Greensheve. I will on with him by myself."

So Greensheve returned to his ambush on the wayside, and Lawless trudged down the hill, whistling as he went, with Dick, still in a dead faint, comfortably settled on his shoulders.

The sun rose as he came out of the skirts of the wood and saw Tunstall hamlet straggling up the opposite hill. All seemed quiet, but a strong post of some half a score of archers lay close by the bridge on either side of the road, and, as soon as they perceived Lawless with his burthen, began to bestir themselves and set arrow to string like vigilant sentries.

"Who goes?" cried the man in command.

"Will Lawless, by the rood—ye know me as well as your own hand," returned the outlaw, contemptuously.

"Give the word, Lawless," returned the other.

"Now, Heaven lighten thee, thou great fool," replied Lawless. "Did I not tell it thee myself? But ye are all mad for this playing at soldiers. When I am in the greenwood, give me greenwood ways; and my word for this tide is: 'A fig for all mock soldiery!'"

"Lawless, ye but show an ill example; give us the word, fool jester," said the commander of the post.

"And if I had forgotten it?" asked the other.

"An ye had forgotten it—as I know y' 'ave not—by the mass, I would clap an arrow into your big body," returned the first.

"Nay, an y'are so ill a jester," said Lawless, "ye shall have your word for me. 'Duckworth and Shelton' is the word; and here, to the illustration, is Shelton on my shoulders, and to Duckworth do I carry him."

"Pass, Lawless," said the sentry.

"And where is John?" asked the Grey Friar.

"He holdeth a court, by the mass, and taketh rents as to the manner born!" cried another of the company.

So it proved. When Lawless got as far up the village as the little inn, he found Ellis Duckworth surrounded by Sir Daniel's tenants, and, by the right of his good company of archers, coolly taking rents, and giving written receipts in return for them. By the faces of the tenants, it was plain how little this proceeding pleased them; for they argued very rightly that they would simply have to pay them twice.

As soon as he knew what had brought Lawless, Ellis dismissed the remainder of the tenants, and, with every mark of interest and apprehension, conducted Dick into an inner chamber of the inn. There the lad's hurts were looked to; and he was recalled, by simple remedies, to consciousness.

"Dear lad," said Ellis, pressing his hand, "y'are in a friend's hands that loved your father, and loves you for his sake. Rest ye a little quietly, for ye are somewhat out of case. Then shall ye tell me your story, and betwixt the two of us we shall find a remedy for all."

A little later in the day, and after Dick had awakened from a comfortable slumber to find himself still very weak, but clearer in mind and easier in body, Ellis returned, and sitting down by the bedside, begged him, in the name of his father, to relate the circumstance of his escape from Tunstall Moat House. There was something in the strength of Duckworth's frame, in the honesty of his brown face, in the clearness and shrewdness of his eyes, that moved Dick to obey him; and from first to last the lad told him the story of his two days' adventures.

"Well," said Ellis, when he had done, "see what the kind saints have done for you, Dick Shelton, not alone to save your body in so numerous and deadly perils, but to bring you into my hands that have no dearer wish than to assist your father's son. Be but true to me—and I see y'are true—and betwixt you and me, we shall bring that false-heart traitor to the death."

"Will ye assault the house?" asked Dick.

"I were mad, indeed, to think of it," returned Ellis. "He hath too much power; his men gather to him; those that gave me the slip last night, and by the mass came in so handily for you—those have made him safe. Nay, Dick, to the contrary, thou and I and my brave bowmen, we must all slip from this forest speedily, and leave Sir Daniel free."

"My mind misgiveth me for Jack," said the lad.

"For Jack!" repeated Duckworth. "O, I see, for the wench! Nay, Dick, I promise you, if there come talk of any marriage we shall act at once; till then, or till the time is ripe, we shall all disappear, even like shadows at morning; Sir Daniel shall look east and west, and see none enemies; he shall think, by the mass, that he hath dreamed awhile, and hath now awakened in his bed. But our four eyes, Dick, shall follow him right close, and our four hands—so help us all the army of the saints!—shall bring that traitor low!"

Two days later Sir Daniel's garrison had grown to such a strength that he ventured on a sally, and at the head of some two-score horsemen, pushed without opposition as far as Tunstall hamlet. Not an arrow flew, not a man stirred in the thicket; the bridge was no longer guarded, but stood open to all comers; and as Sir Daniel crossed it, he saw the villagers looking timidly from their doors.

Presently one of them, taking heart of grace, came forward, and with the lowliest salutations, presented a letter to the knight.

His face darkened as he read the contents. It ran thus:

To the most untrue and cruel gentylman, Sir Daniel Brackley,

Knyght, These:

I fynde ye were untrue and unkynd fro the first. Ye have my father's blood upon your hands; let be, it will not wasshe. Some day ye shall perish by my procurement, so much I let you to wytte; and I let you to wytte farther, that if ye seek to wed to any other the gentylwoman, Mistresse Joan Sedley, whom that I am bound upon a great oath to wed myself, the blow will be very swift. The first step therinne will be thy first step to the grave.

Ric. Shelton.

BOOK III. MY LORD FOXHAM

CHAPTER I. THE HOUSE BY THE SHORE

Months had passed away since Richard Shelton made his escape from the hands of his guardian. These months had been eventful for England. The party of Lancaster, which was then in the very article of death, had once more raised its head. The Yorkists defeated and dispersed, their leader butchered on the field, it seemed, for a very brief season in the winter following upon the events already recorded, as if the House of Lancaster had finally triumphed over its foes.

The small town of Shoreby-on-the-Till was full of the Lancastrian nobles of the neighbourhood. Earl Risingham was there, with three hundred men-at-arms; Lord Shoreby, with two hundred; Sir Daniel himself, high in favour and once more growing rich on confiscations, lay in a house of his own, on the main street, with three-score men. The world had changed indeed.

It was a black, bitter cold evening in the first week of January, with a hard frost, a high wind, and every likelihood of snow before the morning.

In an obscure alehouse in a by-street near the harbour, three or four men sat drinking ale and eating a hasty mess of eggs. They were all likely, lusty, weather-beaten fellows, hard of hand, bold of eye; and though they wore plain tabards, like country ploughmen, even a drunken soldier might have looked twice before he sought a quarrel in such company.

A little apart before the huge fire sat a younger man, almost a boy, dressed in much the same fashion, though it was easy to see by his looks that he was better born, and might have worn a sword, had the time suited.

"Nay," said one of the men at the table, "I like it not. Ill will come of it. This is no place for jolly fellows. A jolly fellow loveth open country, good cover, and scarce foes; but here we are shut in a town, girt about with enemies; and, for the bull's-eye of misfortune, see if it snow not ere the morning."

"'Tis for Master Shelton there," said another, nodding his head towards the lad before the fire.

"I will do much for Master Shelton," returned the first; "but to come to the gallows for any man—nay, brothers, not that!"

The door of the inn opened, and another man entered hastily and approached the youth before the fire.

"Master Shelton," he said, "Sir Daniel goeth forth with a pair of links and four archers."

Dick (for this was our young friend) rose instantly to his feet.

"Lawless," he said, "ye will take John Capper's watch. Greensheve, follow with me. Capper, lead forward. We will follow him this time, an he go to York."

The next moment they were outside in the dark street, and Capper, the man who had just come, pointed to where two torches flared in the wind at a little distance.

The town was already sound asleep; no one moved upon the streets, and there was nothing easier than to follow the party without observation. The two link-bearers went first; next followed a single man, whose long cloak blew about him in the wind; and the rear was brought up by the four archers, each with his bow upon his arm. They moved at a brisk walk, threading the intricate lanes and drawing nearer to the shore.

"He hath gone each night in this direction?" asked Dick, in a whisper.

"This is the third night running, Master Shelton," returned Capper, "and still at the same hour and with the same small following, as though his end were secret."

Sir Daniel and his six men were now come to the outskirts of the country. Shoreby was an open town, and though the Lancastrian lords who lay there kept a strong guard on the main roads, it was still possible to enter or depart unseen by any of the lesser streets or across the open country.

The lane which Sir Daniel had been following came to an abrupt end. Before him there was a stretch of rough down, and the noise of the sea-surf was audible upon one hand. There were no guards in the neighbourhood, nor any light in that quarter of the town.

Dick and his two outlaws drew a little closer to the object of their chase, and presently, as they came forth from between the houses and could see a little farther upon either hand, they were aware of another torch drawing near from another direction.

"Hey," said Dick, "I smell treason."

Meanwhile, Sir Daniel had come to a full halt. The torches were stuck into the sand, and the men lay down, as if to await the arrival of the other party.

This drew near at a good rate. It consisted of four men only—a pair of archers, a varlet with a link, and a cloaked gentleman walking in their midst.

"Is it you, my lord?" cried Sir Daniel.

"It is I, indeed; and if ever true knight gave proof I am that man," replied the leader of the second troop; "for who would not rather face giants, sorcerers, or pagans, than this pinching cold?"

"My lord," returned Sir Daniel, "beauty will be the more beholden, misdoubt it not. But shall we forth? for the sooner ye have seen my merchandise, the sooner shall we both get home."

"But why keep ye her here, good knight?" inquired the other. "An she be so young, and so fair, and so wealthy, why do ye not bring her forth among her mates? Ye would soon make her a good marriage, and no need to freeze your fingers and risk arrow-shots by going abroad at such untimely seasons in the dark."

"I have told you, my lord," replied Sir Daniel, "the reason thereof concerneth me only. Neither do I purpose to explain it further. Suffice it, that if ye be weary of your old gossip, Daniel Brackley, publish it abroad that y'are to wed Joanna Sedley, and I give you my word ye will be quit of him right soon. Ye will find him with an arrow in his back."

Meantime the two gentlemen were walking briskly forward over the down; the three torches going before them, stooping against the wind and scattering clouds of smoke and tufts of flame, and the rear brought up by the six archers.

Close upon the heels of these, Dick followed. He had, of course, heard no word of this conversation; but he had recognised in the second of the speakers old Lord Shoreby himself, a man of an infamous reputation, whom even Sir Daniel affected, in public, to condemn.

Presently they came close down upon the beach. The air smelt salt; the noise of the surf increased; and here, in a large walled garden, there stood a small house of two storeys, with stables and other offices.

The foremost torch-bearer unlocked a door in the wall, and after the whole party had passed into the garden, again closed and locked it on the other side.

Dick and his men were thus excluded from any farther following, unless they should scale the wall and thus put their necks in a trap.

They sat down in a tuft of furze and waited. The red glow of the torches moved up and down and to and fro within the enclosure, as if the link-bearers steadily patrolled the garden.

Twenty minutes passed, and then the whole party issued forth again upon the down; and Sir Daniel and the baron, after an elaborate salutation, separated and turned severally homeward, each with his own following of men and lights.

As soon as the sound of their steps had been swallowed by the wind, Dick got to his feet as briskly as he was able, for he was stiff and aching with the cold.

"Capper, ye will give me a back up," he said.

They advanced, all three, to the wall; Capper stooped, and Dick, getting upon his shoulders, clambered on to the cope-stone.

"Now, Greensheve," whispered Dick, "follow me up here; lie flat upon your face, that ye may be the less seen; and be ever ready to give me a hand if I fall foully on the other side."

And so saying he dropped into the garden.

It was all pitch dark; there was no light in the house. The wind whistled shrill among the poor shrubs, and the surf beat upon the beach; there was no other sound. Cautiously Dick footed it forth, stumbling among bushes, and groping with his hands; and presently the crisp noise of gravel underfoot told him that he had struck upon an alley.

Here he paused, and taking his cross-bow from where he kept it concealed under his long tabard, he prepared it for instant action, and went forward once more with greater resolution and assurance. The path led him straight to the group of buildings.

All seemed to be sorely dilapidated: the windows of the house were secured by crazy shutters; the stables were open and empty; there was no hay in the hay-loft, no corn in the corn-box. Any one would have supposed the place to be deserted. But Dick had good reason to think otherwise. He continued his inspection, visiting the offices, trying all the windows. At length he came round to the sea-side of the house, and there, sure enough, there burned a pale light in one of the upper windows.

He stepped back a little way, till he thought he could see the movement of a shadow on the wall of the apartment. Then he remembered that, in the stable, his groping hand had rested for a moment on a ladder, and he returned with all despatch to bring it. The ladder was very short, but yet, by standing on the topmost round, he could bring his hands as high as the iron bars of the windows; and seizing these, he raised his body by main force until his eyes commanded the interior of the room.

Two persons were within; the first he readily knew to be Dame Hatch;

the second, a tall and beautiful and grave young lady, in a long, embroidered dress—could that be Joanna Sedley? his old wood-companion, Jack, whom he had thought to punish with a belt?

He dropped back again to the top round of the ladder in a kind of amazement. He had never thought of his sweetheart as of so superior a being, and he was instantly taken with a feeling of diffidence. But he had little opportunity for thought. A low "Hist!" sounded from close by, and he hastened to descend the ladder.

"Who goes?" he whispered.

"Greensheve," came the reply, in tones similarly guarded.

"What want ye?" asked Dick.

"The house is watched, Master Shelton," returned the outlaw. "We are not alone to watch it; for even as I lay on my belly on the wall I saw men prowling in the dark, and heard them whistle softly one to the other."

"By my sooth," said Dick, "but this is passing strange! Were they not men of Sir Daniel's?"

"Nay, sir, that they were not," returned Greensheve; "for if I have eyes in my head, every man-Jack of them weareth me a white badge in his bonnet, something chequered with dark."

"White, chequered with dark," repeated Dick. "Faith, 'tis a badge I know not. It is none of this country's badges. Well, an that be so, let us slip as quietly forth from this garden as we may; for here we are in an evil posture for defence. Beyond all question there are men of Sir Daniel's in that house, and to be taken between two shots is a beggarman's position. Take me this ladder; I must leave it where I found it."

They returned the ladder to the stable, and groped their way to the place where they had entered.

Capper had taken Greensheve's position on the cope, and now he leaned down his hand, and, first one and then the other, pulled them up.

Cautiously and silently, they dropped again upon the other side; nor did they dare to speak until they had returned to their old ambush in the gorse.

"Now, John Capper," said Dick, "back with you to Shoreby, even as for your life. Bring me instantly what men ye can collect. Here shall be the rendezvous; or if the men be scattered and the day be near at hand before they muster, let the place be something farther back, and by the entering in of the town. Greensheve and I lie here to watch. Speed ye, John Capper, and the saints aid you to despatch. And now, Greensheve," he continued, as soon as Capper had departed, "let thou and I go round about the garden in a wide circuit. I would fain see whether thine eyes betrayed thee."

Keeping well outwards from the wall, and profiting by every height and hollow, they passed about two sides, beholding nothing. On the third side the garden wall was built close upon the beach, and to preserve the distance necessary to their purpose, they had to go some way down upon the sands. Although the tide was still pretty far out, the surf was so high, and the sands so flat, that at each breaker a great sheet of froth and water came careering over the expanse, and Dick and Greensheve made this part of their inspection wading, now to the ankles, and now as deep as to the knees, in the salt and icy waters of the German Ocean.

Suddenly, against the comparative whiteness of the garden wall, the figure of a man was seen, like a faint Chinese shadow, violently signalling with both arms. As he dropped again to the earth, another arose a little farther on and repeated the same performance. And so, like a silent watchword, these gesticulations made the round of the beleaguered garden.

"They keep good watch," Dick whispered.

"Let us back to land, good master," answered Greensheve. "We stand here too open; for, look ye, when the seas break heavy and white out there behind us, they shall see us plainly against the foam."

"Ye speak sooth," returned Dick. "Ashore with us, right speedily."

CHAPTER II. A SKIRMISH IN THE DARK

Thoroughly drenched and chilled, the two adventurers returned to their position in the gorse.

"I pray Heaven that Capper make good speed!" said Dick. "I vow a candle to St. Mary of Shoreby if he come before the hour!"

"Y'are in a hurry, Master Dick?" asked Greensheve.

"Ay, good fellow," answered Dick; "for in that house lieth my lady, whom I love, and who should these be that lie about her secretly by night? Unfriends, for sure!"

"Well," returned Greensheve, "an John come speedily, we shall give a good account of them. They are not two-score at the outside—I judge so by the spacing of their sentries—and, taken where they are, lying so widely, one score would scatter them like sparrows. And yet, Master Dick, an she be in Sir Daniel's power already, it will little hurt that she should change into another's. Who should these be?"

"I do suspect the Lord of Shoreby," Dick replied. "When came they?"

"They began to come, Master Dick," said Greensheve, "about the time ye crossed the wall. I had not lain there the space of a minute ere I marked the first of the knaves crawling round the corner."

The last light had been already extinguished in the little house when they were wading in the wash of the breakers, and it was impossible to predict at what moment the lurking men about the garden wall might make their onslaught. Of two evils, Dick preferred the least. He preferred that Joanna should remain under the guardianship of Sir Daniel rather than pass into the clutches of Lord Shoreby; and his mind was made up, if the house should be assaulted, to come at once to the relief of the besieged.

But the time passed, and still there was no movement. From quarter of an hour to quarter of an hour the same signal passed about the garden wall, as if the leader desired to assure himself of the vigilance of his scattered followers; but in every other particular the neighbourhood of the little house lay undisturbed.

Presently Dick's reinforcements began to arrive. The night was not yet old before nearly a score of men crouched beside him in the gorse.

Separating these into two bodies, he took the command of the smaller himself, and entrusted the larger to the leadership of Greensheve.

"Now, Kit," said he to this last, "take me your men to the near angle of the garden wall upon the beach. Post them strongly, and wait till that ye hear me falling on upon the other side. It is those upon the sea-front that I would fain make certain of, for there will be the leader. The rest will run; even let them. And now, lads, let no man draw an arrow; ye will but hurt friends. Take to the steel, and keep to the steel; and if we have the uppermost, I promise every man of you a gold noble when I come to mine estate."

Out of the odd collection of broken men, thieves, murderers, and ruined peasantry, whom Duckworth had gathered together to serve the purposes of his revenge, some of the boldest and the most experienced in war had volunteered to follow Richard Shelton. The service of watching Sir Daniel's movements in the town of Shoreby had from the first been irksome to their temper, and they had of late begun to grumble loudly and threaten to disperse. The prospect of a sharp encounter and possible spoils restored them to good-humour, and they joyfully prepared for battle.

Their long tabards thrown aside, they appeared, some in plain green jerkins, and some in stout leathern jacks; under their hoods many wore bonnets strengthened by iron plates; and, for offensive armour, swords, daggers, a few stout boar-spears, and a dozen of bright bills, put them in a posture to engage even regular feudal troops. The bows, quivers, and tabards were concealed among the gorse, and the two bands set resolutely forward.

Dick, when he had reached the other side of the house, posted his six men in a line, about twenty yards from the garden wall, and took position himself a few paces in front. Then they all shouted with one voice, and closed upon the enemy.

These, lying widely scattered, stiff with cold, and taken at unawares, sprang stupidly to their feet, and stood undecided. Before they had time to get their courage about them, or even to form an idea of the number and mettle of their assailants, a similar shout of onslaught sounded in their ears from the far side of the enclosure. Thereupon they gave themselves up for lost and ran.

In this way the two small troops of the men of the Black Arrow closed upon the sea-front of the garden wall, and took a part of the strangers, as it were, between two fires; while the whole of the remainder ran for their lives in different directions, and were soon scattered in the darkness.

For all that, the fight was but beginning. Dick's outlaws, although they had the advantage of the surprise, were still considerably outnumbered by the men they had surrounded. The tide had flowed, in the meanwhile; the beach was narrowed to a strip; and on this wet field, between the surf and the garden wall, there began, in the darkness, a doubtful, furious, and deadly contest.

The strangers were well armed; they fell in silence upon their assailants; and the affray became a series of single combats. Dick, who had come first into the mellay, was engaged by three; the first he cut down at the first blow, but the other two coming upon him, hotly, he was fain to give ground before their onset. One of these two was a huge fellow, almost a giant for stature, and armed with a two-handed sword, which he brandished like a switch. Against this opponent, with his reach of arm and the length and weight of his weapon, Dick and his bill were quite defenceless; and had the other continued to join vigorously in the attack, the lad must have indubitably fallen. This second man, however, less in stature and slower in his movements, paused for a moment to peer about him in the darkness, and to give ear to the sounds of the battle.

The giant still pursued his advantage, and still Dick fled before him, spying for his chance. Then the huge blade flashed and descended, and the lad, leaping on one side and running in, slashed sideways and upwards with his bill. A roar of agony responded, and, before the wounded man could raise his formidable weapon, Dick, twice repeating his blow, had brought him to the ground.

The next moment he was engaged, upon more equal terms, with his second pursuer. Here there was no great difference in size, and though the man, fighting with sword and dagger against a bill, and being wary and quick of fence, had a certain superiority of arms, Dick more than made it up by his greater agility on foot. Neither at first gained any obvious advantage; but the older man was still insensibly profiting by the ardour of the younger to lead him where he would; and presently Dick found that they had crossed the whole width of the beach, and were now fighting above the knees in the spume and bubble of the breakers. Here his own superior activity was rendered useless; he found himself more or less at the discretion of his foe; yet a little, and he had his back turned upon his own men, and saw that this adroit and skilful adversary was bent upon drawing him farther and farther away.

Dick ground his teeth. He determined to decide the combat instantly; and when the wash of the next wave had ebbed and left them dry, he rushed in, caught a blow upon his bill, and leaped right at the throat of his opponent. The man went down backwards, with Dick still upon the top of him; and the next wave, speedily succeeding to the last, buried him below a rush of water.

While he was still submerged, Dick forced his dagger from his grasp, and rose to his feet, victorious.

"Yield ye!" he said. "I give you life."

"I yield me," said the other, getting to his knees. "Ye fight, like a young man, ignorantly and foolhardily; but, by the array of the saints, ye fight bravely!"

Dick turned to the beach. The combat was still raging doubtfully in the night; over the hoarse roar of the breakers steel clanged upon steel, and cries of pain and the shout of battle resounded.

"Lead me to your captain, youth," said the conquered knight. "It is fit this butchery should cease."

"Sir," replied Dick, "so far as these brave fellows have a captain, the poor gentleman who here addresses you is he."

"Call off your dogs, then, and I will bid my villains hold," returned the other.

There was something noble both in the voice and manner of his late opponent, and Dick instantly dismissed all fears of treachery.

"Lay down your arms, men!" cried the stranger knight. "I have yielded me, upon promise of life."

The tone of the stranger was one of absolute command, and almost instantly the din and confusion of the mellay ceased.

"Lawless," cried Dick, "are ye safe?"

"Ay," cried Lawless, "safe and hearty."

"Light me the lantern," said Dick.

"Is not Sir Daniel here?" inquired the knight.

"Sir Daniel?" echoed Dick. "Now, by the rood, I pray not. It would go ill with me if he were."

"Ill with you, fair sir?" inquired the other. "Nay, then, if ye be not of Sir Daniel's party, I profess I comprehend no longer. Wherefore, then, fell ye upon mine ambush? in what quarrel, my young and very fiery friend? to what earthly purpose? and, to make a clear end of questioning, to what good gentleman have I surrendered?"

But before Dick could answer, a voice spoke in the darkness from close by. Dick could see the speaker's black and white badge, and the respectful salute which he addressed to his superior.

"My lord," said he, "if these gentlemen be unfriends to Sir Daniel, it is pity, indeed, we should have been at blows with them; but it were tenfold greater that either they or we should linger here. The watchers in the house——unless they be all dead or deaf——have heard our hammering this quarter-hour agone; instantly they will have signalled to the town; and unless

130

we be the livelier in our departure, we are like to be taken, both of us, by a fresh foe."

"Hawksley is in the right," added the lord. "How please ye, sir? Whither shall we march?"

"Nay, my lord," said Dick, "go where ye will for me. I do begin to suspect we have some ground of friendship, and if, indeed, I began our acquaintance somewhat ruggedly, I would not churlishly continue. Let us, then, separate, my lord, you laying your right hand in mine; and at the hour and place that ye shall name, let us encounter and agree."

"Y'are too trustful, boy," said the other; "but this time your trust is not misplaced. I will meet you at the point of day at St. Bride's Cross. Come, lads, follow!"

The strangers disappeared from the scene with a rapidity that seemed suspicious; and while the outlaws fell to the congenial task of rifling the dead bodies, Dick made once more the circuit of the garden wall to examine the front of the house. In a little upper loophole of the roof he beheld a light set; and as it would certainly be visible in town from the back windows of Sir Daniel's mansion, he doubted not that this was the signal feared by Hawksley, and that ere long the lances of the Knight of Tunstall would arrive upon the scene.

He put his ear to the ground, and it seemed to him as if he heard a jarring and hollow noise from townward. Back to the beach he went hurrying. But the work was already done; the last body was disarmed and stripped to the skin, and four fellows were already wading seaward to commit it to the mercies of the deep.

A few minutes later, when there debouched out of the nearest lanes of Shoreby some two-score horsemen, hastily arrayed and moving at the gallop of their steeds, the neighbourhood of the house beside the sea was entirely silent and deserted.

Meanwhile, Dick and his men had returned to the alehouse of the Goat and Bagpipes to snatch some hours of sleep before the morning tryst.

CHAPTER III. ST. BRIDE'S CROSS

St. Bride's Cross stood a little way back from Shoreby, on the skirts of Tunstall Forest. Two roads met: one, from Holywood across the forest; one, that road from Risingham down which we saw the wrecks of a Lancastrian army fleeing in disorder. Here the two joined issue, and went on together down the hill to Shoreby; and a little back from the point of junction, the summit of a little knoll was crowned by the ancient and weather-beaten cross.

Here, then, about seven in the morning, Dick arrived. It was as cold as ever; the earth was all grey and silver with the hoar-frost, and the day began to break in the east with many colours of purple and orange.

Dick set him down upon the lowest step of the cross, wrapped himself well in his tabard, and looked vigilantly upon all sides. He had not long to wait. Down the road from Holywood a gentleman in very rich and bright armour, and wearing over that a surcoat of the rarest furs, came pacing on a splendid charger. Twenty yards behind him followed a clump of lances; but these halted as soon as they came in view of the trysting-place, while the gentleman in the fur surcoat continued to advance alone.

His visor was raised, and showed a countenance of great command and dignity, answerable to the richness of his attire and arms. And it was with some confusion of manner that Dick arose from the cross and stepped down the bank to meet his prisoner.

"I thank you, my lord, for your exactitude," he said, louting very low. "Will it please your lordship to set foot to earth?"

"Are ye here alone, young man?" inquired the other.

"I was not so simple," answered Dick; "and, to be plain with your lordship, the woods upon either hand of this cross lie full of mine honest fellows lying on their weapons."

"Y' 'ave done wisely," said the lord. "It pleaseth me the rather, since last night ye fought foolhardily, and more like a savage Saracen lunatic than any Christian warrior. But it becomes not me to complain that had the undermost."

"Ye had the undermost indeed, my lord, since ye so fell," returned Dick; "but had the waves not holpen me, it was I that should have had the worst. Ye were pleased to make me yours with several dagger marks, which I still carry. And in fine, my lord, methinks I had all the danger, as well as all the profit, of that little blind-man's mellay on the beach."

"Y'are shrewd enough to make light of it, I see," returned the stranger.

"Nay, my lord, not shrewd," replied Dick, "in that I shoot at no advantage to myself. But when, by the light of this new day, I see how stout a knight hath yielded, not to my arms alone, but to fortune, and the darkness, and the surf—and how easily the battle had gone otherwise, with a soldier so untried and rustic as myself—think it not strange, my lord, if I feel confounded with my victory."

"Ye speak well," said the stranger. "Your name?"

"My name, an't like you, is Shelton," answered Dick.

"Men call me the Lord Foxham," added the other.

"Then, my lord, and under your good favour, ye are guardian to the sweetest maid in England," replied Dick; "and for your ransom, and the ransom of such as were taken with you on the beach, there will be no uncertainty of terms. I pray you, my lord, of your good-will and charity, yield me the hand of my mistress, Joan Sedley; and take ye, upon the other part, your liberty, the liberty of these your followers, and (if ye will have it) my gratitude and service till I die."

"But are ye not ward to Sir Daniel? Methought, if y'are Harry Shelton's son, that I had heard it so reported," said Lord Foxham.

"Will it please you, my lord, to alight? I would fain tell you fully who I am, how situate, and why so bold in my demands. Beseech you, my lord, take place upon these steps, hear me to a full end, and judge me with allowance."

And so saying, Dick lent a hand to Lord Foxham to dismount; led him up the knoll to the cross; installed him in the place where he had himself been sitting; and standing respectfully before his noble prisoner, related the story of his fortunes up to the events of the evening before.

Lord Foxham listened gravely, and when Dick had done, "Master Shelton," he said, "ye are a most fortunate-unfortunate young gentleman; but what fortune y' 'ave had, that ye have amply merited; and what unfortune, ye have noways deserved. Be of a good cheer; for ye have made a friend who is devoid neither of power nor favour. For yourself, although it fits not for a person of your birth to herd with outlaws, I must own ye are both brave and honourable; very dangerous in battle, right courteous in peace; a youth of excellent disposition and brave bearing. For your estates, ye will never see them till the world shall change again; so long as Lancaster hath the strong hand, so long shall Sir Daniel enjoy them for his own. For my ward, it is another matter; I had promised her before to a gentleman a kinsman of my house, one Hamley; the promise is old——"

"Ay, my lord, and now Sir Daniel hath promised her to my Lord Shoreby," interrupted Dick. "And his promise, for all it is but young, is still the likelier to be made good."

"'Tis the plain truth," returned his lordship. "And considering, moreover, that I am your prisoner, upon no better composition than my bare life, and over and above that, that the maiden is unhappily in other hands, I will so far consent. Aid me with your good fellows——"

"My lord," cried Dick, "they are these same outlaws that ye blame me for consorting with."

"Let them be what they will, they can fight," returned Lord Foxham. "Help me, then; and if between us we regain the maid, upon my knightly honour, she shall marry you!"

Dick bent his knee before his prisoner; but he, leaping up lightly from the cross, caught the lad up and embraced him like a son.

"Come," he said, "an y'are to marry Joan, we must be early friends."

CHAPTER IV. THE "GOOD HOPE"

An hour thereafter, Dick was back at the Goat and Bagpipes, breaking his fast, and receiving the report of his messengers and sentries. Duckworth was still absent from Shoreby; and this was frequently the case, for he played many parts in the world, shared many different interests, and conducted many various affairs. He had founded that fellowship of the Black Arrow, as a ruined man longing for vengeance and money; and yet among those who knew him best, he was thought to be the agent and emissary of the great king-maker of England, Richard, Earl of Warwick.

In his absence, at any rate, it fell upon Richard Shelton to command affairs in Shoreby; and, as he sat at meat, his mind was full of care, and his face heavy with consideration. It had been determined, between him and the Lord Foxham, to make one bold stroke that evening, and, by brute force, to set Joanna free. The obstacles, however, were many; and as one after another of his scouts arrived, each brought him more discomfortable news.

Sir Daniel was alarmed by the skirmish of the night before. He had increased the garrison of the house in the garden; but not content with that, he had stationed horsemen in all the neighbouring lanes, so that he might have instant word of any movement. Meanwhile, in the court of his mansion, steeds stood saddled, and the riders, armed at every point, awaited but the signal to ride.

The adventure of the night appeared more and more difficult of execution, till suddenly Dick's countenance lightened.

"Lawless!" he cried, "you that were a shipman, can ye steal me a ship?"

"Master Dick," replied Lawless, "if ye would back me, I would agree to steal York Minster."

Presently after, these two set forth and descended to the harbour. It was a considerable basin, lying among sand-hills, and surrounded with patches of down, ancient ruinous lumber, and tumble-down slums of the town. Many decked ships and many open boats either lay there at anchor, or had been drawn up on the beach. A long duration of bad weather had driven them from the high seas into the shelter of the port; and the great trooping of black clouds, and the cold squalls that followed one another, now with a sprinkling of dry snow, now in a mere swoop of wind, promised no improvement but rather threatened a more serious storm in the immediate future.

The seamen, in view of the cold and the wind, had for the most part slunk ashore, and were now roaring and singing in the shoreside taverns. Many of the ships already rode unguarded at their anchors; and as the day wore on, and the weather offered no appearance of improvement, the number was continually being augmented. It was to these deserted ships, and, above all, to those of them that lay far out, that Lawless directed his attention; while Dick, seated upon an anchor that was half embedded in the sand, and giving ear, now to the rude, potent, and boding voices of the gale, and now to the hoarse singing of the shipmen in a neighbouring tavern, soon forgot his immediate surroundings and concerns in the agreeable recollection of Lord Foxham's promise.

He was disturbed by a touch upon his shoulder. It was Lawless, pointing to a small ship that lay somewhat by itself, and within but a little of the harbour mouth, where it heaved regularly and smoothly on the entering swell. A pale gleam of winter sunshine fell, at that moment, on the vessel's deck, relieving her against a bank of scowling cloud; and in this momentary glitter Dick could see a couple of men hauling the skiff alongside.

"There, sir," said Lawless, "mark ye it well! There is the ship for to-night."

Presently the skiff put out from the vessel's side, and the two men, keeping her head well to the wind, pulled lustily for shore, Lawless turned to a loiterer.

"How call ye her?" he asked, pointing to the little vessel.

"They call her the Good Hope, of Dartmouth," replied the loiterer. "Her captain, Arblaster by name. He pulleth the bow oar in yon skiff."

This was all that Lawless wanted. Hurriedly thanking the man, he moved round the shore to a certain sandy creek, for which the skiff was heading. There he took up his position, and as soon as they were within earshot, opened fire on the sailors of the Good Hope.

"What! Gossip Arblaster!" he cried. "Why, ye be well met; nay, gossip, ye be right well met, upon the rood! And is that the Good Hope? Ay, I would know her among ten thousand!—a sweet shear, a sweet boat! But marry come up, my gossip, will ye drink? I have come into mine estate which doubtless ye remember to have heard on. I am now rich; I have left to sail upon the sea; I do sail now, for the most part, upon spiced ale. Come, fellow; thy hand upon't! Come, drink with an old shipfellow!"

Skipper Arblaster, a long-faced, elderly, weather-beaten man, with a knife hanging about his neck by a plaited cord, and for all the world like any modern seaman in his gait and bearing, had hung back in obvious amazement and distrust. But the name of an estate, and a certain air of tipsified simplicity and good-fellowship which Lawless very well affected, combined to conquer his suspicious jealousy; his countenance relaxed, and he at once extended his open hand and squeezed that of the outlaw in a formidable grasp.

"Nay," he said, "I cannot mind you. But what o' that? I would drink with any man, gossip, and so would my man Tom. Man Tom," he added, addressing his follower, "here is my gossip, whose name I cannot mind, but no doubt a very good seaman. Let's go drink with him and his shore friend."

Lawless led the way, and they were soon seated in an alehouse, which, as it was very new, and stood in an exposed and solitary station, was less crowded than those nearer to the centre of the port. It was but a shed of timber, much like a blockhouse in the backwoods of to-day, and was coarsely furnished with a press or two, a number of naked benches, and boards set upon barrels to play the part of tables. In the middle, and besieged by half a hundred violent draughts, a fire of wreck-wood blazed and vomited thick smoke.

"Ay, now," said Lawless, "here is a shipman's joy—a good fire and a good stiff cup ashore, with foul weather without and an off-sea gale a-snoring in the roof! Here's to the Good Hope! May she ride easy!"

"Ay," said Skipper Arblaster, "'tis good weather to be ashore in, that is sooth. Man Tom, how say ye to that? Gossip, ye speak well, though I can never think upon your name; but ye speak very well. May the Good Hope ride easy! Amen!"

"Friend Dickon," resumed Lawless, addressing his commander, "ye have certain matters on hand, unless I err? Well, prithee be about them incontinently. For here I be with the choice of all good company, two tough old shipmen; and till that ye return I will go warrant these brave fellows will bide here and drink me cup for cup. We are not like shore-men, we old, tough tarry-Johns!"

"It is well meant," returned the skipper. "Ye can go, boy; for I will keep your good friend and my good gossip company till curfew—ay, and by St. Mary, till the sun get up again! For, look ye, when a man hath been long enough at sea, the salt getteth me into the clay upon his bones; and let him drink a draw-well, he will never be quenched."

Thus encouraged upon all hands, Dick rose, saluted his company, and going forth again into the gusty afternoon, got him as speedily as he might to the Goat and Bagpipes. Thence he sent word to my Lord Foxham that, so soon as ever the evening closed, they would have a stout boat to keep the sea in. And then leading along with him a couple of outlaws who had some experience of the sea, he returned himself to the harbour and the little sandy creek.

The skiff of the Good Hope lay among many others, from which it was easily distinguished by its extreme smallness and fragility. Indeed, when Dick and his two men had taken their places, and begun to put forth out of the creek into the open harbour, the little cockle dipped into the swell and staggered under every gust of wind, like a thing upon the point of sinking.

The Good Hope, as we have said, was anchored far out, where the swell was heaviest. No other vessel lay nearer than several cables' length; those that were the nearest were themselves entirely deserted; and as the skiff approached, a thick flurry of snow and a sudden darkening of the weather further concealed the movements of the outlaws from all possible espial. In a trice they had leaped upon the heaving deck, and the skiff was dancing at the stern. The Good Hope was captured.

She was a good stout boat, decked in the bows and amid-ships, but open in the stern. She carried one mast, and was rigged between a felucca and a lugger. It would seem that Skipper Arblaster had made an excellent venture, for the hold was full of pieces of French wine; and in the little cabin, besides the Virgin Mary in the bulkhead which proved the captain's piety, there were many lock-fast chests and cupboards, which showed him to be rich and careful.

A dog, who was the sole occupant of the vessel, furiously barked and bit the heels of the boarders; but he was soon kicked into the cabin, and the door shut upon his just resentment. A lamp was lit and fixed in the shrouds to mark the vessel clearly from the shore; one of the wine pieces in the hold was broached, and a cup of excellent Gascony emptied to the adventure of the evening; and then, while one of the outlaws began to get ready his bow and arrows and prepare to hold the ship against all comers, the other hauled in the skiff and got overboard, where he held on, waiting for Dick.

"Well, Jack, keep me a good watch," said the young commander, preparing to follow his subordinate. "Ye will do right well."

"Why," returned Jack, "I shall do excellent well indeed, so long as we lie here; but once we put the nose of this poor ship outside the harbour— See, there she trembles! Nay, the poor shrew heard the words, and the heart misgave her in her oak-tree ribs. But look, Master Dick! how black the weather gathers!"

The darkness ahead was, indeed, astonishing. Great billows heaved up out of the blackness, one after another; and one after another the Good Hope buoyantly climbed, and giddily plunged upon the farther side. A thin sprinkle of snow and thin flakes of foam came flying, and powdered the deck; and the wind harped dismally among the rigging.

"In sooth, it looketh evilly," said Dick, "But what cheer! 'Tis but a squall, and presently it will blow over." But, in spite of his words, he was depressingly affected by the bleak disorder of the sky and the wailing and fluting of the wind; and as he got over the side of the Good Hope and made once more for the landing-creek with the best speed of oars, he crossed himself devoutly, and recommended to Heaven the lives of all who should adventure on the sea.

At the landing-creek there had already gathered about a dozen of the outlaws. To these the skiff was left, and they were bidden embark without delay.

A little farther up the beach Dick found Lord Foxham hurrying in quest of him, his face concealed with a dark hood, and his bright armour covered by a long russet mantle of a poor appearance.

"Young Shelton," he said, "are ye for sea, then, truly?"

"My lord," replied Richard, "they lie about the house with horsemen; it may not be reached from the land side without alarum; and Sir Daniel once advertised of our adventure, we can no more carry it to a good end than, saving your presence, we could ride upon the wind. Now, in going round by sea, we do run some peril by the elements; but, what much outweighteth all, we have a chance to make good our purpose and bear off the maid."

"Well," returned Lord Foxham, "lead on. I will, in some sort, follow you for shame's sake; but I own I would I were in bed."

"Here, then," said Dick. "Hither we go to fetch our pilot."

And he led the way to the rude alehouse where he had given rendezvous to a portion of his men. Some of these he found lingering round the door outside; others had pushed more boldly in, and, choosing places as near as possible to where they saw their comrade, gathered close about Lawless and the two shipmen. These, to judge by the distempered countenance and cloudy eye, had long since gone beyond the boundaries of moderation; and as Richard entered, closely followed by Lord Foxham, they were all three tuning up an old, pitiful sea-ditty, to the chorus of the wailing of the gale.

The young leader cast a rapid glance about the shed. The fire had just been replenished, and gave forth volumes of black smoke, so that it was difficult to see clearly in the farther corners. It was plain, however, that the outlaws very largely outnumbered the remainder of the guests. Satisfied upon this point, in case of any failure in the operation of his plan, Dick strode up to the table and resumed his place upon the bench.

"Hey?" cried the skipper, tipsily, "who are ye, hey?"

"I want a word with you without, Master Arblaster," returned Dick; "and here is what we shall talk of." And he showed him a gold noble in the glimmer of the firelight.

The shipman's eyes burned, although he still failed to recognise our hero.

"Ay, boy," he said, "I am with you. Gossip, I will be back anon. Drink fair, gossip"; and, taking Dick's arm to steady his uneven steps, he walked to the door of the alehouse.

As soon as he was over the threshold, ten strong arms had seized and bound him; and in two minutes more, with his limbs trussed one to another, and a good gag in his mouth, he had been tumbled neck and crop into a neighbouring hay-barn. Presently, his man Tom, similarly secured, was tossed beside him, and the pair were left to their uncouth reflections for the night.

And now, as the time for concealment had gone by, Lord Foxham's followers were summoned by a preconcerted signal, and the party, boldly taking possession of as many boats as their numbers required, pulled in a flotilla for the light in the rigging of the ship. Long before the last man had climbed to the deck of the Good Hope, the sound of furious shouting from the shore showed that a part, at least, of the seamen had discovered the loss of their skiffs.

But it was now too late, whether for recovery or revenge. Out of some forty fighting men now mustered in the stolen ship, eight had been to sea, and could play the part of mariners. With the aid of these, a slice of sail was got upon her. The cable was cut. Lawless, vacillating on his feet, and still shouting the chorus of sea-ballads, took the long tiller in his hands: and the Good Hope began to flit forward into the darkness of the night, and to face the great waves beyond the harbour bar.

Richard took his place beside the weather rigging. Except for the ship's own lantern, and for some lights in Shoreby town, that were already fading to leeward, the whole world of air was as black as in a pit. Only from time to time, as the Good Hope swooped dizzily down into the valley of the rollers, a crest would break—a great cataract of snowy foam would leap in one instant into being—and, in an instant more, would stream into the wake and vanish.

Many of the men lay holding on and praying aloud; many more were sick, and had crept into the bottom, where they sprawled among the cargo. And what with the extreme violence of the motion, and the continued drunken bravado of Lawless, still shouting and singing at the helm, the stoutest heart on board may have nourished a shrewd misgiving as to the result.

But Lawless, as if guided by an instinct, steered the ship across the breakers, struck the lee of a great sand-bank, where they sailed for awhile in smooth water, and presently after laid her alongside a rude stone pier, where she was hastily made fast, and lay ducking and grinding in the dark.

CHAPTER V. THE "GOOD HOPE" (CONTINUED)

The pier was not far distant from the house in which Joanna lay; it now only remained to get the men on shore, to surround the house with a strong party, burst in the door and carry off the captive. They might then regard themselves as done with the Good Hope; it had placed them on the rear of their enemies; and the retreat, whether they should succeed or fail in the main enterprise, would be directed with a greater measure of hope in the direction of the forest and my Lord Foxham's reserve.

To get the men on shore, however, was no easy task; many had been sick, all were pierced with cold; the promiscuity and disorder on board had shaken their discipline; the movement of the ship and the darkness of the night had cowed their spirits. They made a rush upon the pier; my lord, with his sword drawn on his own retainers, must throw himself in front; and this impulse of rabblement was not restrained without a certain clamour of voices, highly to be regretted in the case.

When some degree of order had been restored, Dick, with a few chosen men, set forth in advance. The darkness on shore, by contrast with the flashing of the surf, appeared before him like a solid body; and the howling and whistling of the gale drowned any lesser noise.

He had scarce reached the end of the pier, however, when there fell a lull of the wind; and in this he seemed to hear on shore the hollow footing of horses and the clash of arms. Checking his immediate followers, he passed forward a step or two alone, even setting foot upon the down; and here he made sure he could detect the shape of men and horses moving. A strong discouragement assailed him. If their enemies were really on the watch, if they had beleaguered the shoreward end of the pier, he and Lord Foxham were taken in a posture of very poor defence, the sea behind, the men jostled in the dark upon a narrow causeway. He gave a cautious whistle, the signal previously agreed upon.

It proved to be a signal far more than he desired. Instantly there fell, through the black night, a shower of arrows sent at a venture; and so close were the men huddled on the pier that more than one was hit, and the arrows were answered with cries of both fear and pain. In this first discharge, Lord Foxham was struck down; Hawksley had him carried on board again at once; and his men, during the brief remainder of the skirmish, fought (when they fought at all) without guidance. That was perhaps the chief cause of the disaster which made haste to follow.

At the shore end of the pier, for perhaps a minute, Dick held his own with a handful; one or two were wounded upon either side; steel crossed steel; nor had there been the least signal of advantage, when in the twinkling of an eye the tide turned against the party from the ship. Some one cried out that all was lost; the men were in the very humour to lend an ear to a discomfortable counsel; the cry was taken up. "On board, lads, for your lives!" cried another. A third, with the true instinct of the coward, raised that inevitable report on all retreats: "We are betrayed!" And in a moment the whole mass of men went surging and jostling backward down the pier, turning their defenceless backs on their pursuers and piercing the night with craven outcry.

One coward thrust off the ship's stern, while another still held her by the bows. The fugitives leaped, screaming, and were hauled on board, or fell back and perished in the sea. Some were cut down upon the pier by the pursuers. Many were injured on the ship's deck in the blind haste and terror of the moment, one man leaping upon another, and a third on both. At last, and whether by design or accident, the bows of the Good Hope were liberated; and the ever-ready Lawless, who had maintained his place at the helm through all the hurly-burly by sheer strength of body and a liberal use of the cold steel, instantly clapped her on the proper tack. The ship began to move once more forward on the stormy sea, its scuppers running blood, its deck heaped with fallen men, sprawling and struggling in the dark.

Thereupon, Lawless sheathed his dagger, and turning to his next neighbour, "I have left my mark on them, gossip," said he, "the yelping, coward hounds."

Now, while they were all leaping and struggling for their lives, the men

144

had not appeared to observe the rough shoves and cutting stabs with which Lawless had held his post in the confusion. But perhaps they had already begun to understand somewhat more clearly, or perhaps another ear had overheard, the helmsman's speech.

Panic-stricken troops recover slowly, and men who have just disgraced themselves by cowardice, as if to wipe out the memory of their fault, will sometimes run straight into the opposite extreme of insubordination. So it was now; and the same men who had thrown away their weapons and been hauled, feet-foremost, into the Good Hope, began to cry out upon their leaders, and demand that some one should be punished.

This growing ill-feeling turned upon Lawless.

In order to get a proper offing, the old outlaw had put the head of the Good Hope to seaward.

"What!" bawled one of the grumblers, "he carrieth us to seaward!"

"'Tis sooth," cried another. "Nay, we are betrayed for sure."

And they all began to cry out in chorus that they were betrayed, and in shrill tones and with abominable oaths bade Lawless go about-ship and bring them speedily ashore. Lawless, grinding his teeth, continued in silence to steer the true course, guiding the Good Hope among the formidable billows. To their empty terrors, as to their dishonourable threats, between drink and dignity he scorned to make reply. The malcontents drew together a little abaft the mast, and it was plain they were like barnyard cocks, "crowing for courage." Presently they would be fit for any extremity of injustice or ingratitude. Dick began to mount by the ladder, eager to interpose; but one of the outlaws, who was also something of a seaman, got beforehand.

"Lads," he began, "y'are right wooden heads, I think. For to get back, by the mass, we must have an offing, must we not? And this old Lawless——"

Some one struck the speaker on the mouth, and the next moment, as a fire springs among dry straw, he was felled upon the deck, trampled under the feet, and despatched by the daggers of his cowardly companions. At this the wrath of Lawless rose and broke.

"Steer yourselves," he bellowed, with a curse; and, careless of the result, he left the helm.

The Good Hope was, at that moment, trembling on the summit of a swell. She subsided, with sickening velocity, upon the farther side. A wave, like a great black bulwark, hove immediately in front of her; and, with a staggering blow, she plunged head-foremost through that liquid hill. The green water passed right over her from stem to stern, as high as a man's knees; the sprays ran higher than the mast; and she rose again upon the other side, with an appalling, tremulous indecision, like a beast that has been deadly wounded.

Six or seven of the malcontents had been carried bodily overboard; and as for the remainder, when they found their tongues again, it was to bellow to the saints and wail upon Lawless to come back and take the tiller.

Nor did Lawless wait to be twice bidden. The terrible result of his fling of just resentment sobered him completely. He knew, better than any one on board, how nearly the Good Hope had gone bodily down below their feet; and he could tell, by the laziness with which she met the sea, that the peril was by no means over.

Dick, who had been thrown down by the concussion and half drowned, rose wading to his knees in the swamped well of the stern, and crept to the old helmsman's side.

"Lawless," he said, "we do all depend on you; y'are a brave, steady man, indeed, and crafty in the management of ships; I shall put three sure men to watch upon your safety."

"Bootless, my master, bootless," said the steersman, peering forward through the dark. "We come every moment somewhat clearer of these sand-banks; with every moment, then, the sea packeth upon us heavier, and for all these whimperers, they will presently be on their backs. For, my master, 'tis a right mystery, but true, there never yet was a bad man that was a good shipman. None but the honest and the bold can endure me this tossing of a ship."

"Nay, Lawless," said Dick, laughing, "that is a right shipman's by-word, and hath no more of sense than the whistle of the wind. But, prithee, how go we? Do we lie well? Are we in good case?"

"Master Shelton," replied Lawless, "I have been a Grey Friar—I praise fortune—an archer, a thief, and a shipman. Of all these coats, I had the best fancy to die in the Grey Friar's, as ye may readily conceive, and the least fancy to die in John Shipman's tarry jacket; and that for two excellent good reasons: first, that the death might take a man suddenly; and second, for the horror of that great, salt smother and welter under my foot here"—and Lawless stamped with his foot. "Howbeit," he went on, "an I die not a sailor's death, and that this night, I shall owe a tall candle to our Lady."

"Is it so?" asked Dick.

"It is right so," replied the outlaw. "Do ye not feel how heavy and dull she moves upon the waves? Do ye not hear the water washing in her hold? She will scarce mind the rudder even now. Bide till she has settled a bit lower; and she will either go down below your boots like a stone image, or drive ashore here, under our lee, and come all to pieces like a twist of string."

"Ye speak with a good courage," returned Dick. "Ye are not then appalled?"

"Why, master," answered Lawless, "if ever a man had an ill crew to come to port with, it is I—a renegade friar, a thief, and all the rest on't. Well, ye may wonder, but I keep a good hope in my wallet; and if that I be to drown, I will drown with a bright eye, Master Shelton, and a steady hand."

Dick returned no answer; but he was surprised to find the old vagabond of so resolute a temper, and fearing some fresh violence or treachery, set forth upon his quest for three sure men. The great bulk of the men had now deserted the deck, which was continually wetted with the flying sprays, and where they lay exposed to the shrewdness of the winter wind. They had gathered, instead, into the hold of the merchandise, among the butts of wine, and lighted by two swinging lanterns.

Here a few kept up the form of revelry, and toasted each other deep in Arblaster's Gascony wine. But as the Good Hope continued to tear through the smoking waves, and toss her stem and stern alternately high in air and deep into white foam, the number of these jolly companions diminished with every moment and with every lurch. Many sat apart, tending their hurts, but the majority were already prostrated with sickness, and lay moaning in the bilge.

Greensheve, Cuckow, and a young fellow of Lord Foxham's whom Dick had already remarked for his intelligence and spirit, were still, however, both fit to understand and willing to obey. These Dick set, as a body-guard, about the person of the steersman, and then, with a last look at the black sky and sea, he turned and went below into the cabin, whither Lord Foxham had been carried by his servants.

CHAPTER VI. THE "GOOD HOPE" (CONCLUDED)

The moans of the wounded baron blended with the wailing of the ship's dog. The poor animal, whether he was merely sick at heart to be separated from his friends, or whether he indeed recognised some peril in the labouring of the ship, raised his cries, like minute-guns, above the roar of wave and weather; and the more superstitious of the men heard, in these sounds, the knell of the Good Hope.

Lord Foxham had been laid in a berth upon a fur cloak. A little lamp burned dim before the Virgin in the bulkhead, and by its glimmer Dick could see the pale countenance and hollow eyes of the hurt man.

"I am sore hurt," said he. "Come near to my side, young Shelton; let there be one by me who, at least, is gentle born; for after having lived nobly and richly all the days of my life, this is a sad pass that I should get my hurt in a little ferreting skirmish, and die here, in a foul, cold ship upon the sea, among broken men and churls."

"Nay, my lord," said Dick, "I pray rather to the saints that ye will recover you of your hurt, and come soon and sound ashore."

"How!" demanded his lordship. "Come sound ashore? There is, then, a question of it?"

"The ship laboureth—the sea is grievous and contrary," replied the lad; "and by what I can learn of my fellow that steereth us, we shall do well, indeed, if we come dry-shod to land."

"Ha!" said the baron, gloomily, "thus shall every terror attend upon the passage of my soul! Sir, pray rather to live hard, that ye may die easy, than to be fooled and fluted all through life, as to the pipe and tabour, and, in the last hour, be plunged among misfortunes! Howbeit, I have that upon my mind that must not be delayed. We have no priest aboard?"

"None," replied Dick.

"Here, then, to my secular interests," resumed Lord Foxham: "ye must be as good a friend to me dead, as I found you a gallant enemy when I was living. I fall in an evil hour for me, for England, and for them that trusted me. My men are being brought by Hamley—he that was your rival; they will rendezvous in the long holm at Holywood; this ring from off my finger will accredit you to represent mine orders; and I shall write, besides, two words upon this paper, bidding Hamley yield to you the damsel. Will he obey? I know not."

"But, my lord, what orders?" inquired Dick.

"Ay," quoth the baron, "ay—the orders"; and he looked upon Dick with hesitation. "Are ye Lancaster or York?" he asked, at length.

"I shame to say it," answered Dick, "I can scarce clearly answer. But so much I think is certain: since I serve with Ellis Duckworth, I serve the house of York. Well, if that be so, I declare for York."

"It is well," returned the other; "it is exceeding well. For, truly, had ye said Lancaster, I wot not for the world what I had done. But sith ye are for York, follow me. I came hither but to watch these lords at Shoreby, while mine excellent young lord, Richard of Gloucester,[1] prepareth a sufficient force to fall upon and scatter them. I have made me notes of their strength, what watch they keep, and how they lie; and these I was to deliver to my young lord on Sunday, an hour before noon, at St. Bride's Cross beside the forest. This tryst I am not like to keep, but I pray you, of courtesy, to keep it in my stead; and see that not pleasure, nor pain, tempest, wound, nor pestilence withhold you from the hour and place, for the welfare of England lieth upon this cast."

"I do soberly take this upon me," said Dick. "In so far as in me lieth, your purpose shall be done."

"It is good," said the wounded man. "My lord duke shall order you further, and if ye obey him with spirit and good-will, then is your fortune made. Give me the lamp a little nearer to mine eyes, till that I write these words for you."

He wrote a note "to his worshipful kinsman, Sir John Hamley"; and then a second, which he left without external superscripture.

"This is for the duke," he said. "The word is 'England and Edward,' and the counter, 'England and York.'"

"And Joanna, my lord?" asked Dick.

"Nay, ye must get Joanna how ye can," replied the baron. "I have named you for my choice in both these letters; but ye must get her for yourself, boy. I have tried, as ye see here before you, and have lost my life. More could no man do."

By this time the wounded man began to be very weary; and Dick, putting the precious papers in his bosom, bade him be of good cheer, and left him to repose.

The day was beginning to break, cold and blue, with flying squalls of snow. Close under the lee of the Good Hope, the coast lay in alternate rocky headlands and sandy bays; and farther inland the wooded hill-tops of Tunstall showed along the sky. Both the wind and the sea had gone down; but the vessel wallowed deep, and scarce rose upon the waves.

Lawless was still fixed at the rudder; and by this time nearly all the men had crawled on deck, and were now gazing, with blank faces, upon the inhospitable coast.

"Are we going ashore?" asked Dick.

"Ay," said Lawless, "unless we get first to the bottom."

And just then the ship rose so languidly to meet a sea, and the water weltered so loudly in her hold, that Dick involuntarily seized the steersman by the arm.

"By the mass!" cried Dick, as the bows of the Good Hope reappeared above the foam, "I thought we had foundered, indeed; my heart was at my throat."

In the waist, Greensheve, Hawksley, and the better men of both companies were busy breaking up the deck to build a raft; and to these Dick joined himself, working the harder to drown the memory of his predicament. But, even as he worked, every sea that struck the poor ship, and every one of her dull lurches, as she tumbled wallowing among the waves, recalled him with a horrid pang to the immediate proximity of death.

Presently, looking up from his work, he saw that they were close in below a promontory; a piece of ruinous cliff, against the base of which the sea broke white and heavy, almost overplumbed the deck; and, above that, again, a house appeared, crowning a down.

Inside the bay the seas ran gaily, raised the Good Hope upon their foam-flecked shoulders, carried her beyond the control of the steersman, and in a moment dropped her, with a great concussion, on the sand, and began to break over her half-mast high, and roll her to and fro. Another great wave followed, raised her again, and carried her yet farther in; and then a third succeeded, and left her far inshore of the more dangerous breakers, wedged upon a bank.

"Now, boys," cried Lawless, "the saints have had a care of us, indeed. The tide ebbs; let us but sit down and drink a cup of wine, and before half an hour ye may all march me ashore as safe as on a bridge."

A barrel was broached, and, sitting in what shelter they could find from the flying snow and spray, the shipwrecked company handed the cup around, and sought to warm their bodies and restore their spirits.

Dick, meanwhile, returned to Lord Foxham, who lay in great perplexity and fear, the floor of his cabin washing knee-deep in water, and the lamp, which had been his only light, broken and extinguished by the violence of the blow.

"My lord," said young Shelton, "fear not at all; the saints are plainly for us; the seas have cast us high upon a shoal, and as soon as the tide hath somewhat ebbed, we may walk ashore upon our feet."

It was nearly an hour before the vessel was sufficiently deserted by the ebbing sea, and they could set forth for the land, which appeared dimly before them through a veil of driving snow.

Upon a hillock on one side of their way a party of men lay huddled together, suspiciously observing the movements of the new arrivals.

"They might draw near and offer us some comfort," Dick remarked.

"Well, an' they come not to us, let us even turn aside to them," said Hawksley. "The sooner we come to a good fire and a dry bed the better for my poor lord."

But they had not moved far in the direction of the hillock, before the men, with one consent, rose suddenly to their feet, and poured a flight of well-directed arrows on the shipwrecked company.

"Back! back!" cried his lordship. "Beware, in Heaven's name, that ye reply not."

"Nay," cried Greensheve, pulling an arrow from his leather jack. "We are in no posture to fight, it is certain, being drenching wet, dog-weary, and three-parts frozen; but for the love of old England, what aileth them to shoot thus cruelly on their poor country people in distress?"

"They take us to be French pirates," answered Lord Foxham. "In these most troublesome and degenerate days we cannot keep our own shores of England; but our old enemies, whom we once chased on sea and land, do now range at pleasure, robbing and slaughtering and burning. It is the pity and reproach of this poor land."

The men upon the hillock lay, closely observing them, while they trailed upward from the beach and wound inland among desolate sand-hills; for a mile or so they even hung upon the rear of the march, ready, at a sign, to pour another volley on the weary and dispirited fugitives; and it was only when, striking at length upon a firm highroad, Dick began to call his men to some more martial order, that these jealous guardians of the coast of England silently disappeared among the snow. They had done what they desired; they had protected their own homes and farms, their own families and cattle; and their private interest being thus secured, it mattered not the weight of a straw to any one of them, although the Frenchmen should carry blood and fire to every other parish in the realm of England.

BOOK IV. THE DISGUISE

CHAPTER I. THE DEN

The place where Dick had struck the line of a highroad was not far from Holywood, and within nine or ten miles of Shoreby-on-the-Till; and here, after making sure that they were pursued no longer, the two bodies separated. Lord Foxham's followers departed, carrying their wounded master towards the comfort and security of the great abbey; and Dick, as he saw them wind away and disappear in the thick curtain of the falling snow, was left alone with near upon a dozen outlaws, the last remainder of his troop of volunteers.

Some were wounded; one and all were furious at their ill-success and long exposure; and though they were now too cold and hungry to do more, they grumbled and cast sullen looks upon their leaders. Dick emptied his purse among them, leaving himself nothing; thanked them for the courage they had displayed, though he could have found it more readily in his heart to rate them for poltroonery; and having thus somewhat softened the effect of his prolonged misfortune, despatched them to find their way, either severally or in pairs, to Shoreby and the Goat and Bagpipes.

For his own part, influenced by what he had seen on board of the Good Hope, he chose Lawless to be his companion on the walk. The snow was falling, without pause or variation, in one even, blinding cloud; the wind had been strangled, and now blew no longer; and the whole world was blotted out and sheeted down below that silent inundation. There was great danger of wandering by the way and perishing in drifts; and Lawless, keeping half a step in front of his companion, and holding his head forward like a hunting dog upon the scent, inquired his way of every tree, and studied out their path as though he were conning a ship among dangers.

About a mile into the forest they came to a place where several ways met, under a grove of lofty and contorted oaks. Even in the narrow horizon of the falling snow, it was a spot that could not fail to be recognised; and Lawless evidently recognised it with particular delight.

"Now, Master Richard," said he, "an y'are not too proud to be the guest of a man who is neither a gentleman by birth nor so much as a good Christian, I can offer you a cup of wine and a good fire to melt the marrow in your frozen bones."

"Lead on, Will," answered Dick. "A cup of wine and a good fire! Nay, I would go a far way round to see them."

Lawless turned aside under the bare branches of the grove, and, walking resolutely forward for some time, came to a steepish hollow or den, that had now drifted a quarter full of snow. On the verge, a great beech-tree hung, precariously rooted; and here the old outlaw, pulling aside some bushy underwood, bodily disappeared into the earth.

The beech had, in some violent gale, been half uprooted, and had torn up a considerable stretch of turf; and it was under this that old Lawless had dug out his forest hiding-place. The roots served him for rafters, the turf was his thatch; for walls and floor he had his mother the earth. Rude as it was, the hearth in one corner, blackened by fire, and the presence in another of a large oaken chest well fortified with iron, showed it at one glance to be the den of a man, and not the burrow of a digging beast.

Though the snow had drifted at the mouth and sifted in upon the floor of this earth cavern, yet was the air much warmer than without; and when Lawless had struck a spark, and the dry furze bushes had begun to blaze and crackle on the hearth, the place assumed, even to the eye, an air of comfort and of home.

With a sigh of great contentment, Lawless spread his broad hands before the fire, and seemed to breathe the smoke.

"Here, then," he said, "is this old Lawless's rabbit-hole; pray Heaven there come no terrier! Far I have rolled hither and thither, and here and about, since that I was fourteen years of mine age and first ran away from mine abbey, with the sacrist's gold chain and a mass-book that I sold for four marks. I have been in England and France and Burgundy, and in Spain, too, on a pilgrimage for my poor soul; and upon the sea, which is no man's country. But here is my place, Master Shelton. This is my native land, this burrow in the earth! Come rain or wind—and whether it's April, and the birds all sing, and the blossoms fall about my bed—or whether it's winter, and I sit alone with my good gossip the fire, and robin redbreast twitters in the woods— here, is my church and market, and my wife and child. It's here I come back to, and it's here, so please the saints, that I would like to die."

"'Tis a warm corner, to be sure," replied Dick, "and a pleasant, and a well hid."

"It had need to be," returned Lawless, "for an they found it, Master Shelton, it would break my heart. But here," he added, burrowing with his stout fingers in the sandy floor, "here is my wine cellar; and ye shall have a flask of excellent strong stingo."

Sure enough, after but a little digging, he produced a big leathern bottle of about a gallon, nearly three-parts full of a very heady and sweet wine; and when they had drunk to each other comradely, and the fire had been replenished and blazed up again, the pair lay at full length, thawing and steaming, and divinely warm.

"Master Shelton," observed the outlaw, "y' 'ave had two mischances this last while, and y'are like to lose the maid—do I take it aright?"

"Aright!" returned Dick, nodding his head.

"Well, now," continued Lawless, "hear an old fool that hath been nigh-hand everything, and seen nigh-hand all! Ye go too much on other people's errands, Master Dick. Ye go on Ellis's; but he desireth rather the death of Sir Daniel. Ye go on Lord Foxham's; well the saints preserve him!—doubtless he meaneth well. But go ye upon your own, good Dick. Come right to the maid's side. Court her, lest that she forget you. Be ready; and when the chance shall come, off with her at the saddle-bow."

"Ay, but, Lawless, beyond doubt she is now in Sir Daniel's own mansion," answered Dick.

"Thither, then, go we," replied the outlaw.

Dick stared at him.

"Nay, I mean it," nodded Lawless. "And if y'are of so little faith, and stumble at a word, see here!"

And the outlaw, taking a key from about his neck, opened the oak chest, and dipping and groping deep among its contents, produced first a friar's robe, and next a girdle of rope; and then a huge rosary of wood, heavy enough to be counted as a weapon.

"Here," he said, "is for you. On with them!"

And then, when Dick had clothed himself in this clerical disguise, Lawless produced some colours and a pencil, and proceeded, with the greatest cunning, to disguise his face. The eyebrows he thickened and produced; to the moustache, which was yet hardly visible, he rendered a little service; while, by a few lines around the eye, he changed the expression and increased the apparent age of this young monk.

"Now," he resumed, "when I have done the like, we shall make as bonny a pair of friars as the eye could wish. Boldly to Sir Daniel's we shall go, and there be hospitably welcome for the love of Mother Church."

"And how, dear Lawless," cried the lad, "shall I repay you?"

"Tut, brother," replied the outlaw, "I do naught but for my pleasure. Mind not for me. I am one, by the mass, that mindeth for himself. When that I lack, I have a long tongue and a voice like the monastery bell—I do ask, my son; and where asking faileth, I do most usually take."

The old rogue made a humorous grimace; and although Dick was displeased to lie under so great favours to so equivocal a personage, he was yet unable to restrain his mirth.

With that, Lawless returned to the big chest, and was soon similarly disguised; but, below his gown, Dick wondered to observe him conceal a sheaf of black arrows.

"Wherefore do ye that?" asked the lad. "Wherefore arrows, when ye take no bow?"

"Nay," replied Lawless, lightly, "'tis like there will be heads broke—not to say backs—ere you and I win sound from where we're going to; and if any fall, I would our fellowship should come by the credit on't. A black arrow, Master Dick, is the seal of our abbey; it showeth you who writ the bill."

"An ye prepare so carefully," said Dick, "I have here some papers that, for mine own sake, and the interest of those that trusted me, were better left behind than found upon my body. Where shall I conceal them, Will?"

"Nay," replied Lawless, "I will go forth into the wood and whistle me three verses of a song; meanwhile, do you bury them where ye please, and smooth the sand upon the place."

"Never!" cried Richard. "I trust you, man. I were base indeed if I not trusted you."

"Brother, y'are but a child," replied the old outlaw, pausing and turning his face upon Dick from the threshold of the den. "I am a kind old Christian, and no traitor to men's blood, and no sparer of mine own in a friend's jeopardy. But, fool, child, I am a thief by trade and birth and habit. If my bottle were empty and my mouth dry, I would rob you, dear child, as sure as I love, honour, and admire your parts and person! Can it be clearer spoken? No."

And he stumped forth through the bushes with a snap of his big fingers.

Dick, thus left alone, after a wondering thought upon the inconsistencies of his companion's character, hastily produced, reviewed, and buried his papers. One only he reserved to carry along with him, since it in nowise compromised his friends, and yet might serve him, in a pinch, against Sir Daniel. That was the knight's own letter to Lord Wensleydale, sent by Throgmorton, on the morrow of the defeat at Risingham, and found next day by Dick upon the body of the messenger.

Then, treading down the embers of the fire, Dick left the den, and rejoined the old outlaw, who stood awaiting him under the leafless oaks, and was already beginning to be powdered by the falling snow. Each looked upon the other, and each laughed, so thorough and so droll was the disguise.

"Yet I would it were but summer and a clear day," grumbled the outlaw, "that I might see myself in the mirror of a pool. There be many of Sir Daniel's men that know me; and if we fell to be recognised, there might be two words for you, brother, but as for me, in a paternoster while, I should be kicking in a rope's-end."

Thus they set forth together along the road to Shoreby, which, in this part of its course, kept near along the margin of the forest, coming forth, from time to time, in the open country, and passing beside poor folks' houses and small farms.

Presently at sight of one of these, Lawless pulled up.

"Brother Martin," he said, in a voice capitally disguised, and suited to his monkish robe, "let us enter and seek alms from these poor sinners. Pax vobiscum! Ay," he added, in his own voice, "'tis as I feared; I have somewhat lost the whine of it; and by your leave, good Master Shelton, ye must suffer me to practise in these country places, before that I risk my fat neck by entering Sir Daniel's. But look ye a little, what an excellent thing it is to be a Jack-of-all-trades! An I had not been a shipman, ye had infallibly gone down in the Good Hope; an I had not been a thief, I could not have painted me your face; and but that I had been a Grey Friar, and sung loud in the choir, and ate hearty at the board, I could not have carried this disguise, but the very dogs would have spied us out and barked at us for shams."

He was by this time close to the window of the farm, and he rose on his tip-toes and peeped in.

"Nay," he cried, "better and better. We shall here try our false faces with a vengeance, and have a merry jest on Brother Capper to boot."

And so saying, he opened the door and led the way into the house.

Three of their own company sat at the table, greedily eating. Their daggers, stuck beside them in the board, and the black and menacing looks which they continued to shower upon the people of the house, proved that they owed their entertainment rather to force than favour. On the two monks, who now, with a sort of humble dignity, entered the kitchen of the farm, they seemed to turn with a particular resentment; and one—it was John Capper in person—who seemed to play the leading part, instantly and rudely ordered them away.

"We want no beggars here!" he cried.

But another—although he was as far from recognising Dick and Lawless—inclined to more moderate counsels.

"Not so," he cried. "We be strong men, and take; these be weak, and crave; but in the latter end these shall be uppermost and we below. Mind him not, my father; but come, drink of my cup, and give me a benediction."

"Y'are men of a light mind, carnal, and accursed," said the monk. "Now, may the saints forbid that ever I should drink with such companions! But here, for the pity I bear to sinners, here I do leave you a blessed relic, the which, for your souls' interest, I bid you kiss and cherish."

So far Lawless thundered upon them like a preaching friar; but with these words he drew from under his robe a black arrow, tossed it on the board in front of the three startled outlaws, turned in the same instant, and, taking Dick along with him, was out of the room and out of sight among the falling snow before they had time to utter a word or move a finger.

"So," he said, "we have proved our false faces, Master Shelton. I will now adventure my poor carcase where ye please."

"Good!" returned Richard. "It irks me to be doing. Set we on for Shoreby!"

CHAPTER II. "IN MINE ENEMIES' HOUSE"

Sir Daniel's residence in Shoreby was a tall, commodious, plastered mansion, framed in carven oak, and covered by a low-pitched roof of thatch. To the back there stretched a garden, full of fruit-trees, alleys, and thick arbours, and overlooked from the far end by the tower of the abbey church.

The house might contain, upon a pinch, the retinue of a greater person than Sir Daniel; but even now it was filled with hubbub. The court rang with arms and horseshoe-iron; the kitchens roared with cookery like a bees'-hive; minstrels, and the players of instruments, and the cries of tumblers, sounded from the hall. Sir Daniel, in his profusion, in the gaiety and gallantry of his establishment, rivalled with Lord Shoreby, and eclipsed Lord Risingham.

All guests were made welcome. Minstrels, tumblers, players of chess, the sellers of relics, medicines, perfumes, and enchantments, and along with these every sort of priest, friar, or pilgrim, were made welcome to the lower table, and slept together in the ample lofts, or on the bare boards of the long dining-hall.

On the afternoon following the wreck of the Good Hope, the buttery, the kitchens, the stables, the covered cartshed that surrounded two sides of the court, were all crowded by idle people, partly belonging to Sir Daniel's establishment, and attired in his livery of murrey and blue, partly nondescript strangers attracted to the town by greed, and received by the knight through policy, and because it was the fashion of the time.

The snow, which still fell without interruption, the extreme chill of the air, and the approach of night, combined to keep them under shelter. Wine, ale, and money were all plentiful; many sprawled gambling in the straw of the barn, many were still drunken from the noontide meal. To the eye of a modern it would have looked like the sack of a city; to the eye of a contemporary it was like any other rich and noble household at a festive season.

Two monks—a young and an old—had arrived late, and were now

warming themselves at a bonfire in a corner of the shed. A mixed crowd surrounded them—jugglers, mountebanks, and soldiers; and with these the elder of the two had soon engaged so brisk a conversation, and exchanged so many loud guffaws and country witticisms, that the group momentarily increased in number.

The younger companion, in whom the reader has already recognised Dick Shelton, sat from the first somewhat backward, and gradually drew himself away. He listened, indeed, closely, but he opened not his mouth; and by the grave expression of his countenance, he made but little account of his companion's pleasantries.

At last his eye, which travelled continually to and fro, and kept a guard upon all the entrances of the house, lit upon a little procession entering by the main gate and crossing the court in an oblique direction. Two ladies, muffled in thick furs, led the way, and were followed by a pair of waiting-women and four stout men-at-arms. The next moment they had disappeared within the house; and Dick, slipping through the crowd of loiterers in the shed, was already giving hot pursuit.

"The taller of these twain was Lady Brackley," he thought; "and where Lady Brackley is, Joan will not be far."

At the door of the house the four men-at-arms had ceased to follow, and the ladies were now mounting the stairway of polished oak, under no better escort than that of the two waiting-women. Dick followed close behind. It was already the dusk of the day; and in the house the darkness of the night had almost come. On the stair-landings, torches flared in iron holders; down the long, tapestried corridors, a lamp burned by every door. And where the door stood open, Dick could look in upon arras-covered walls and rush-bescattered floors, glowing in the light of the wood fires.

Two floors were passed, and at every landing the younger and shorter of the two ladies had looked back keenly at the monk. He, keeping his eyes lowered, and affecting the demure manners that suited his disguise, had but seen her once, and was unaware that he had attracted her attention. And now, on the third floor, the party separated, the younger lady continuing to ascend alone, the other, followed by the Waiting-maids, descending the corridor to the right.

Dick mounted with a swift foot, and holding to the corner, thrust forth his head and followed the three women with his eyes. Without turning or looking behind them, they continued to descend the corridor.

"It is right well," thought Dick. "Let me but know my Lady Brackley's chamber, and it will go hard an I find not Dame Hatch upon an errand."

And just then a hand was laid upon his shoulder, and, with a bound and a choked cry, he turned to grapple his assailant.

He was somewhat abashed to find, in the person whom he had so roughly seized, the short young lady in the furs. She, on her part, was shocked and terrified beyond expression, and hung trembling in his grasp.

"Madam," said Dick, releasing her, "I cry you a thousand pardons; but I have no eyes behind, and, by the mass, I could not tell ye were a maid."

The girl continued to look at him, but, by this time, terror began to be succeeded by surprise, and surprise by suspicion. Dick, who could read these changes on her face, became alarmed for his own safety in that hostile house.

"Fair maid," he said, affecting easiness, "suffer me to kiss your hand, in token ye forgive my roughness, and I will even go."

"Y'are a strange monk, young sir," returned the young lady, looking him both boldly and shrewdly in the face; "and now that my first astonishment hath somewhat passed away, I can spy the layman in each word you utter. What do ye here? Why are ye thus sacrilegiously tricked out? Come ye in peace or war? And why spy ye after Lady Brackley like a thief?"

"Madam," quoth Dick, "of one thing I pray you to be very sure: I am no thief. And even if I come here in war, as in some degree I do, I make no war upon fair maids, and I hereby entreat them to copy me so far, and to leave me be. For, indeed, fair mistress, cry out—if such be your pleasure—cry but once, and say what ye have seen, and the poor gentleman before you is merely a dead man. I cannot think ye would be cruel," added Dick; and taking the girl's hand gently in both of his, he looked at her with courteous admiration.

"Are ye, then, a spy—a Yorkist?" asked the maid.

"Madam," he replied, "I am indeed a Yorkist, and, in some sort, a spy. But that which bringeth me into this house, the same which will win for me the pity and interest of your kind heart, is neither of York nor Lancaster. I will wholly put my life in your discretion. I am a lover, and my name——"

But here the young lady clapped her hand suddenly upon Dick's mouth, looked hastily up and down and east and west, and, seeing the coast clear, began to drag the young man, with great strength and vehemence, up-stairs.

"Hush!" she said, "and come! Shalt talk hereafter."

Somewhat bewildered, Dick suffered himself to be pulled up-stairs, bustled along a corridor, and thrust suddenly into a chamber, lit, like so many of the others, by a blazing log upon the hearth.

"Now," said the young lady, forcing him down upon a stool, "sit ye there and attend my sovereign good pleasure. I have life and death over you, and I will not scruple to abuse my power. Look to yourself; y' 'ave cruelly mauled my arm. He knew not I was a maid, quoth he! Had he known I was a maid, he had ta'en his belt to me, forsooth!"

And with these words, she whipped out of the room and left Dick gaping with wonder, and not very sure if he were dreaming or awake.

"Ta'en my belt to her!" he repeated. "Ta'en my belt to her!" And the recollection of that evening in the forest flowed back upon his mind, and he once more saw Matcham's wincing body and beseeching eyes.

And then he was recalled to the dangers of the present. In the next room he heard a stir, as of a person moving; then followed a sigh, which sounded strangely near; and then the rustle of skirts and tap of feet once more began. As he stood hearkening, he saw the arras wave along the wall; there was the sound of a door being opened, the hangings divided, and, lamp in hand, Joanna Sedley entered the apartment.

She was attired in costly stuffs of deep and warm colours, such as befit the winter and the snow. Upon her head, her hair had been gathered together and became her as a crown. And she, who had seemed so little and so awkward in the attire of Matcham, was now tall like a young willow, and swam across the floor as though she scorned the drudgery of walking.

Without a start, without a tremor, she raised her lamp and looked at the young monk.

"What make ye here, good brother?" she inquired. "Ye are doubtless ill-directed. Whom do ye require?" And she set her lamp upon the bracket.

"Joanna," said Dick; and then his voice failed him. "Joanna," he began again, "ye said ye loved me; and the more fool I, but I believed it!"

"Dick!" she cried. "Dick!"

And then, to the wonder of the lad, this beautiful and tall young lady made but one step of it, and threw her arms about his neck and gave him a hundred kisses all in one.

"Oh, the fool fellow!" she cried. "Oh, dear Dick! Oh, if ye could see yourself! Alack!" she added, pausing. "I have spoilt you, Dick! I have knocked some of the paint off. But that can be mended. What cannot be mended, Dick—or I much fear it cannot!—is my marriage with Lord Shoreby."

"Is it decided, then?" asked the lad.

"To-morrow, before noon, Dick, in the abbey church," she answered, "John Matcham and Joanna Sedley both shall come to a right miserable end. There is no help in tears, or I could weep mine eyes out. I have not spared myself to pray, but Heaven frowns on my petition. And, dear Dick—good Dick—but that ye can get me forth of this house before the morning, we must even kiss and say good-bye."

"Nay," said Dick, "not I; I will never say that word. 'Tis like despair; but while there's life, Joanna, there is hope. Yet will I hope. Ay, by the mass, and triumph! Look ye, now, when ye were but a name to me, did I not follow—did I not rouse good men—did I not stake my life upon the quarrel? And now that I have seen you for what ye are—the fairest maid and stateliest of England—think ye I would turn?—if the deep sea were there, I would straight through it; if the way were full of lions, I would scatter them like mice."

"Ay," she said, drily, "ye make a great ado about a sky-blue robe!"

"Nay, Joan," protested Dick, "'tis not alone the robe. But, lass, ye were disguised. Here am I disguised; and, to the proof, do I not cut a figure of fun—a right fool's figure?"

"Ay, Dick, an' that ye do!" she answered, smiling.

"Well, then!" he returned, triumphant. "So was it with you, poor Matcham, in the forest. In sooth, ye were a wench to laugh at. But now!"

So they ran on, holding each other by both hands, exchanging smiles and lovely looks, and melting minutes into seconds; and so they might have continued all night long. But presently there was a noise behind them; and they were aware of the short young lady, with her finger on her lips.

"Saints!" she cried, "but what a noise ye keep! Can ye not speak in compass? And now, Joanna, my fair maid of the woods, what will ye give your gossip for bringing you your sweetheart?"

Joanna ran to her, by way of answer, and embraced her fierily.

"And you, sir," added the young lady, "what do ye give me?"

"Madam," said Dick, "I would fain offer to pay you in the same money." "Come, then," said the lady, "it is permitted you."

But Dick, blushing like a peony, only kissed her hand.

"What ails ye at my face, fair sir?" she inquired, curtseying to the very ground; and then, when Dick had at length and most tepidly embraced her, "Joanna," she added, "your sweetheart is very backwards under your eyes; but I warrant you, when first we met, he was more ready. I am all black and blue, wench; trust me never, if I be not black and blue! And now," she continued, "have ye said your sayings? for I must speedily dismiss the paladin."

But at this they both cried out that they had said nothing, that the night

166

was still very young, and that they would not be separated so early.

"And supper?" asked the young lady. "Must we not go down to supper?"

"Nay, to be sure!" cried Joan. "I had forgotten."

"Hide me, then," said Dick, "put me behind the arras, shut me in a chest, or what ye will, so that I may be here on your return. Indeed, fair lady," he added, "bear this in mind, that we are sore bested, and may never look upon each other's face from this night forward till we die."

At this the young lady melted; and when, a little after, the bell summoned Sir Daniel's household to the board, Dick was planted very stiffly against the wall, at a place where a division in the tapestry permitted him to breathe the more freely, and even to see into the room.

He had not been long in this position, when he was somewhat strangely disturbed. The silence in that upper storey of the house, was only broken by the flickering of the flames and the hissing of a green log in the chimney; but presently, to Dick's strained hearing, there came the sound of some one walking with extreme precaution; and soon after the door opened, and a little black-faced, dwarfish fellow, in Lord Shoreby's colours, pushed first his head, and then his crooked body, into the chamber. His mouth was open, as though to hear the better; and his eyes, which were very bright, flitted restlessly and swiftly to and fro. He went round and round the room, striking here and there upon the hangings; but Dick, by a miracle, escaped his notice. Then he looked below the furniture, and examined the lamp; and, at last, with an air of cruel disappointment, was preparing to go away as silently as he had come, when down he dropped upon his knees, picked up something from among the rushes on the floor, examined it, and, with every signal of delight, concealed it in the wallet at his belt.

Dick's heart sank, for the object in question was a tassel from his own girdle; and it was plain to him that this dwarfish spy, who took a malign delight in his employment, would lose no time in bearing it to his master, the baron. He was half tempted to throw aside the arras, fall upon the scoundrel, and, at the risk of his life, remove the tell-tale token. And while he was still hesitating, a new cause of concern was added. A voice, hoarse and broken by drink, began to be audible from the stair; and presently after, uneven, wandering, and heavy footsteps sounded without along the passage.

"What make ye here, my merry men, among the greenwood shaws?" sang the voice. "What make ye here? Hey! sots, what make ye here?" it added, with a rattle of drunken laughter; and then, once more breaking into song:

"If ye should drink the clary wine,

Fat Friar John, ye friend o' mine—

If I should eat, and ye should drink,

Who shall sing the mass, d'ye think?"

Lawless, alas! rolling drunk, was wandering the house, seeking for a corner wherein to slumber off the effect of his potations. Dick inwardly raged. The spy, at first terrified, had grown reassured as he found he had to deal with an intoxicated man, and now, with a movement of cat-like rapidity, slipped from the chamber, and was gone from Richard's eyes.

What was to be done? If he lost touch of Lawless for the night, he was left impotent, whether to plan or carry forth Joanna's rescue. If, on the other hand, he dared to address the drunken outlaw, the spy might still be lingering within sight, and the most fatal consequences ensue.

It was, nevertheless, upon this last hazard that Dick decided. Slipping from behind the tapestry, he stood ready in the doorway of the chamber, with a warning hand upraised. Lawless, flushed crimson, with his eyes injected, vacillating on his feet, drew still unsteadily nearer. At last he hazily caught sight of his commander, and, in despite of Dick's imperious signals, hailed him instantly and loudly by his name.

Dick leaped upon and shook the drunkard furiously.

"Beast!" he hissed—"beast and no man! It is worse than treachery to be so witless. We may all be shent for thy sotting."

But Lawless only laughed and staggered, and tried to clap young Shelton

168

on the back.

And just then Dick's quick ear caught a rapid brushing in the arras. He leaped towards the sound, and the next moment a piece of the wall-hanging had been torn down, and Dick and the spy were sprawling together in its folds. Over and over they rolled, grappling for each other's throat, and still baffled by the arras, and still silent in their deadly fury. But Dick was by much the stronger, and soon the spy lay prostrate under his knee, and, with a single stroke of the long poniard, ceased to breathe.

CHAPTER III. THE DEAD SPY

Throughout this furious and rapid passage, Lawless had looked on helplessly, and even when all was over, and Dick, already re-arisen to his feet, was listening with the most passionate attention to the distant bustle in the lower storeys of the house, the old outlaw was still wavering on his legs like a shrub in a breeze of wind, and still stupidly staring on the face of the dead man.

"It is well," said Dick, at length; "they have not heard us, praise the saints! But, now, what shall I do with this poor spy? At least, I will take my tassel from his wallet."

So saying, Dick opened the wallet; within he found a few pieces of money, the tassel, and a letter addressed to Lord Wensleydale, and sealed with my Lord Shoreby's seal. The name awoke Dick's recollection; and he instantly broke the wax and read the contents of the letter. It was short, but, to Dick's delight, it gave evident proof that Lord Shoreby was treacherously corresponding with the House of York.

The young fellow usually carried his ink-horn and implements about him, and so now, bending a knee beside the body of the dead spy, he was able to write these words upon a corner of the paper:

My Lord of Shoreby, ye that writt the letter, wot ye why your man is ded? But let me rede you, marry not.

Jon Amend-all.

He laid this paper on the breast of the corpse; and the Lawless, who had been looking on upon these last manœuvres with some flickering returns of intelligence, suddenly drew a black arrow from below his robe, and therewith pinned the paper in its place. The sight of this disrespect, or, as it almost seemed, cruelty to the dead, drew a cry of horror from young Shelton; but the old outlaw only laughed.

"Nay, I will have the credit for mine order," he hiccuped. "My jolly boys must have the credit on't—the credit, brother"; and then, shutting his eyes tight and opening his mouth like a precentor, he began to thunder, in a formidable voice:

"If ye should drink the clary wine"—

"Peace, sot!" cried Dick, and thrust him hard against the wall. "In two words—if so be that such a man can understand me who hath more wine than wit in him—in two words, and, a-Mary's name, begone out of this house, where, if ye continue to abide, ye will not only hang yourself, but me also! Faith, then, up foot! be yare, or, by the mass, I may forget that I am in some sort your captain and in some your debtor! Go!"

The sham monk was now, in some degree, recovering the use of his intelligence; and the ring in Dick's voice, and the glitter in Dick's eye, stamped home the meaning of his words.

"By the mass," cried Lawless, "an I be not wanted, I can go"; and he turned tipsily along the corridor and proceeded to flounder down-stairs, lurching against the wall.

So soon as he was out of sight, Dick returned to his hiding-place, resolutely fixed to see the matter out. Wisdom, indeed, moved him to be gone; but love and curiosity were stronger.

Time passed slowly for the young man, bolt upright behind the arras. The fire in the room began to die down, and the lamp to burn low and to smoke. And still there was no word of the return of any one to these upper quarters of the house; still the faint hum and clatter of the supper party sounded from far below; and still, under the thick fall of the snow, Shoreby town lay silent upon every side.

At length, however, feet and voices began to draw near upon the stair; and presently after several of Sir Daniel's guests arrived upon the landing, and, turning down the corridor, beheld the torn arras and the body of the spy.

Some ran forward and some back, and all together began to cry aloud.

At the sound of their cries, guests, men-at-arms, ladies, servants, and, in a word, all the inhabitants of that great house, came flying from every direction, and began to join their voices to the tumult.

Soon a way was cleared, and Sir Daniel came forth in person, followed by the bridegroom of the morrow, my Lord Shoreby.

"My lord," said Sir Daniel, "have I not told you of this knave Black Arrow? To the proof, behold it! There it stands, and, by the rood, my gossip, in a man of yours, or one that stole your colours!"

"In good sooth, it was a man of mine," replied Lord Shoreby, hanging back. "I would I had more such. He was keen as a beagle and secret as a mole."

"Ay, gossip, truly?" asked Sir Daniel, keenly. "And what came he smelling up so many stairs in my poor mansion? But he will smell no more."

"An't please you, Sir Daniel," said one, "here is a paper written upon with some matter, pinned upon his breast."

"Give it me, arrow and all," said the knight. And when he had taken into his hand the shaft, he continued for some time to gaze upon it in a sullen musing. "Ay," he said, addressing Lord Shoreby, "here is a hate that followeth hard and close upon my heels. This black stick, or its just likeness, shall yet bring me down. And, gossip, suffer a plain knight to counsel you; and if these hounds begin to wind you, flee! 'Tis like a sickness—it still hangeth, hangeth upon the limbs. But let us see what they have written. It is as I thought, my lord; y'are marked, like an old oak, by the woodman; to-morrow or next day, by will come the axe. But what wrote ye in a letter?"

Lord Shoreby snatched the paper from the arrow, read it, crumpled it between his hands, and overcoming the reluctance which had hitherto withheld him from approaching, threw himself on his knees beside the body and eagerly groped in the wallet.

He rose to his feet with a somewhat unsettled countenance.

"Gossip," he said, "I have indeed lost a letter here that much imported; and could I lay my hand upon the knave that took it, he should incontinently grace a halter. But let us, first of all, secure the issues of the house. Here is enough harm already, by St. George!"

Sentinels were posted close around the house and garden; a sentinel on every landing of the stair, a whole troop in the main entrance-hall; and yet another about the bonfire in the shed. Sir Daniel's followers were supplemented by Lord Shoreby's; there was thus no lack of men or weapons to make the house secure, or to entrap a lurking enemy, should one be there.

Meanwhile, the body of the spy was carried out through the falling snow and deposited in the abbey church.

It was not until these dispositions had been taken, and all had returned to a decorous silence, that the two girls drew Richard Shelton from his place of concealment, and made a full report to him of what had passed. He, upon his side, recounted the visit of the spy, his dangerous discovery, and speedy end.

Joanna leaned back very faint against the curtained wall.

"It will avail but little," she said. "I shall be wed to-morrow, in the morning, after all!"

"What!" cried her friend. "And here is our paladin that driveth lions like mice! Ye have little faith, of a surety. But come, friend lion-driver, give us some comfort; speak, and let us hear bold counsels."

Dick was confounded to be thus outfaced with his own exaggerated words; but though he coloured, he still spoke stoutly.

"Truly," said he, "we are in straits. Yet, could I but win out of this house for half an hour, I do honestly tell myself that all might still go well; and for the marriage, it should be prevented."

"And for the lions," mimicked the girl, "they shall be driven."

"I crave your excuse," said Dick. "I speak not now in any boasting humour, but rather as one inquiring after help or counsel; for if I get not forth of this house and through these sentinels, I can do less than naught. Take me, I pray you, rightly."

"Why said ye he was rustic, Joan?" the girl inquired. "I warrant he hath a tongue in his head; ready, soft, and bold is his speech at pleasure. What would ye more?"

"Nay," sighed Joanna, with a smile, "they have changed me my friend Dick, 'tis sure enough. When I beheld him, he was rough indeed. But it matters little; there is no help for my hard case, and I must still be Lady Shoreby!"

"Nay, then," said Dick, "I will even make the adventure. A friar is not much regarded; and if I found a good fairy to lead me up, I may find another belike to carry me down. How call they the name of this spy?"

"Rutter," said the young lady; "and an excellent good name to call him by. But how mean ye, lion-driver? What is in your mind to do?"

"To offer boldly to go forth," returned Dick; "and if any stop me, to keep an unchanged countenance, and say I go to pray for Rutter. They will be praying over his poor clay even now."

"The device is somewhat simple," replied the girl, "yet it may hold."

"Nay," said young Shelton, "it is no device, but mere boldness, which serveth often better in great straits."

"Ye say true," she said. "Well, go, a-Mary's name, and may Heaven speed you! Ye leave here a poor maid that loves you entirely, and another that is most heartily your friend. Be wary, for their sakes, and make not shipwreck of your safety."

"Ay," added Joanna, "go, Dick. Ye run no more peril, whether ye go or stay. Go; ye take my heart with you; the saints defend you!"

Dick passed the first sentry with so assured a countenance that the fellow merely fidgeted and stared; but at the second landing the man carried his spear across and bade him name his business.

"Pax vobiscum," answered Dick. "I go to pray over the body of this poor Rutter."

"Like enough," returned the sentry; "but to go alone is not permitted you." He leaned over the oaken balusters and whistled shrill. "One cometh!" he cried; and then motioned Dick to pass.

At the foot of the stair he found the guard afoot and awaiting his arrival; and when he had once more repeated his story, the commander of the post ordered four men out to accompany him to the church.

"Let him not slip, my lads," he said. "Bring him to Sir Oliver, on your lives!"

The door was then opened; one of the men took Dick by either arm, another marched ahead with a link, and the fourth, with bent bow and the arrow on the string, brought up the rear. In this order they proceeded through the garden, under the thick darkness of the night and the scattering snow, and drew near to the dimly illuminated windows of the abbey church.

At the western portal a picket of archers stood, taking what shelter they could find in the hollow of the arched doorways, and all powdered with the snow; and it was not until Dick's conductors had exchanged a word with these, that they were suffered to pass forth and enter the nave of the sacred edifice.

The church was doubtfully lighted by the tapers upon the great altar, and by a lamp or two that swung from the arched roof before the private chapels of illustrious families. In the midst of the choir the dead spy lay, his limbs piously composed, upon a bier.

A hurried mutter of prayer sounded along the arches; cowled figures knelt in the stalls of the choir, and on the steps of the high altar a priest in pontifical vestments celebrated mass.

Upon this fresh entrance, one of the cowled figures arose, and, coming down the steps which elevated the level of the choir above that of the nave, demanded from the leader of the four men what business brought him to the church. Out of respect for the service and the dead, they spoke in guarded tones; but the echoes of that huge, empty building caught up their words, and hollowly repeated and repeated them along the aisles.

"A monk!" returned Sir Oliver (for he it was), when he had heard the report of the archer. "My brother, I looked not for your coming," he added, turning to young Shelton. "In all civility, who are ye? and at whose instance do ye join your supplications to ours?"

Dick, keeping his cowl about his face, signed to Sir Oliver to move a pace or two aside from the archers; and, so soon as the priest had done so, "I cannot hope to deceive you, sir," he said. "My life is in your hands."

Sir Oliver violently started; his stout cheeks grew pale, and for a space he was silent.

"Richard," he said, "what brings you here, I know not; but I much misdoubt it to be evil. Nevertheless, for the kindness that was, I would not willingly deliver you to harm. Ye shall sit all night beside me in the stalls: ye shall sit there till my Lord of Shoreby be married, and the party gone safe home; and if all goeth well, and ye have planned no evil, in the end ye shall go whither ye will. But if your purpose be bloody, it shall return upon your head. Amen!"

And the priest devoutly crossed himself, and turned and louted to the altar.

With that, he spoke a few words more to the soldiers, and taking Dick by the hand, led him up to the choir, and placed him in the stall beside his own, where, for mere decency, the lad had instantly to kneel and appear to be busy with his devotions.

His mind and his eyes, however, were continually wandering. Three of the soldiers, he observed, instead of returning to the house, had got them quietly into a point of vantage in the aisle; and he could not doubt that they had done so by Sir Oliver's command. Here, then, he was trapped. Here he must spend the night in the ghostly glimmer and shadow of the church, and looking on the pale face of him he slew; and here, in the morning, he must see his sweetheart married to another man before his eyes.

But, for all that, he obtained a command upon his mind, and built himself up in patience to await the issue.

CHAPTER IV. IN THE ABBEY CHURCH

In Shoreby Abbey Church the prayers were kept up all night without cessation, now with the singing of psalms, now with a note or two upon the bell.

Rutter, the spy, was nobly waked. There he lay, meanwhile, as they had arranged him, his dead hands crossed upon his bosom, his dead eyes staring on the roof; and hard by, in the stall, the lad who had slain him waited, in sore disquietude, the coming of the morning.

Once only, in the course of the hours, Sir Oliver leaned across to his captive.

"Richard," he whispered, "my son, if ye mean me evil, I will certify, on my soul's welfare, ye design upon an innocent man. Sinful in the eye of Heaven I do declare myself; but sinful as against you I am not, neither have been ever."

"My father," returned Dick, in the same tone of voice, "trust me, I design nothing; but as for your innocence, I may not forget that ye cleared yourself but lamely."

"A man may be innocently guilty," replied the priest. "He may be set blindfolded upon a mission, ignorant of its true scope. So it was with me. I did decoy your father to his death; but as Heaven sees us in this sacred place, I knew not what I did."

"It may be," returned Dick. "But see what a strange web ye have woven, that I should be, at this hour, at once your prisoner and your judge; that ye should both threaten my days and deprecate my anger. Methinks, if ye had been all your life a true man and good priest, ye would neither thus fear nor thus detest me. And now to your prayers. I do obey you, since needs must; but I will not be burthened with your company."

The priest uttered a sigh so heavy that it had almost touched the lad into some sentiment of pity, and he bowed his head upon his hands like a man borne down below a weight of care. He joined no longer in the psalms; but Dick could hear the beads rattle though his fingers and the prayers a-pattering between his teeth.

Yet a little, and the grey of the morning began to struggle through the painted casements of the church, and to put to shame the glimmer of the tapers. The light slowly broadened and brightened, and presently through the southeastern clerestories a flush of rosy sunlight flickered on the walls. The storm was over; the great clouds had disburthened their snow and fled farther on, and the new day was breaking on a merry winter landscape sheathed in white.

A bustle of church officers followed; the bier was carried forth to the deadhouse, and the stains of blood were cleansed from off the tiles, that no such ill-omened spectacle should disgrace the marriage of Lord Shoreby. At the same time, the very ecclesiastics who had been so dismally engaged all night began to put on morning faces, to do honour to the merrier ceremony which was about to follow. And further to announce the coming of the day, the pious of the town began to assemble and fall to prayer before their favourite shrines, or wait their turn at the confessionals.

Favoured by this stir, it was of course easily possible for any man to avoid the vigilance of Sir Daniel's sentries at the door; and presently Dick, looking about him wearily, caught the eye of no less a person than Will Lawless, still in his monk's habit.

The outlaw, at the same moment, recognised his leader, and privily signed to him with hand and eye.

Now, Dick was far from having forgiven the old rogue his most untimely drunkenness, but he had no desire to involve him in his own predicament; and he signalled back to him, as plain as he was able, to begone.

Lawless, as though he had understood, disappeared at once behind a pillar, and Dick breathed again.

What, then, was his dismay to feel himself plucked by the sleeve and to find the old robber installed beside him, upon the next seat, and, to all appearance, plunged in his devotions!

Instantly Sir Oliver arose from his place, and, gliding behind the stalls, made for the soldiers in the aisle. If the priest's suspicions had been so lightly wakened, the harm was already done, and Lawless a prisoner in the church.

"Move not," whispered Dick. "We are in the plaguiest pass, thanks, before all things, to thy swinishness of yestereven. When ye saw me here, so strangely seated where I have neither right nor interest, what a murrain! could ye not smell harm and get ye gone from evil?"

"Nay," returned Lawless, "I thought ye had heard from Ellis, and were here on duty."

"Ellis!" echoed Dick. "Is Ellis, then, returned?"

"For sure," replied the outlaw. "He came last night, and belted me sore for being in wine—so there ye are avenged, my master. A furious man is Ellis Duckworth! He hath ridden me hot-spur from Craven to prevent this marriage; and, Master Dick, ye know the way of him—do so he will!"

"Nay, then," returned Dick, with composure, "you and I, my poor brother, are dead men; for I sit here a prisoner upon suspicion, and my neck was to answer for this very marriage that he purposeth to mar. I had a fair choice, by the rood! to lose my sweetheart or else lose my life! Well, the cast is thrown—it is to be my life."

"By the mass," cried Lawless, half arising, "I am gone!"

But Dick had his hand at once upon his shoulder.

"Friend Lawless, sit ye still," he said. "An ye have eyes, look yonder at the corner by the chancel arch; see ye not that, even upon the motion of your rising, yon armed men are up and ready to intercept you? Yield ye, friend. Ye were bold aboard ship, when ye thought to die a sea-death; be bold again, now that y'are to die presently upon the gallows."

"Master Dick," gasped Lawless, "the thing hath come upon me somewhat of the suddenest. But give me a moment till I fetch my breath again; and, by the mass, I will be as stout-hearted as yourself."

"Here is my bold fellow!" returned Dick. "And yet, Lawless, it goes hard against the grain with me to die; but where whining mendeth nothing, wherefore whine?"

"Nay, that indeed!" chimed Lawless. "And a fig for death, at worst! It has to be done, my master, soon or late. And hanging in a good quarrel is an easy death, they say, though I could never hear of any that came back to say so."

And so saying, the stout old rascal leaned back in his stall, folded his arms, and began to look about him with the greatest air of insolence and unconcern.

"And for the matter of that," Dick added, "it is yet our best chance to keep quiet. We wot not yet what Duckworth purposes; and when all is said, and if the worst befall, we may yet clear our feet of it."

Now that they ceased talking, they were aware of a very distant and thin strain of mirthful music which steadily drew nearer, louder, and merrier. The bells in the tower began to break forth into a doubling peal, and a greater and greater concourse of people to crowd into the church, shuffling the snow from off their feet, and clapping and blowing in their hands. The western door was flung wide open, showing a glimpse of sunlit, snowy street, and admitting in a great gust the shrewd air of the morning; and in short, it became plain by every sign that Lord Shoreby desired to be married very early in the day, and that the wedding-train was drawing near.

Some of Lord Shoreby's men now cleared a passage down the middle aisle, forcing the people back with lance-stocks; and just then, outside the portal, the secular musicians could be descried drawing near over the frozen snow, the fifers and trumpeters scarlet in the face with lusty blowing, the drummers and the cymbalists beating as for a wager.

These, as they drew near the door of the sacred building, filed off on either side, and, marking time to their own vigorous music, stood stamping in the snow. As they thus opened their ranks, the leaders of this noble bridal train appeared behind and between them; and such was the variety and gaiety of their attire, such the displays of silk and velvet, fur and satin, embroidery and lace, that the procession showed forth upon the snow like a flower-bed in a path or a painted window in a wall.

First came the bride, a sorry sight, as pale as winter, clinging to Sir Daniel's arm, and attended, as bridesmaid, by the short young lady who had befriended Dick the night before. Close behind, in the most radiant toilet, followed the bridegroom, halting on a gouty foot; and as he passed the threshold of the sacred building and doffed his hat, his bald head was seen to be rosy with emotion.

And now came the hour of Ellis Duckworth.

Dick, who sat stunned among contrary emotions, grasping the desk in front of him, beheld a movement in the crowd, people jostling backward, and eyes and arms uplifted. Following these signs, he beheld three or four men with bent bows, leaning from the clerestory gallery. At the same instant they delivered their discharge, and before the clamour and cries of the astounded populace had time to swell fully upon the ear, they had flitted from their perch and disappeared.

The nave was full of swaying heads and voices screaming; the ecclesiastics thronged in terror from their places; the music ceased, and though the bells overhead continued for some seconds to clang upon the air, some wind of the disaster seemed to find its way at last even to the chamber where the ringers were leaping on their ropes, and they also desisted from their merry labours.

Right in the midst of the nave the bridegroom lay stone-dead, pierced by two black arrows. The bride had fainted. Sir Daniel stood, towering above the crowd in his surprise and anger, a cloth-yard shaft quivering in his left forearm, and his face streaming blood from another which had grazed his brow.

Long before any search could be made for them, the authors of this tragic interruption had clattered down a turn-pike stair and decamped by a postern door.

But Dick and Lawless still remained in pawn; they had, indeed, arisen on the first alarm, and pushed manfully to gain the door; but what with the narrowness of the stalls and the crowding of terrified priests and choristers, the attempt had been in vain, and they had stoically resumed their places.

And now, pale with horror, Sir Oliver rose to his feet and called upon Sir Daniel, pointing with one hand to Dick.

"Here," he cried, "is Richard Shelton—alas the hour!—blood guilty! Seize him!—bid him be seized! For all our lives' sakes, take him and bind him surely! He hath sworn our fall."

Sir Daniel was blinded by anger—blinded by the hot blood that still streamed across his face.

"Where?" he bellowed. "Hale him forth! By the cross of Holywood, but he shall rue this hour!"

The crowd fell back, and a party of archers invaded the choir, laid rough hands on Dick, dragged him head-foremost from the stall, and thrust him by the shoulders down the chancel steps. Lawless, on his part, sat as still as a mouse.

Sir Daniel, brushing the blood out of his eyes, stared blinkingly upon his captive.

"Ay," he said, "treacherous and insolent, I have thee fast; and by all potent oaths, for every drop of blood that now trickles in mine eyes, I will wring a groan out of thy carcase. Away with him!" he added. "Here is no place! Off with him to my house. I will number every joint of thy body with a torture."

But Dick, putting off his captors, uplifted his voice.

"Sanctuary!" he shouted. "Sanctuary! Ho, there, my fathers! They would drag me from the church!"

"From the church thou hast defiled with murder, boy," added a tall man, magnificently dressed.

"On what probation?" cried Dick. "They do accuse me, indeed, of some complicity, but have not proved one tittle. I was, in truth, a suitor for this damsel's hand; and she, I will be bold to say it, repaid my suit with favour. But what then? To love a maid is no offence, I trow—nay, nor to gain her love. In all else, I stand here free from guiltiness."

There was a murmur of approval among the bystanders, so boldly Dick declared his innocence; but at the same time a throng of accusers arose upon the other side, crying how he had been found last night in Sir Daniel's house, how he wore a sacrilegious disguise; and in the midst of the babel, Sir Oliver indicated Lawless, both by voice and gesture, as accomplice to the fact. He, in his turn, was dragged from his seat and set beside his leader. The feelings of the crowd rose high on either side, and while some dragged the prisoners to and fro to favour their escape, others cursed and struck them with their fists. Dick's ears rang and his brain swam dizzily, like a man struggling in the eddies of a furious river.

But the tall man who had already answered Dick, by a prodigious exercise of voice restored silence and order in the mob.

"Search them," he said, "for arms. We may so judge of their intentions."

Upon Dick they found no weapon but his poniard, and this told in his favour, until one man officiously drew it from its sheath, and found it still uncleansed of the blood of Rutter. At this there was a great shout among Sir Daniel's followers, which the tall man suppressed by a gesture and an imperious glance. But when it came to the turn of Lawless, there was found under his gown a sheaf of arrows identical with those that had been shot.

"How say ye now?" asked the tall man, frowningly, of Dick.

"Sir," replied Dick, "I am here in sanctuary, is it not so? Well, sir, I see by your bearing that ye are high in station, and I read in your countenance the marks of piety and justice. To you, then, I will yield me prisoner, and that blithely, foregoing the advantage of this holy place. But rather than to be yielded into the discretion of that man—whom I do here accuse with a loud voice to be the murderer of my natural father and the unjust retainer of my lands and revenues—rather than that, I would beseech you, under favour, with your own gentle hand, to despatch me on the spot. Your own ears have heard him, how before that I was proven guilty he did threaten me with torments. It standeth not with your own honour to deliver me to my sworn enemy and old oppressor, but to try me fairly by the way of law, and, if that I be guilty indeed, to slay me mercifully."

"My lord," cried Sir Daniel, "ye will not hearken to this wolf? His bloody dagger reeks him the lie into his face."

"Nay, but suffer me, good knight," returned the tall stranger; "your own vehemence doth somewhat tell against yourself."

And here the bride, who had come to herself some minutes past and looked wildly on upon this scene, broke loose from those that held her, and fell upon her knees before the last speaker.

"My Lord of Risingham," she cried, "hear me, in justice. I am here in this man's custody by mere force, reft from mine own people. Since that day I had never pity, countenance, nor comfort from the face of man—but from him only—Richard Shelton—whom they now accuse and labour to undo. My lord, if he was yesternight in Sir Daniel's mansion, it was I that brought him there; he came but at my prayer, and thought to do no hurt. While yet Sir Daniel was a good lord to him, he fought with them of the Black Arrow loyally; but when his foul guardian sought his life by practices, and he fled by night, for his soul's sake, out of that bloody house, whither was he to turn—he, helpless and penniless? Or if he be fallen among ill company, whom should ye blame—the lad that was unjustly handled, or the guardian that did abuse his trust?"

And then the short young lady fell on her knees by Joanna's side.

"And I, my good lord and natural uncle," she added, "I can bear testimony, on my conscience and before the face of all, that what this maiden saith is true. It was I, unworthy, that did lead the young man in."

Earl Risingham had heard in silence, and when the voices ceased, he still stood silent for a space. Then he gave Joanna his hand to arise, though it was to be observed that he did not offer the like courtesy to her who had called herself his niece.

"Sir Daniel," he said, "here is a right intricate affair, the which, with your good leave, it shall be mine to examine and adjust. Content ye, then; your business is in careful hands; justice shall be done you; and in the meanwhile, get ye incontinently home, and have your hurts attended. The air is shrewd, and I would not ye took cold upon these scratches."

He made a sign with his hand; it was passed down the nave by obsequious servants, who waited there upon his smallest gesture. Instantly, without the church, a tucket sounded shrill, and through the open portal archers and men-at-arms, uniformly arrayed in the colours and wearing the badge of Lord Risingham, began to file into the church, took Dick and Lawless from those who still detained them, and closing their files about the prisoners, marched forth again and disappeared.

As they were passing, Joanna held both her hands to Dick and cried him her farewell; and the bridesmaid, nothing downcast by her uncle's evident displeasure, blew him a kiss, with a "Keep your heart up, lion-driver!" that for the first time since the accident called up a smile to the faces of the crowd.

CHAPTER V. EARL RISINGHAM

Earl Risingham, although by far the most important person then in Shoreby, was poorly lodged in the house of a private gentleman upon the extreme outskirts of the town. Nothing but the armed men at the doors, and the mounted messengers that kept arriving and departing, announced the temporary residence of a great lord.

Thus it was that, from lack of space, Dick and Lawless were clapped into the same apartment.

"Well spoken, Master Richard," said the outlaw; "it was excellently well spoken, and, for my part, I thank you cordially. Here we are in good hands; we shall be justly tried, and, some time this evening, decently hanged on the same tree."

"Indeed, my poor friend, I do believe it," answered Dick.

"Yet have we a string to our bow," returned Lawless. "Ellis Duckworth is a man out of ten thousand; he holdeth you right near his heart, both for your own and for your father's sake; and knowing you guiltless of this fact, he will stir earth and heaven to bear you clear."

"It may not be," said Dick. "What can he do? He hath but a handful. Alack, if it were but to-morrow—could I but keep a certain tryst an hour before noon to-morrow—all were, I think, otherwise. But now there is no help."

"Well," concluded Lawless, "an ye will stand to it for my innocence, I will stand to it for yours, and that stoutly. It shall naught avail us; but an I be to hang, it shall not be for lack of swearing."

And then, while Dick gave himself over to his reflections, the old rogue curled himself down into a corner, pulled his monkish hood about his face, and composed himself to sleep. Soon he was loudly snoring, so utterly had his long life of hardship and adventure blunted the sense of apprehension.

It was long after noon, and the day was already failing, before the door was opened and Dick taken forth and led up-stairs to where, in a warm cabinet, Earl Risingham sat musing over the fire.

On his captive's entrance he looked up.

"Sir," he said, "I knew your father, who was a man of honour, and this inclineth me to be the more lenient; but I may not hide from you that heavy charges lie against your character. Ye do consort with murderers and robbers; upon a clear probation ye have carried war against the king's peace; ye are suspected to have piratically seized upon a ship; ye are found skulking with a counterfeit presentment in your enemy's house; a man is slain that very evening——"

"An it like you, my lord," Dick interposed, "I will at once avow my guilt, such as it is. I slew this fellow Rutter; and to the proof"—searching in his bosom—"here is a letter from his wallet."

Lord Risingham took the letter, and opened and read it twice.

"Ye have read this?" he inquired.

"I have read it," answered Dick.

"Are ye for York or Lancaster?" the earl demanded.

"My lord, it was but a little while back that I was asked that question, and knew not how to answer it," said Dick; "but having answered once, I will not vary. My lord, I am for York."

The earl nodded approvingly.

"Honestly replied," he said. "But wherefore, then, deliver me this letter?"

"Nay, but against traitors, my lord, are not all sides arrayed?" cried Dick.

"I would they were, young gentleman," returned the earl; "and I do at least approve your saying. There is more youth than guile in you, I do perceive; and were not Sir Daniel a mighty man upon our side, I were half tempted to espouse your quarrel. For I have inquired, and it appears ye have been hardly dealt with, and have much excuse. But look ye, sir, I am, before all else, a leader in the Queen's interest; and though by nature a just man, as I believe, and leaning even to the excess of mercy, yet must I order my goings for my party's interest, and, to keep Sir Daniel, I would go far about."

"My lord," returned Dick, "ye will think me very bold to counsel you; but do ye count upon Sir Daniel's faith? Methought he had changed sides intolerably often."

"Nay, it is the way of England. What would ye have?" the earl demanded. "But ye are unjust to the knight of Tunstall; and as faith goes, in this unfaithful generation, he hath of late been honourably true to us of Lancaster. Even in our last reverses he stood firm."

"An it pleased you, then," said Dick, "to cast your eye upon this letter, ye might somewhat change your thought of him"; and he handed to the earl Sir Daniel's letter to Lord Wensleydale.

The effect upon the earl's countenance was instant; he lowered like an angry lion, and his hand, with a sudden movement, clutched at his dagger.

"Ye have read this also?" he asked.

"Even so," said Dick. "It is your lordship's own estate he offers to Lord Wensleydale?"

"It is my own estate, even as ye say!" returned the earl. "I am your bedesman for this letter. It hath shown me a fox's hole. Command me, Master Shelton; I will not be backward in gratitude, and to begin with, York or Lancaster, true man or thief, I do now set you at freedom. Go, a-Mary's name! But judge it right that I retain and hang your fellow, Lawless. The crime hath been most open, and it were fitting that some open punishment should follow."

"My lord, I make it my first suit to you to spare him also," pleaded Dick.

"It is an old, condemned rogue, thief, and vagabond, Master Shelton," said the earl. "He hath been gallows-ripe this score of years. And, whether for one thing or another, whether to-morrow or the day after, where is the great choice?"

"Yet, my lord, it was through love to me that he came hither," answered Dick, "and I were churlish and thankless to desert him."

"Master Shelton, ye are troublesome," replied the earl, severely. "It is an evil way to prosper in this world. Howbeit, and to be quit of your importunity, I will once more humour you. Go, then, together; but go warily, and get swiftly out of Shoreby town. For this Sir Daniel (whom may the saints confound!) thirsteth most greedily to have your blood."

"My lord, I do now offer you in words my gratitude, trusting at some brief date to pay you some of it in service," replied Dick, as he turned from the apartment.

CHAPTER VI. ARBLASTER AGAIN

When Dick and Lawless were suffered to steal, by a back way, out of the house where Lord Risingham held his garrison, the evening had already come.

They paused in shelter of the garden wall to consult on their best course. The danger was extreme. If one of Sir Daniel's men caught sight of them and raised the view-hallo, they would be run down and butchered instantly. And not only was the town of Shoreby a mere net of peril for their lives, but to make for the open country was to run the risk of the patrols.

A little way off, upon some open ground, they spied a windmill standing; and hard by that, a very large granary with open doors.

"How if we lay there until the night fall?" Dick proposed.

And Lawless having no better suggestion to offer, they made a straight push for the granary at a run, and concealed themselves behind the door among some straw. The daylight rapidly departed; and presently the moon was silvering the frozen snow. Now or never was their opportunity to gain the Goat and Bagpipes unobserved and change their tell-tale garments. Yet even then it was advisable to go round by the outskirts, and not run the gauntlet of the market-place, where, in the concourse of people, they stood the more imminent peril to be recognised and slain.

This course was a long one. It took them not far from the house by the beach, now lying dark and silent, and brought them forth at last by the margin of the harbour. Many of the ships, as they could see by the clear moonshine, had weighed anchor, and, profiting by the calm sky, proceeded for more distant parts; answerably to this, the rude alehouses along the beach (although, in defiance of the curfew law, they still shone with fire and candle) were no longer thronged with customers, and no longer echoed to the chorus of sea-songs.

Hastily, half running, with their monkish raiment kilted to the knee, they plunged through the deep snow and threaded the labyrinth of marine lumber; and they were already more than half-way round the harbour when, as they were passing close before an alehouse, the door suddenly opened and let out a gush of light upon their fleeting figures.

Instantly they stopped, and made believe to be engaged in earnest conversation.

Three men, one after another, came out of the alehouse, and the last closed the door behind him. All three were unsteady upon their feet, as if they had passed the day in deep potations, and they now stood wavering in the moonlight, like men who knew not what they would be after. The tallest of the three was talking in a loud, lamentable voice.

"Seven pieces of as good Gascony as ever a tapster broached," he was saying, "the best ship out o' the port o' Dartmouth, a Virgin Mary parcel-gilt, thirteen pounds of good gold money——"

"I have had losses, too," interrupted one of the others. "I have had losses of mine own, gossip Arblaster. I was robbed at Martinmas of five shillings and a leather wallet well worth ninepence farthing."

Dick's heart smote him at what he heard. Until that moment he had not perhaps thought twice of the poor skipper who had been ruined by the loss of the Good Hope; so careless, in those days, were men who wore arms of the goods and interests of their inferiors. But this sudden encounter reminded him sharply of the high-handed manner and ill-ending of his enterprise; and both he and Lawless turned their heads the other way, to avoid the chance of recognition.

The ship's dog had, however, made his escape from the wreck and found his way back again to Shoreby. He was now at Arblaster's heels, and suddenly sniffing and pricking his ears, he darted forward and began to bark furiously at the two sham friars.

His master unsteadily followed him.

"Hey, shipmates!" he cried. "Have ye ever a penny piece for a poor old shipman, clean destroyed by pirates? I am a man that would have paid for you both o' Thursday morning; and now here I be, o' Saturday night, begging for a flagon of ale! Ask my man Tom, if ye misdoubt me. Seven pieces of good Gascon wine, a ship that was mine own, and was my father's before me, a Blessed Mary of plane-tree wood and parcel-gilt, and thirteen pounds in gold and silver. Hey! what say ye? A man that fought the French, too; for I have fought the French; I have cut more French throats upon the high seas than ever a man that sails out of Dartmouth. Come, a penny piece."

Neither Dick nor Lawless durst answer him a word, lest he should recognise their voices; and they stood there as helpless as a ship ashore, not knowing where to turn nor what to hope.

"Are ye dumb, boy?" inquired the skipper. "Mates," he added, with a hiccup, "they be dumb. I like not this manner of discourtesy; for an a man be dumb, so be as he's courteous, he will still speak when he was spoken to, methinks."

By this time the sailor, Tom, who was a man of great personal strength, seemed to have conceived some suspicion of these two speechless figures; and being soberer than his captain, stepped suddenly before him, took Lawless roughly by the shoulder, and asked him, with an oath, what ailed him that he held his tongue. To this the outlaw, thinking all was over, made answer by a wrestling feint that stretched the sailor on the sand, and, calling upon Dick to follow him, took to his heels among the lumber.

The affair passed in a second. Before Dick could run at all, Arblaster had him in his arms; Tom, crawling on his face, had caught him by one foot, and the third man had a drawn cutlass brandishing above his head.

It was not so much the danger, it was not so much the annoyance, that now bowed down the spirits of young Shelton; it was the profound humiliation to have escaped Sir Daniel, convinced Lord Risingham, and now fall helpless in the hands of this old, drunken sailor; and not merely helpless, but, as his conscience loudly told him when it was too late, actually guilty— actually the bankrupt debtor of the man whose ship he had stolen and lost.

"Bring me him back into the alehouse, till I see his face," said Arblaster.

"Nay, nay," returned Tom; "but let us first unload his wallet, lest the other lads cry share."

But though he was searched from head to foot, not a penny was found upon him; nothing but Lord Foxham's signet, which they plucked savagely from his finger.

"Turn me him to the moon," said the skipper; and taking Dick by the chin, he cruelly jerked his head into the air. "Blessed Virgin!" he cried, "it is the pirate!"

"Hey!" cried Tom.

"By the Virgin of Bordeaux, it is the man himself!" repeated Arblaster. "What, sea-thief, do I hold you?" he cried. "Where is my ship? Where is my wine? Hey! have I you in my hands? Tom, give me one end of a cord here; I will so truss me this sea-thief, hand and foot together, like a basting turkey— marry, I will so bind him up—and thereafter I will so beat—so beat him!"

And so he ran on, winding the cord meanwhile about Dick's limbs with the dexterity peculiar to seamen, and at every turn and cross securing it with a knot, and tightening the whole fabric with a savage pull.

When he had done, the lad was a mere package in his hands—as helpless as the dead. The skipper held him at arm's length, and laughed aloud. Then he fetched him a stunning buffet on the ear; and then turned him about, and furiously kicked and kicked him. Anger rose up in Dick's bosom like a storm; anger strangled him, and he thought to have died; but when the sailor, tired of this cruel play, dropped him all his length upon the sand and turned to consult with his companions, he instantly regained command of his temper. Here was a momentary respite; ere they began again to torture him, he might have found some method to escape from this degrading and fatal misadventure.

Presently, sure enough, and while his captors were still discussing what to do with him, he took heart of grace, and, with a pretty steady voice, addressed them.

"My masters," he began, "are ye gone clean foolish? Here hath Heaven put into your hands as pretty an occasion to grow rich as ever shipman had—such as ye might make thirty over-sea adventures and not find again—and, by the mass! what do ye? Beat me?—nay; so would an angry child! But for long-headed tarry-Johns, that fear not fire nor water, and that love gold as they love beef, methinks ye are not wise."

"Ay," said Tom, "now y'are trussed ye would cozen us."

"Cozen you!" repeated Dick. "Nay, if ye be fools, it would be easy. But if ye be shrewd fellows, as I trow ye are, ye can see plainly where your interest lies. When I took your ship from you, we were many, we were well clad and armed; but now, bethink you a little, who mustered that array? One incontestably that hath much gold. And if he, being already rich, continueth to hunt after more even in the face of storms—bethink you once more—shall there not be a treasure somewhere hidden?"

"What meaneth he?" asked one of the men.

"Why, if ye have lost an old skiff and a few jugs of vinegary wine," continued Dick, "forget them, for the trash they are; and do ye rather buckle to an adventure worth the name, that shall, in twelve hours, make or mar you for ever. But take me up from where I lie, and let us go somewhere near at hand and talk across a flagon, for I am sore and frozen, and my mouth is half among the snow."

"He seeks but to cozen us," said Tom, contemptuously.

"Cozen! cozen!" cried the third man. "I would I could see the man that could cozen me! He were a cozener indeed! Nay, I was not born yesterday. I can see a church when it hath a steeple on it; and for my part, gossip Arblaster, methinks there is some sense in this young man. Shall we go hear him, indeed? Say, shall we go hear him?"

"I would look gladly on a pottle of strong ale, good Master Pirret," returned Arblaster. "How say ye, Tom? But then the wallet is empty."

"I will pay," said the other—"I will pay. I would fain see this matter out; I do believe, upon my conscience, there is gold in it."

"Nay, if ye get again to drinking, all is lost!" cried Tom.

"Gossip Arblaster, ye suffer your fellow to have too much liberty," returned Master Pirret. "Would ye be led by a hired man? Fy, fy!"

"Peace, fellow!" said Arblaster, addressing Tom. "Will ye put your oar in? Truly a fine pass, when the crew is to correct the skipper!"

"Well, then, go your way," said Tom; "I wash my hands of you."

"Set him, then, upon his feet," said Master Pirret. "I know a privy place where we may drink and discourse."

"If I am to walk, my friends, ye must set my feet at liberty," said Dick, when he had been once more planted upright like a post.

"He saith true," laughed Pirret. "Truly, he could not walk accoutred as he is. Give it a slit—out with your knife and slit it, gossip."

Even Arblaster paused at this proposal; but as his companion continued to insist, and Dick had the sense to keep the merest wooden indifference of expression, and only shrugged his shoulders over the delay, the skipper consented at last, and cut the cords which tied his prisoner's feet and legs. Not only did this enable Dick to walk; but the whole network of his bonds being proportionately loosened, he felt the arm behind his back begin to move more freely, and could hope, with time and trouble, to entirely disengage it. So much he owed already to the owlish silliness and greed of Master Pirret.

That worthy now assumed the lead, and conducted them to the very same rude alehouse where Lawless had taken Arblaster on the day of the gale. It was now quite deserted; the fire was a pile of red embers, radiating the most ardent heat; and when they had chosen their places, and the landlord had set before them a measure of mulled ale, both Pirret and Arblaster stretched forth their legs and squared their elbows like men bent upon a pleasant hour.

The table at which they sat, like all the others in the alehouse, consisted of a heavy, square board, set on a pair of barrels; and each of the four curiously-assorted cronies sat at one side of the square, Pirret facing Arblaster, and Dick opposite to the common sailor.

"And now, young man," said Pirret, "to your tale. It doth appear, indeed, that ye have somewhat abused our gossip Arblaster; but what then? Make it up to him—show him but this chance to become wealthy—and I will go pledge he will forgive you."

So far Dick had spoken pretty much at random; but it was now necessary, under the supervision of six eyes, to invent and tell some marvellous story, and, if it were possible, get back into his hands the all-important signet. To squander time was the first necessity. The longer his stay lasted, the more would his captors drink, and the surer should he be when he attempted his escape.

Well, Dick was not much of an inventor, and what he told was pretty much the tale of Ali Baba, with Shoreby and Tunstall Forest substituted for the East, and the treasures of the cavern rather exaggerated than diminished. As the reader is aware, it is an excellent story, and has but one drawback—that it is not true; and so, as these three simple shipmen now heard it for the first time, their eyes stood out of their faces, and their mouths gaped like codfish at a fishmonger's.

Pretty soon a second measure of mulled ale was called for; and while Dick was still artfully spinning out the incidents a third followed the second.

Here was the position of the parties towards the end:

Arblaster, three-parts drunk and one-half asleep, hung helpless on his stool. Even Tom had been much delighted with the tale, and his vigilance had abated in proportion. Meanwhile, Dick had gradually wormed his right arm clear of its bonds, and was ready to risk all.

"And so," said Pirret, "y'are one of these?"

"I was made so," replied Dick, "against my will; but an I could but get a sack or two of gold coin to my share, I should be a fool indeed to continue dwelling in a filthy cave, and standing shot and buffet like a soldier. Here be we four; good! Let us, then, go forth into the forest to-morrow ere the sun be up. Could we come honestly by a donkey, it were better; but an we cannot, we have our four strong backs, and I warrant me we shall come home staggering."

Pirret licked his lips.

"And this magic," he said—"this password, whereby the cave is opened— how call ye it, friend?"

"Nay, none know the word but the three chiefs," returned Dick; "but here is your great good fortune, that, on this very evening, I should be the bearer of a spell to open it. It is a thing not trusted twice a year beyond the captain's wallet."

"A spell!" said Arblaster, half awakening, and squinting upon Dick with one eye. "Aroint thee! no spells! I be a good Christian. Ask my man Tom, else."

"Nay, but this is white magic," said Dick. "It doth naught with the devil; only the powers of numbers, herbs, and planets."

"Ay, ay," said Pirret; "'tis but white magic, gossip. There is no sin therein, I do assure you. But proceed, good youth. This spell—in what should it consist?"

"Nay, that I will incontinently show you," answered Dick. "Have ye there the ring ye took from my finger? Good! Now hold it forth before you by the extreme finger-ends, at the arm's length, and over against the shining of these embers. 'Tis so exactly. Thus, then, is the spell."

With a haggard glance, Dick saw the coast was clear between him and the door. He put up an internal prayer. Then whipping forth his arm, he made but one snatch of the ring, and at the same instant, levering up the table, he sent it bodily over upon the seaman Tom. He, poor soul, went down bawling under the ruins; and before Arblaster understood that anything was wrong, or Pirret could collect his dazzled wits, Dick had run to the door and escaped into the moonlit night.

The moon, which now rode in the mid-heavens, and the extreme whiteness of the snow, made the open ground about the harbour bright as day; and young Shelton leaping, with kilted robe, among the lumber, was a conspicuous figure from afar.

Tom and Pirret followed him with shouts; from every drinking-shop they were joined by others whom their cries aroused; and presently a whole fleet of sailors was in full pursuit. But Jack ashore was a bad runner, even in the fifteenth century, and Dick, besides, had a start, which he rapidly improved, until, as he drew near the entrance of a narrow lane, he even paused and looked laughingly behind him.

Upon the white floor of snow, all the shipmen of Shoreby came clustering in an inky mass, and tailing out rearward in isolated clumps. Every man was shouting or screaming; every man was gesticulating with both arms in air; some one was continually falling; and to complete the picture, when one fell, a dozen would fall upon the top of him.

The confused mass of sound which they rolled up as high as to the moon was partly comical and partly terrifying to the fugitive whom they were hunting. In itself, it was impotent, for he made sure no seaman in the port could run him down. But the mere volume of noise, in so far as it must awake all the sleepers in Shoreby and bring all the skulking sentries to the street, did really threaten him with danger in the front. So, spying a dark doorway at a corner, he whipped briskly into it, and let the uncouth hunt go by him, still shouting and gesticulating, and all red with hurry and white with tumbles in the snow.

It was a long while, indeed, before this great invasion of the town by the harbour came to an end, and it was long before silence was restored. For long, lost sailors were still to be heard pounding and shouting through the streets in all directions and in every quarter of the town. Quarrels followed, sometimes among themselves, sometimes with the men of the patrols; knives were drawn, blows given and received, and more than one dead body remained behind upon the snow.

When, a full hour later, the last seaman returned grumblingly to the harbour side and his particular tavern, it may fairly be questioned if he had ever known what manner of man he was pursuing, but it was absolutely sure that he had now forgotten. By next morning there were many strange stories flying; and a little while after, the legend of the devil's nocturnal visit was an article of faith with all the lads of Shoreby.

But the return of the last seaman did not, even yet, set free young Shelton from his cold imprisonment in the doorway.

For some time after, there was a great activity of patrols; and special parties came forth to make the round of the place and report to one or other of the great lords, whose slumbers had been thus unusually broken.

The night was already well spent before Dick ventured from his hiding-place and came, safe and sound, but aching with cold and bruises, to the door of the Goat and Bagpipes. As the law required, there was neither fire nor candle in the house; but he groped his way into a corner of the icy guest-room, found an end of a blanket, which he hitched around his shoulders, and creeping close to the nearest sleeper, was soon lost in slumber.

BOOK V. CROOKBACK

CHAPTER I. THE SHRILL TRUMPET

Very early the next morning, before the first peep of the day, Dick arose, changed his garments, armed himself once more like a gentleman, and set forth for Lawless's den in the forest. There, it will be remembered, he had left Lord Foxham's papers; and to get these and be back in time for the tryst with the young Duke of Gloucester could only be managed by an early start and the most vigorous walking.

The frost was more rigorous than ever; the air windless and dry, and stinging to the nostril. The moon had gone down, but the stars were still bright and numerous, and the reflection from the snow was clear and cheerful. There was no need for a lamp to walk by; nor, in that still but ringing air, the least temptation to delay.

Dick had crossed the greater part of the open ground between Shoreby and the forest, and had reached the bottom of the little hill, some hundred yards below the Cross of St. Bride, when, through the stillness of the black morn, there rang forth the note of a trumpet, so shrill, clear, and piercing, that he thought he had never heard the match of it for audibility. It was blown once, and then hurriedly a second time; and then the clash of steel succeeded.

At this young Shelton pricked his ears, and drawing his sword, ran forward up the hill.

Presently he came in sight of the cross, and was aware of a most fierce encounter raging on the road before it. There were seven or eight assailants, and but one to keep head against them; but so active and dexterous was this one, so desperately did he charge and scatter his opponents, so deftly keep his footing on the ice, that already, before Dick could intervene, he had slain one, wounded another, and kept the whole in check.

Still, it was by a miracle that he continued his defence, and at any moment, any accident, the least slip of foot or error of hand, his life would be a forfeit.

"Hold ye well, sir! Here is help!" cried Richard; and forgetting that he was alone, and that the cry was somewhat irregular, "To the Arrow! to the Arrow!" he shouted, as he fell upon the rear of the assailants.

These were stout fellows also, for they gave not an inch at this surprise, but faced about, and fell with astonishing fury upon Dick. Four against one, the steel flashed about him in the starlight; the sparks flew fiercely; one of the men opposed to him fell—in the stir of the fight he hardly knew why; then he himself was struck across the head, and though the steel cap below his hood protected him, the blow beat him down upon one knee, with a brain whirling like a windmill-sail.

Meanwhile the man whom he had come to rescue, instead of joining in the conflict, had, on the first sign of intervention, leaped aback and blown again, and yet more urgently and loudly, on that same shrill-voiced trumpet that began the alarm. Next moment, indeed, his foes were on him, and he was once more charging and fleeing, leaping, stabbing, dropping to his knee, and using indifferently sword and dagger, foot and hand, with the same unshaken courage and feverish energy and speed.

But that ear-piercing summons had been heard at last. There was a muffled rushing in the snow; and in a good hour for Dick, who saw the sword-points glitter already at his throat, there poured forth out of the wood upon both sides a disorderly torrent of mounted men-at-arms, each cased in iron, and with visor lowered, each bearing his lance in rest, or his sword bared and raised, and each carrying, so to speak, a passenger, in the shape of an archer or page, who leaped one after another from their perches, and had presently doubled the array.

The original assailants, seeing themselves outnumbered and surrounded, threw down their arms without a word.

"Seize me these fellows!" said the hero of the trumpet; and when his order had been obeyed, he drew near to Dick and looked him in the face.

Dick, returning this scrutiny, was surprised to find in one who had displayed such strength, skill, and energy, a lad no older than himself—slightly deformed, with one shoulder higher than the other, and of a pale, painful, and distorted countenance.[2] The eyes, however, were very clear and bold.

"Sir," said this lad, "ye came in good time for me, and none too early."

"My lord," returned Dick, with a faint sense that he was in the presence of a great personage, "ye are yourself so marvellous a good swordsman that I believe ye had managed them single-handed. Howbeit, it was certainly well for me that your men delayed no longer than they did."

"How knew ye who I was?" demanded the stranger.

"Even now, my lord," Dick answered, "I am ignorant of whom I speak with."

"Is it so?" asked the other. "And yet ye threw yourself head-first into this unequal battle."

"I saw one man valiantly contending against many," replied Dick, "and I had thought myself dishonoured not to bear him aid."

A singular sneer played about the young nobleman's mouth as he made answer:

"These are very brave words. But to the more essential—are ye Lancaster or York?"

"My lord, I make no secret; I am clear for York," Dick answered.

"By the mass!" replied the other, "it is well for you."

And so saying, he turned towards one of his followers.

"Let me see," he continued, in the same sneering and cruel tones—"let me see a clean end of these brave gentlemen. Truss me them up."

There were but five survivors of the attacking party. Archers seized them by the arms; they were hurried to the borders of the wood, and each placed below a tree of suitable dimension; the rope was adjusted; an archer, carrying the end of it, hastily clambered overhead; and before a minute was over, and without a word passing upon either hand, the five men were swinging by the neck.

"And now," cried the deformed leader, "back to your posts, and when I summon you next, be readier to attend."

"My lord duke," said one man, "beseech you, tarry not here alone. Keep but a handful of lances at your hand."

"Fellow," said the duke, "I have forborne to chide you for your slowness. Cross me not, therefore. I trust my hand and arm, for all that I be crooked. Ye were backwards when the trumpet sounded; and ye are now too forward with your counsels. But it is ever so; last with the lance and first with tongue. Let it be reversed."

And with a gesture that was not without a sort of dangerous nobility, he waved them off.

The footmen climbed again to their seats behind the men-at-arms, and the whole party moved slowly away and disappeared in twenty different directions, under the cover of the forest.

The day was by this time beginning to break, and the stars to fade. The first grey glimmer of dawn shone upon the countenances of the two young men, who now turned once more to face each other.

"Here," said the duke, "ye have seen my vengeance, which is, like my blade, both sharp and ready. But I would not have you, for all Christendom, suppose me thankless. You that came to my aid with a good sword and a better courage—unless that ye recoil from my misshapeness—come to my heart."

And so saying, the young leader held out his arms for an embrace.

In the bottom of his heart Dick already entertained a great terror and some hatred for the man whom he had rescued; but the invitation was so worded that it would not have been merely discourteous, but cruel, to refuse or hesitate; and he hastened to comply.

"And now, my lord duke," he said, when he had regained his freedom, "do I suppose aright? Are ye my Lord Duke of Gloucester?"

"I am Richard of Gloucester," returned the other. "And you—how call they you?"

Dick told him his name, and presented Lord Foxham's signet, which the duke immediately recognised.

"Ye come too soon," he said; "but why should I complain? Ye are like me, that was here at watch two hours before the day. But this is the first sally of mine arms; upon this adventure, Master Shelton, shall I make or mar the quality of my renown. There lie mine enemies, under two old, skilled captains—Risingham and Brackley—well posted for strength, I do believe, but yet upon two sides without retreat, enclosed betwixt the sea, the harbour, and the river. Methinks, Shelton, here were a great blow to be stricken, an we could strike it silently and suddenly."

"I do think so, indeed," cried Dick, warming.

"Have ye my Lord Foxham's notes?" inquired the duke.

And then, Dick, having explained how he was without them for the moment, made himself bold to offer information every jot as good, of his own knowledge.

"And for mine own part, my lord duke," he added, "an ye had men enough, I would fall on even at this present. For, look ye, at the peep of day the watches of the night are over; but by day they keep neither watch nor ward—only scour the outskirts with horsemen. Now, then, when the night watch is already unarmed, and the rest are at their morning cup—now were the time to break them."

"How many do ye count?" asked Gloucester.

"They number not two thousand," Dick replied.

"I have seven hundred in the woods behind us," said the duke; "seven hundred follow from Kettley, and will be here anon; behind these, and further, are four hundred more; and my Lord Foxham hath five hundred half a day from here, at Holywood. Shall we attend their coming, or fall on?"

"My lord," said Dick, "when ye hanged these five poor rogues ye did decide the question. Churls although they were, in these uneasy times they will be lacked and looked for, and the alarm be given. Therefore, my lord, if ye do count upon the advantage of a surprise, ye have not, in my poor opinion, one whole hour in front of you."

"I do think so indeed," returned Crookback. "Well, before an hour, ye shall be in the thick on't, winning spurs. A swift man to Holywood, carrying Lord Foxham's signet; another along the road to speed my laggards! Nay, Shelton, by the rood, it may be done!"

Therewith he once more set his trumpet to his lips and blew.

This time he was not long kept waiting. In a moment the open space about the cross was filled with horse and foot. Richard of Gloucester took his place upon the steps, and despatched messenger after messenger to hasten the concentration of the seven hundred men that lay hidden in the immediate neighbourhood among the woods; and before a quarter of an hour had passed, all his dispositions being taken, he put himself at their head, and began to move down the hill towards Shoreby.

His plan was simple. He was to seize a quarter of the town of Shoreby lying on the right hand of the highroad and make his position good there in the narrow lanes until his reinforcements followed.

If Lord Risingham chose to retreat, Richard would follow upon his rear, and take him between two fires; or, if he preferred to hold the town, he would be shut in a trap, there to be gradually overwhelmed by force of numbers.

There was but one danger, but that was imminent and great—Gloucester's seven hundred might be rolled up and cut to pieces in the first encounter, and, to avoid this, it was needful to make the surprise of their arrival as complete as possible.

The footmen, therefore, were all once more taken up behind the riders, and Dick had the signal honour meted out to him of mounting behind Gloucester himself. For as far as there was any cover the troops moved slowly, and when they came near the end of the trees that lined the highway, stopped to breathe and reconnoitre.

The sun was now well up, shining with a frosty brightness out of a yellow halo, and right over against the luminary, Shoreby, a field of snowy roofs and ruddy gables, was rolling up its columns of morning smoke.

Gloucester turned round to Dick.

"In that poor place," he said, "where people are cooking breakfast, either you shall gain your spurs and I begin a life of mighty honour and glory in the world's eye, or both of us, as I conceive it, shall fall dead and be unheard of. Two Richards are we. Well, then, Richard Shelton, they shall be heard about, these two! Their swords shall not ring more loudly on men's helmets than their names shall ring in people's ears."

Dick was astonished at so great a hunger after fame, expressed with so great vehemence of voice and language, and he answered very sensibly and quietly, that, for his part, he promised he would do his duty, and doubted not of victory if every one did the like.

By this time the horses were well breathed, and the leader holding up his, sword and giving rein, the whole troop of chargers broke into the gallop and thundered, with their double load of fighting men, down the remainder of the hill and across the snow-covered plain that still divided them from Shoreby.

CHAPTER II. THE BATTLE OF SHOREBY

The whole distance to be crossed was not above a quarter of a mile. But they had no sooner debouched beyond the cover of the trees than they were aware of people fleeing and screaming in the snowy meadows upon either hand. Almost at the same moment a great rumour began to arise, and spread and grow continually louder in the town; and they were not yet half-way to the nearest house before the bells began to ring backwards from the steeple.

The young duke ground his teeth together. By these so early signals of alarm he feared to find his enemies prepared; and if he failed to gain a footing in the town, he knew that his small party would soon be broken and exterminated in the open.

In the town, however, the Lancastrians were far from being in so good a posture. It was as Dick had said. The night-guard had already doffed their harness; the rest were still hanging—unlatched, unbraced, all unprepared for battle—about their quarters; and in the whole of Shoreby there were not, perhaps, fifty men full armed, or fifty chargers ready to be mounted.

The beating of the bells, the terrifying summons of men who ran about the streets crying and beating upon the doors, aroused in an incredibly short space at least two-score out of that half-hundred. These got speedily to horse, and, the alarm still flying wild and contrary, galloped in different directions.

Thus it befell that, when Richard of Gloucester reached the first house of Shoreby, he was met in the mouth of the street by a mere handful of lances, whom he swept before his onset as the storm chases the bark.

A hundred paces into the town, Dick Shelton touched the duke's arm; the duke, in answer, gathered his reins, put the shrill trumpet to his mouth, and blowing a concerted point, turned to the right hand out of the direct advance. Swerving like a single rider, his whole command turned after him, and, still at the full gallop of the chargers, swept up the narrow by-street. Only the last score of riders drew rein and faced about in the entrance; the footmen, whom they carried behind them, leapt at the same instant to the earth, and began, some to bend their bows, and others to break into and secure the houses upon either hand.

Surprised at this sudden change of direction, and daunted by the firm front of the rear-guard, the few Lancastrians, after a momentary consultation, turned and rode farther into town to seek for reinforcements.

The quarter of the town upon which, by the advice of Dick, Richard of Gloucester had now seized, consisted of five small streets of poor and ill-inhabited houses, occupying a very gentle eminence, and lying open towards the back.

The five streets being each secured by a good guard, the reserve would thus occupy the centre, out of shot, and yet ready to carry aid wherever it was needed.

Such was the poorness of the neighbourhood that none of the Lancastrian lords, and but few of their retainers, had been lodged therein; and the inhabitants, with one accord, deserted their houses and fled, squalling, along the streets or over garden walls.

In the centre, where the five ways all met, a somewhat ill-favoured alehouse displayed the sign of the Chequers; and here the Duke of Gloucester chose his headquarters for the day.

To Dick he assigned the guard of one of the five streets.

"Go," he said, "win your spurs. Win glory for me: one Richard for another. I tell you, if I rise, ye shall rise by the same ladder. Go," he added, shaking him by the hand.

But, as soon as Dick was gone, he turned to a little shabby archer at his elbow.

"Go, Dutton, and that right speedily," he added. "Follow that lad. If ye find him faithful, ye answer for his safety, a head for a head. Woe unto you, if ye return without him! But if he be faithless—or, for one instant, ye misdoubt him—stab him from behind."

In the meanwhile Dick hastened to secure his post. The street he had to guard was very narrow, and closely lined with houses, which projected and overhung the roadway; but narrow and dark as it was, since it opened upon the market-place of the town, the main issue of the battle would probably fall to be decided on that spot.

The market-place was full of townspeople fleeing in disorder; but there was as yet no sign of any foeman ready to attack, and Dick judged he had some time before him to make ready his defence.

The two houses at the end stood deserted, with open doors, as the inhabitants had left them in their flight, and from these he had the furniture hastily tossed forth and piled into a barrier in the entry of the lane. A hundred men were placed at his disposal, and of these he threw the more part into the houses, where they might lie in shelter and deliver their arrows from the windows. With the rest, under his own immediate eye, he lined the barricade.

Meanwhile the utmost uproar and confusion had continued to prevail throughout the town; and what with the hurried clashing of bells, the sounding of trumpets, the swift movement of bodies of horse, the cries of the commanders, and the shrieks of women, the noise was almost deafening to the ear. Presently, little by little, the tumult began to subside; and soon after, files of men in armour and bodies of archers began to assemble and form in line of battle in the market-place.

A large portion of this body were in murrey and blue, and in the mounted knight who ordered their array Dick recognised Sir Daniel Brackley.

Then there befell a long pause, which was followed by the almost simultaneous sounding of four trumpets from four different quarters of the town. A fifth rang in answer from the market-place, and at the same moment the files began to move, and a shower of arrows rattled about the barricade, and sounded like blows upon the walls of the two flanking houses.

The attack had begun, by a common signal, on all the five issues of the quarter. Gloucester was beleaguered upon every side; and Dick judged, if he would make good his post, he must rely entirely on the hundred men of his command.

Seven volleys of arrows followed one upon the other, and in the very thick of the discharges Dick was touched from behind upon the arm, and found a page holding out to him a leathern jack, strengthened with bright plates of mail.

"It is from my Lord of Gloucester," said the page. "He hath observed, Sir Richard, that ye went unarmed."

Dick, with a glow at his heart at being so addressed, got to his feet and, with the assistance of the page, donned the defensive coat. Even as he did so, two arrows rattled harmlessly upon the plates, and a third struck down the page, mortally wounded, at his feet.

Meantime the whole body of the enemy had been steadily drawing nearer across the market-place; and by this time were so close at hand that Dick gave the order to return their shot. Immediately, from behind the barrier and from the windows of the houses, a counterblast of arrows sped, carrying death. But the Lancastrians, as if they had but waited for a signal, shouted loudly in answer; and began to close at a run upon the barrier, the horsemen still hanging back, with visors lowered.

Then followed an obstinate and deadly struggle, hand to hand. The assailants, wielding their falchions with one hand, strove with the other to drag down the structure of the barricade. On the other side, the parts were reversed; and the defenders exposed themselves like madmen to protect their rampart. So for some minutes the contest raged almost in silence, friend and foe falling one upon another. But it is always the easier to destroy; and when a single note upon the tucket recalled the attacking party from this desperate service, much of the barricade had been removed piecemeal, and the whole fabric had sunk to half its height, and tottered to a general fall.

And now the footmen in the market-place fell back, at a run, on every side. The horsemen, who had been standing in a line two deep, wheeled suddenly, and made their flank into their front; and as swift as a striking adder, the long, steel-clad column was launched upon the ruinous barricade.

Of the first two horsemen, one fell, rider and steed, and was ridden down by his companions. The second leaped clean upon the summit of the rampart, transpiercing an archer with his lance. Almost in the same instant he was dragged from the saddle and his horse despatched.

And then the full weight and impetus of the charge burst upon and scattered the defenders. The men-at-arms, surmounting their fallen comrades, and carried onward by the fury of their onslaught, dashed through Dick's broken line and poured thundering up the lane beyond, as a stream bestrides and pours across a broken dam.

Yet was the fight not over. Still, in the narrow jaws of the entrance, Dick and a few survivors plied their bills like woodmen; and already, across the width of the passage, there had been formed a second, a higher, and a more effectual rampart of fallen men and disembowelled horses, lashing in the agonies of death.

Baffled by this fresh obstacle, the remainder of the cavalry fell back; and as, at the sight of this movement, the flight of arrows redoubled from the casements of the houses, their retreat had, for a moment, almost degenerated into flight.

Almost at the same time, those who had crossed the barricade and charged farther up the street, being met before the door of the Chequers by the formidable hunchback and the whole reserve of the Yorkists, began to come scattering backwards, in the excess of disarray and terror.

Dick and his fellows faced about, fresh men poured out of the houses; a cruel blast of arrows met the fugitives full in the face, while Gloucester was already riding down their rear; in the inside of a minute and a half there was no living Lancastrian in the street.

Then, and not till then, did Dick hold up his reeking blade and give the word to cheer.

Meanwhile Gloucester dismounted from his horse and came forward to inspect the post. His face was as pale as linen; but his eyes shone in his head like some strange jewel, and his voice, when he spoke, was hoarse and broken with the exultation of battle and success. He looked at the rampart, which neither friend nor foe could now approach without precaution, so fiercely did the horses struggle in the throes of death, and at the sight of that great carnage he smiled upon one side.

"Despatch these horses," he said; "they keep you from your vantage. Richard Shelton," he added, "ye have pleased me. Kneel."

The Lancastrians had already resumed their archery, and the shafts fell thick in the mouth of the street; but the duke, minding them not at all, deliberately drew his sword and dubbed Richard a knight upon the spot.

"And now, Sir Richard," he continued, "if that ye see Lord Risingham, send me an express upon the instant. Were it your last man, let me hear of it incontinently. I had rather venture the post than lose my stroke at him. For mark me, all of ye," he added, raising his voice, "if Earl Risingham fall by another hand than mine, I shall count this victory a defeat."

"My lord duke," said one of his attendants, "is your grace not weary of exposing his dear life unneedfully? Why tarry we here?"

"Catesby," returned the duke, "here is the battle, not elsewhere. The rest are but feigned onslaughts. Here must we vanquish. And for the exposure—if ye were an ugly hunchback, and the children gecked at you upon the street, ye would count your body cheaper, and an hour of glory worth a life. Howbeit, if ye will, let us ride on and visit the other posts. Sir Richard here, my namesake, he shall still hold this entry, where he wadeth to the ankles in hot blood. Him can we trust. But mark it, Sir Richard, ye are not yet done. The worst is yet to ward. Sleep not."

He came right up to young Shelton, looking him hard in the eyes, and taking his hand in both of his, gave it so extreme a squeeze that the blood had nearly spurted. Dick quailed before his eyes. The insane excitement, the courage, and the cruelty that he read therein filled him with dismay about the future. This young duke's was indeed a gallant spirit, to ride foremost in the ranks of war; but after the battle, in the days of peace and in the circle of his trusted friends, that mind, it was to be dreaded, would continue to bring forth the fruits of death.

CHAPTER III. THE BATTLE OF SHOREBY (CONCLUDED)

Dick, once more left to his own counsels, began to look about him. The arrow-shot had somewhat slackened. On all sides the enemy were falling back; and the greater part of the market-place was now left empty, the snow here trampled into orange mud, there splashed with gore, scattered all over with dead men and horses, and bristling thick with feathered arrows.

On his own side the loss had been cruel. The jaws of the little street and the ruins of the barricade were heaped with the dead and dying; and out of the hundred men with whom he had begun the battle, there were not seventy left who could still stand to arms.

At the same time, the day was passing. The first reinforcements might be looked for to arrive at any moment; and the Lancastrians, already shaken by the result of their desperate but unsuccessful onslaught, were in an ill temper to support a fresh invader.

There was a dial in the wall of one of the two flanking houses; and this, in the frosty winter sunshine, indicated ten of the forenoon.

Dick turned to the man who was at his elbow, a little insignificant archer, binding a cut in his arm.

"It was well fought," he said, "and, by my sooth, they will not charge us twice."

"Sir," said the little archer, "ye have fought right well for York, and better for yourself. Never hath man in so brief space prevailed so greatly on the duke's affections. That he should have entrusted such a post to one he knew not is a marvel. But look to your head, Sir Richard! If ye be vanquished—ay, if ye give way one foot's breadth—axe or cord shall punish it; and I am set if ye do aught doubtful, I will tell you honestly, here to stab you from behind."

Dick looked at the little man in amaze.

"You!" he cried. "And from behind!"

"It is right so," returned the archer; "and because I like not the affair I tell it you. Ye must make the post good, Sir Richard, at your peril. O, our Crookback is a bold blade and a good warrior; but, whether in cold blood or in hot, he will have all things done exact to his commandment. If any fail or hinder, they shall die the death."

"Now, by the saints!" cried Richard, "is this so? And will men follow such a leader?"

"Nay, they follow him gleefully," replied the other; "for if he be exact to punish, he is most open-handed to reward. And if he spare not the blood and sweat of others, he is ever liberal of his own, still in the first front of battle, still the last to sleep. He will go far, will Crookback Dick o' Gloucester!"

The young knight, if he had before been brave and vigilant, was now all the more inclined to watchfulness and courage. His sudden favour, he began to perceive, had brought perils in its train. And he turned from the archer, and once more scanned anxiously the market-place. It lay empty as before.

"I like not this quietude," he said. "Doubtless they prepare us some surprise."

And, as if in answer to his remark, the archers began once more to advance against the barricade, and the arrows to fall thick. But there was something hesitating in the attack. They came not on roundly, but seemed rather to await a further signal.

Dick looked uneasily about him, spying for a hidden danger. And sure enough, about half-way up the little street, a door was suddenly opened from within, and the house continued, for some seconds, to disgorge a torrent of Lancastrian archers. These, as they leaped down, hurriedly stood to their ranks, bent their bows, and proceeded to pour upon Dick's rear a flight of arrows.

At the same time, the assailants in the market-place redoubled their shot, and began to close in stoutly upon the barricade.

Dick called down his whole command out of the houses, and facing them both ways, and encouraging their valour both by word and gesture, returned as best he could the double shower of shafts that fell about his post.

Meanwhile house after house was opened in the street, and the Lancastrians continued to pour out of the doors and leap down from the windows, shouting victory, until the number of enemies upon Dick's rear was almost equal to the number in his face. It was plain that he could hold the post no longer; what was worse, even if he could have held it, it had now become useless; and the whole Yorkist army lay in a posture of helplessness upon the brink of a complete disaster.

The men behind him formed the vital flaw in the general defence; and it was upon these that Dick turned, charging at the head of his men. So vigorous was the attack, that the Lancastrian archers gave ground and staggered, and, at last, breaking their ranks, began to crowd back into the houses from which they had so recently and so vain-gloriously sallied.

Meanwhile the men from the market-place had swarmed across the undefended barricade, and fell on hotly upon the other side; and Dick must once again face about, and proceed to drive them back. Once again the spirit of his men prevailed; they cleared the street in a triumphant style, but even as they did so the others issued again out of the houses, and took them, a third time, upon the rear.

The Yorkists began to be scattered; several times Dick found himself alone among his foes and plying his bright sword for life; several times he was conscious of a hurt. And meanwhile the fight swayed to and fro in the street without determinate result.

Suddenly Dick was aware of a great trumpeting about the outskirts of the town. The war-cry of York began to be rolled up to heaven, as by many and triumphant voices. And at the same time the men in front of him began to give ground rapidly, streaming out of the street and back upon the market-place. Some one gave the word to fly. Trumpets were blown distractedly, some for a rally, some to charge. It was plain that a great blow had been struck, and the Lancastrians were thrown, at least for the moment, into full disorder, and some degree of panic.

And then, like a theatre trick, there followed the last act of Shoreby Battle. The men in front of Richard turned tail, like a dog that has been whistled home, and fled like the wind. At the same moment there came through the market-place a storm of horsemen, fleeing and pursuing, the Lancastrians turning back to strike with the sword, the Yorkists riding them down at the point of the lance.

Conspicuous in the mellay, Dick beheld the Crookback. He was already giving a foretaste of that furious valour and skill to cut his way across the ranks of war, which, years afterwards upon the field of Bosworth, and when he was stained with crimes, almost sufficed to change the fortunes of the day and the destiny of the English throne. Evading, striking, riding down, he so forced and so manœuvred his strong horse, so aptly defended himself, and so liberally scattered death to his opponents, that he was now far ahead of the foremost of his knights, hewing his way, with the truncheon of a bloody sword, to where Lord Risingham was rallying the bravest. A moment more and they had met; the tall, splendid, and famous warrior against the deformed and sickly boy.

Yet Shelton had never a doubt of the result; and when the fight next opened for a moment, the figure of the earl had disappeared; but still, in the first of the danger, Crookback Dick was launching his big horse and plying the truncheon of his sword.

Thus, by Shelton's courage in holding the mouth of the street against the first attack, and by the opportune arrival of his seven hundred reinforcements, the lad, who was afterwards to be handed down to the execration of posterity under the name of Richard III., had won his first considerable fight.

CHAPTER IV. THE SACK OF SHOREBY

There was not a foe left within striking distance; and Dick, as he looked ruefully about him on the remainder of his gallant force, began to count the cost of victory. He was himself, now that the danger was ended, so stiff and sore, so bruised and cut and broken, and, above all, so utterly exhausted by his desperate and unremitting labours in the fight, that he seemed incapable of any fresh exertion.

But this was not yet the hour for repose. Shoreby had been taken by assault; and though an open town, and not in any manner to be charged with the resistance, it was plain that these rough fighters would be not less rough now that the fight was over, and that the more horrid part of war would fall to be enacted. Richard of Gloucester was not the captain to protect the citizens from his infuriated soldiery; and even if he had the will, it might be questioned if he had the power.

It was, therefore, Dick's business to find and to protect Joanna; and with that end he looked about him at the faces of his men. The three or four who seemed likeliest to be obedient and to keep sober he drew aside; and promising them a rich reward and a special recommendation to the duke, led them across the market-place, now empty of horsemen, and into the streets upon the farther side.

Every here and there small combats of from two to a dozen still raged upon the open street; here and there a house was being besieged, the defenders throwing out stools and tables on the heads of the assailants. The snow was strewn with arms and corpses; but except for these partial combats the streets were deserted, and the houses, some standing open, and some shuttered and barricaded, had for the most part ceased to give out smoke.

Dick, threading the skirts of these skirmishers, led his followers briskly in the direction of the abbey church; but when he came the length of the main street, a cry of horror broke from his lips. Sir Daniel's great house had been carried by assault. The gates hung in splinters from the hinges, and a double throng kept pouring in and out through the entrance, seeking and carrying booty. Meanwhile, in the upper storeys, some resistance was still being offered to the pillagers; for just as Dick came within eyeshot of the building, a casement was burst open from within, and a poor wretch in murrey and blue, screaming and resisting, was forced through the embrasure and tossed into the street below.

The most sickening apprehension fell upon Dick. He ran forward like one possessed, forced his way into the house among the foremost, and mounted without pause to the chamber on the third floor where he had last parted from Joanna. It was a mere wreck; the furniture had been overthrown, the cupboards broken open, and in one place a trailing corner of the arras lay smouldering on the embers of the fire.

Dick, almost without thinking, trod out the incipient conflagration, and then stood bewildered. Sir Daniel, Sir Oliver, Joanna, all were gone; but whether butchered in the rout or safe escaped from Shoreby, who should say?

He caught a passing archer by the tabard.

"Fellow," he asked, "were ye here when this house was taken?"

"Let be," said the archer. "A murrain! let be, or I strike."

"Hark ye," returned Richard, "two can play at that. Stand and be plain."

But the man, flushed with drink and battle, struck Dick upon the shoulder with one hand, while with the other he twitched away his garment. Thereupon the full wrath of the young leader burst from his control. He seized the fellow in his strong embrace, and crushed him on the plates of his mailed bosom like a child; then, holding him at arm's length, he bid him speak as he valued life.

"I pray you mercy!" gasped the archer. "An I had thought ye were so angry I would 'a' been charier of crossing you. I was here indeed."

"Know ye Sir Daniel?" pursued Dick.

"Well do I know him," returned the man.

"Was he in the mansion?"

"Ay, sir, he was," answered the archer; "but even as we entered by the yard gate he rode forth by the garden."

"Alone?" cried Dick.

"He may 'a' had a score of lances with him," said the man.

"Lances! No women, then?" asked Shelton.

"Troth, I saw not," said the archer. "But there were none in the house, if that be your quest."

"I thank you," said Dick. "Here is a piece for your pains." But groping in his wallet, Dick found nothing. "Inquire for me to-morrow," he added—"Richard Shelt—Sir Richard Shelton," he corrected, "and I will see you handsomely rewarded."

And then an idea struck Dick. He hastily descended to the courtyard, ran with all his might across the garden, and came to the great door of the church. It stood wide open; within, every corner of the pavement was crowded with fugitive burghers, surrounded by their families and laden with the most precious of their possessions, while, at the high altar, priests in full canonicals were imploring the mercy of God. Even as Dick entered, the loud chorus began to thunder in the vaulted roofs.

He hurried through the groups of refugees, and came to the door of the stair that led into the steeple. And here a tall churchman stepped before him and arrested his advance.

"Whither, my son?" he asked, severely.

"My father," answered Dick, "I am here upon an errand of expedition. Stay me not. I command here for my Lord of Gloucester."

"For my Lord of Gloucester?" repeated the priest. "Hath, then, the battle gone so sore?"

"The battle, father, is at an end, Lancaster clean sped, my Lord of

Risingham—Heaven rest him!—left upon the field. And now, with your good leave, I follow mine affairs." And thrusting on one side the priest, who seemed stupefied at the news, Dick pushed open the door and rattled up the stairs four at a bound, and without pause or stumble, till he stepped upon the open platform at the top.

Shoreby Church tower not only commanded the town, as in a map, but looked far, on both sides, over sea and land. It was now near upon noon; the day exceeding bright, the snow dazzling. And as Dick looked around him, he could measure the consequences of the battle.

A confused, growling uproar reached him from the streets, and now and then, but very rarely, the clash of steel. Not a ship, not so much as a skiff remained in harbour; but the sea was dotted with sails and row-boats laden with fugitives. On shore, too, the surface of the snowy meadows was broken up with bands of horsemen, some cutting their way towards the borders of the forest, others, who were doubtless of the Yorkist side, stoutly interposing and beating them back upon the town. Over all the open ground there lay a prodigious quantity of fallen men and horses, clearly defined upon the snow.

To complete the picture, those of the foot soldiers as had not found place upon a ship still kept up an archery combat on the borders of the port, and from the cover of the shoreside taverns. In that quarter, also, one or two houses had been fired, and the smoke towered high in the frosty sunlight, and blew off to sea in voluminous folds.

Already close upon the margin of the woods, and somewhat in the line of Holywood, one particular clump of fleeing horsemen riveted the attention of the young watcher on the tower. It was fairly numerous; in no other quarter of the field did so many Lancastrians still hold together; thus they had left a wide, discoloured wake upon the snow, and Dick was able to trace them step by step from where they had left the town.

While Dick stood watching them, they had gained, unopposed, the first fringe of the leafless forest, and, turning a little from their direction, the sun fell for a moment full on their array, as it was relieved against the dusky wood.

"Murrey and blue!" cried Dick. "I swear it—murrey and blue!"

220

The next moment he was descending the stairway.

It was now his business to seek out the Duke of Gloucester, who alone, in the disorder of the forces, might be able to supply him with a sufficiency of men. The fighting in the main town was now practically at an end; and as Dick ran hither and thither, seeking the commander, the streets were thick with wandering soldiers, some laden with more booty than they could well stagger under, others shouting drunk. None of them, when questioned, had the least notion of the duke's whereabouts; and, at last, it was by sheer good fortune that Dick found him, where he sat in the saddle directing operations to dislodge the archers from the harbour side.

"Sir Richard Shelton, ye are well found," he said. "I owe you one thing that I value little, my life; and one that I can never pay you for, this victory. Catesby, if I had ten such captains as Sir Richard, I would march forthright on London. But now, sir, claim your reward."

"Freely, my lord," said Dick, "freely and loudly. One hath escaped to whom I owe some grudges, and taken with him one whom I owe love and service. Give me, then, fifty lances, that I may pursue; and for any obligation that your graciousness is pleased to allow, it shall be clean discharged."

"How call ye him?" inquired the duke.

"Sir Daniel Brackley," answered Richard.

"Out upon him, double-face!" cried Gloucester. "Here is no reward, Sir Richard; here is fresh service offered, and, if that ye bring his head to me, a fresh debt upon my conscience. Catesby, get him these lances; and you, sir, bethink ye, in the meanwhile, what pleasure, honour, or profit it shall be mine to give you."

Just then the Yorkist skirmishers carried one of the shoreside taverns, swarming in upon it on three sides, and driving out or taking its defenders. Crookback Dick was pleased to cheer the exploit, and pushing his horse a little nearer, called to see the prisoners.

There were four or five of them—two men of my Lord Shoreby's and one of Lord Risingham's among the number, and last, but in Dick's eyes not least, a tall, shambling, grizzled old shipman, between drunk and sober, and with a dog whimpering and jumping at his heels.

The young duke passed them for a moment under a severe review.

"Good," he said. "Hang them."

And he turned the other way to watch the progress of the fight.

"My lord," said Dick, "so please you, I have found my reward. Grant me the life and liberty of yon old shipman."

Gloucester turned and looked the speaker in the face.

"Sir Richard," he said, "I make not war with peacock's feathers, but steel shafts. Those that are mine enemies I slay, and that without excuse or favour. For, bethink ye, in this realm of England, that is so torn in pieces, there is not a man of mine but hath a brother or a friend upon the other party. If, then, I did begin to grant these pardons, I might sheathe my sword."

"It may be so, my lord; and yet I will be overbold, and, at the risk of your disfavour, recall your lordship's promise," replied Dick.

Richard of Gloucester flushed.

"Mark it right well," he said, harshly. "I love not mercy, nor yet mercymongers. Ye have this day laid the foundations of high fortune. If ye oppose to me my word, which I have plighted, I will yield. But, by the glory of heaven, there your favour dies!"

"Mine is the loss," said Dick.

"Give him his sailor," said the duke; and wheeling his horse, he turned his back upon young Shelton.

Dick was nor glad nor sorry. He had seen too much of the young duke to set great store on his affection; and the origin and growth of his own favour had been too flimsy and too rapid to inspire much confidence. One thing alone he feared—that the vindictive leader might revoke the offer of the lances. But here he did justice neither to Gloucester's honour (such as it was) nor, above all, to his decision. If he had once judged Dick to be the right man to pursue Sir Daniel, he was not one to change; and he soon proved it by shouting after Catesby to be speedy, for the paladin was waiting.

In the meanwhile, Dick turned to the old shipman, who had seemed equally indifferent to his condemnation and to his subsequent release.

"Arblaster," said Dick, "I have done you ill; but now, by the rood, I think I have cleared the score."

But the old skipper only looked upon him dully and held his peace.

"Come," continued Dick, "a life is a life, old shrew, and it is more than ships or liquor. Say ye forgive me; for if your life be worth nothing to you, it hath cost me the beginnings of my fortune. Come, I have paid for it dearly; be not so churlish."

"An I had had my ship," said Arblaster, "I would 'a' been forth and safe on the high seas—I and my man Tom. But ye took my ship, gossip, and I'm a beggar; and for my man Tom, a knave fellow in russet shot him down. 'Murrain!' quoth he, and spake never again. 'Murrain' was the last of his words, and the poor spirit of him passed. 'A will never sail no more, will my Tom."

Dick was seized with unavailing penitence and pity; he sought to take the skipper's hand, but Arblaster avoided his touch.

"Nay," said he, "let be. Y' have played the devil with me, and let that content you."

The words died in Richard's throat. He saw, through tears, the poor old man, bemused with liquor and sorrow, go shambling away, with bowed head, across the snow, and the unnoticed dog whimpering at his heels, and for the first time began to understand the desperate game that we play in life; and how a thing once done is not to be changed or remedied, by any penitence.

But there was no time left to him for vain regret. Catesby had now collected the horsemen, and riding up to Dick he dismounted, and offered him his own horse.

"This morning," he said, "I was somewhat jealous of your favour; it hath not been of a long growth; and now, Sir Richard, it is with a very good heart that I offer you this horse—to ride away with."

"Suffer me yet a moment," replied Dick. "This favour of mine— whereupon was it founded?"

"Upon your name," answered Catesby. "It is my lord's chief superstition. Were my name Richard, I should be an earl to-morrow."

"Well, sir, I thank you," returned Dick; "and since I am little likely to follow these great fortunes, I will even say farewell. I will not pretend I was displeased to think myself upon the road to fortune; but I will not pretend, neither, that I am over-sorry to be done with it. Command and riches, they are brave things, to be sure; but a word in your ear—yon duke of yours, he is a fearsome lad."

Catesby laughed.

"Nay," said he, "of a verity he that rides with Crooked Dick will ride deep. Well, God keep us all from evil! Speed ye well."

Thereupon Dick put himself at the head of his men, and giving the word of command, rode off.

He made straight across the town, following what he supposed to be the route of Sir Daniel, and spying around for any signs that might decide if he were right.

The streets were strewn with the dead and the wounded, whose fate, in the bitter frost, was far the more pitiable. Gangs of the victors went from house to house, pillaging and stabbing, and sometimes singing together as they went.

From different quarters, as he rode on, the sounds of violence and outrage came to young Shelton's ears; now the blows of the sledge-hammer on some barricaded door, and now the miserable shrieks of women.

Dick's heart had just been awakened. He had just seen the cruel consequences of his own behaviour; and the thought of the sum of misery that was now acting in the whole of Shoreby filled him with despair.

At length he reached the outskirts, and there, sure enough, he saw straight before him the same broad, beaten track across the snow that he had marked from the summit of the church. Here, then, he went the faster on; but still, as he rode, he kept a bright eye upon the fallen men and horses that lay beside the track. Many of these, he was relieved to see, wore Sir Daniel's colours, and the faces of some, who lay upon their back, he even recognised.

About half-way between the town and the forest, those whom he was following had plainly been assailed by archers; for the corpses lay pretty closely scattered, each pierced by an arrow. And here Dick spied among the rest the body of a very young lad, whose face was somehow hauntingly familiar to him.

He halted his troop, dismounted, and raised the lad's head. As he did so, the hood fell back, and a profusion of long brown hair unrolled itself. At the same time the eyes opened.

"Ah! lion driver!" said a feeble voice. "She is farther on. Ride—ride fast!"

And then the poor young lady fainted once again.

One of Dick's men carried a flask of some strong cordial, and with this Dick succeeded in reviving consciousness. Then he took Joanna's friend upon his saddle-bow, and once more pushed toward the forest.

"Why do ye take me?" said the girl. "Ye but delay your speed."

"Nay, Mistress Risingham," replied Dick. "Shoreby is full of blood and drunkenness and riot. Here ye are safe; content ye."

"I will not be beholden to any of your faction," she cried; "set me down."

"Madam, ye know not what ye say," returned Dick. "Y'are hurt——"

"I am not," she said. "It was my horse was slain."

"It matters not one jot," replied Richard. "Ye are here in the midst of open snow, and compassed about with enemies. Whether ye will or not, I carry you with me. Glad am I to have the occasion; for thus shall I repay some portion of our debt."

For a little while she was silent. Then, very suddenly, she asked:

"My uncle?"

"My Lord Risingham?" returned Dick. "I would I had good news to give you, madam; but I have none. I saw him once in the battle, and once only. Let us hope the best."

CHAPTER V. NIGHT IN THE WOODS: ALICIA RISINGHAM

It was almost certain that Sir Daniel had made for the Moat House; but, considering the heavy snow, the lateness of the hour, and the necessity under which he would lie of avoiding the few roads and striking across the wood, it was equally certain that he could not hope to reach it ere the morrow.

There were two courses open to Dick: either to continue to follow in the knight's trail, and, if he were able, to fall upon him that very night in camp, or to strike out a path of his own, and seek to place himself between Sir Daniel and his destination.

Either scheme was open to serious objection, and Dick, who feared to expose Joanna to the hazards of a fight, had not yet decided between them when he reached the borders of the wood.

At this point Sir Daniel had turned a little to his left, and then plunged straight under a grove of very lofty timber. His party had then formed to a narrower front, in order to pass between the trees, and the track was trod proportionally deeper in the snow. The eye followed it, under the leafless tracery of the oaks, running direct and narrow; the trees stood over it, with knotty joints and the great, uplifted forest of their boughs; there was no sound, whether of man or beast—not so much as the stirring of a robin; and over the field of snow the winter sun lay golden among netted shadows.

"How say ye," asked Dick of one of the men, "to follow straight on, or strike across for Tunstall?"

"Sir Richard," replied the man-at-arms, "I would follow the line until they scatter."

"Ye are, doubtless, right," returned Dick; "but we came right hastily upon the errand, even as the time commanded. Here are no houses, neither for food nor shelter, and by the morrow's dawn we shall know both cold fingers and an empty belly. How say ye, lads? Will ye stand a pinch for expedition's sake, or shall we turn by Holywood and sup with Mother Church? The case being somewhat doubtful, I will drive no man; yet if ye would suffer me to lead you, ye would choose the first."

The men answered, almost with one voice, that they would follow Sir Richard where he would.

And Dick, setting spur to his horse, began once more to go forward.

The snow in the trail had been trodden very hard, and the pursuers had thus a great advantage over the pursued. They pushed on, indeed, at a round trot, two hundred hoofs beating alternately on the dull pavement of the snow, and the jingle of weapons and the snorting of horses raising a warlike noise along the arches of the silent wood.

Presently, the wide slot of the pursued came out upon the highroad from Holywood; it was there, for a moment, indistinguishable; and, where it once more plunged into the unbeaten snow upon the farther side, Dick was surprised to see it narrower and lighter trod. Plainly, profiting by the road, Sir Daniel had begun already to scatter his command.

At all hazards, one chance being equal to another, Dick continued to pursue the straight trail; and that, after an hour's riding, in which it led into the very depths of the forest, suddenly split, like a bursting shell, into two dozen others, leading to every point of the compass.

Dick drew bridle in despair. The short winter's day was near an end; the sun, a dull red orange, shorn of rays, swam low among the leafless thickets; the shadows were a mile long upon the snow; the frost bit cruelly at the finger-nails; and the breath and steam of the horses mounted in a cloud.

"Well, we are outwitted," Dick confessed. "Strike we for Holywood, after all. It is still nearer us than Tunstall—or should be by the station of the sun."

So they wheeled to their left, turning their backs on the red shield of sun, and made across country for the abbey. But now times were changed with them; they could no longer spank forth briskly on a path beaten firm by the passage of their foes, and for a goal to which that path itself conducted them. Now they must plough at a dull pace through the encumbering snow, continually pausing to decide their course, continually floundering in drifts. The sun soon left them; the glow of the west decayed; and presently they were wandering in a shadow of blackness, under frosty stars.

Presently, indeed, the moon would clear the hill-tops, and they might resume their march. But till then, every random step might carry them wider of their march. There was nothing for it but to camp and wait.

Sentries were posted; a spot of ground was cleared of snow, and, after some failures, a good fire blazed in the midst. The men-at-arms sat close about this forest hearth, sharing such provisions as they had, and passing about the flask; and Dick, having collected the most delicate of the rough and scanty fare, brought it to Lord Risingham's niece, where she sat apart from the soldiery against a tree.

She sat upon one horse-cloth, wrapped in another, and stared straight before her at the firelit scene. At the offer of food she started, like one wakened from a dream, and then silently refused.

"Madam," said Dick, "let me beseech you, punish me not so cruelly. Wherein I have offended you, I know not; I have, indeed, carried you away, but with a friendly violence; I have, indeed, exposed you to the inclemency of night, but the hurry that lies upon me hath for its end the preservation of another, who is no less frail and no less unfriended than yourself. At least, madam, punish not yourself; and eat, if not for hunger, then for strength."

"I will eat nothing at the hands that slew my kinsman," she replied.

"Dear madam," Dick cried, "I swear to you upon the rood I touched him not."

"Swear to me that he still lives," she returned.

"I will not palter with you," answered Dick. "Pity bids me to wound you. In my heart I do believe him dead."

"And ye ask me to eat!" she cried. "Ay, and they call you 'sir'! Y' have won your spurs by my good kinsman's murder. And had I not been fool and traitor both, and saved you in your enemy's house, ye should have died the death, and he—he that was worth twelve of you—were living."

"I did but my man's best, even as your kinsman did upon the other party," answered Dick. "Were he still living—as I vow to Heaven I wish it!—he would praise, not blame me."

"Sir Daniel hath told me," she replied. "He marked you at the barricade. Upon you, he saith, their party foundered; it was you that won the battle. Well, then, it was you that killed my good Lord Risingham, as sure as though ye had strangled him. And ye would have me eat with you—and your hands not washed from killing? But Sir Daniel hath sworn your downfall. He 'tis that will avenge me!"

The unfortunate Dick was plunged in gloom. Old Arblaster returned upon his mind, and he groaned aloud.

"Do ye hold me so guilty?" he said; "you that defended me—you that are Joanna's friend?"

"What made ye in the battle?" she retorted. "Y'are of no party; y'are but a lad—but legs and body, without government of wit or counsel! Wherefore did ye fight? For the love of hurt, pardy!"

"Nay," cried Dick, "I know not. But as the realm of England goes, if that a poor gentleman fight not upon the one side, perforce he must fight upon the other. He may not stand alone; 'tis not in nature."

"They that have no judgment should not draw the sword," replied the young lady. "Ye that fight but for a hazard, what are ye but a butcher? War is but noble by the cause, and y' have disgraced it."

"Madam," said the miserable Dick, "I do partly see mine error. I have made too much haste; I have been busy before my time. Already I stole a ship—thinking, I do swear it, to do well—and thereby brought about the death of many innocent, and the grief and ruin of a poor old man whose face this very day hath stabbed me like a dagger. And for this morning, I did but design to do myself credit, and get fame to marry with, and, behold! I have brought about the death of your dear kinsman that was good to me. And what besides, I know not. For, alas! I may have set York upon the throne, and that may be the worser cause, and may do hurt to England. O, madam, I do see my sin. I am unfit for life. I will, for penance' sake and to avoid worse evil, once I have finished this adventure, get me to a cloister. I will forswear Joanna and the trade of arms. I will be a friar, and pray for your good kinsman's spirit all my days."

It appeared to Dick, in this extremity of his humiliation and repentance, that the young lady had laughed.

Raising his countenance, he found her looking down upon him, in the firelight, with a somewhat peculiar but not unkind expression.

"Madam," he cried, thinking the laughter to have been an illusion of his hearing, but still, from her changed looks, hoping to have touched her heart, "madam, will not this content you? I give up all to undo what I have done amiss; I make heaven certain for Lord Risingham. And all this upon the very day that I have won my spurs, and thought myself the happiest young gentleman on ground."

"O boy," she said—"good boy!"

And then, to the extreme surprise of Dick, she first very tenderly wiped the tears away from his cheeks, and then, as if yielding to a sudden impulse, threw both her arms about his neck, drew up his face, and kissed him. A pitiful bewilderment came over simple-minded Dick.

"But come," she said, with great cheerfulness, "you that are a captain, ye must eat. Why sup ye not?"

"Dear Mistress Risingham," replied Dick, "I did but wait first upon my prisoner; but, to say truth, penitence will no longer suffer me to endure the sight of food. I were better to fast, dear lady, and to pray."

"Call me Alicia," she said; "are we not old friends? And now, come, I will eat with you, bit for bit and sup for sup; so if ye eat not, neither will I; but if ye eat hearty, I will dine like a ploughman."

So there and then she fell to; and Dick, who had an excellent stomach, proceeded to bear her company, at first with great reluctance, but gradually, as he entered into the spirit, with more and more vigour and devotion: until, at last, he forgot even to watch his model, and most heartily repaired the expenses of his day of labour and excitement.

"Lion-driver," she said, at length, "ye do not admire a maid in a man's jerkin?"

The moon was now up; and they were only waiting to repose the wearied horses. By the moon's light, the still penitent but now well-fed Richard beheld her looking somewhat coquettishly down upon him.

"Madam—" he stammered, surprised at this new turn in her manners.

"Nay," she interrupted, "it skills not to deny; Joanna hath told me, but come, sir lion-driver, look at me—am I so homely—come!"

And she made bright eyes at him.

"Ye are something smallish, indeed—" began Dick.

And here again she interrupted him, this time with a ringing peal of laughter that completed his confusion and surprise.

"Smallish!" she cried. "Nay, now, be honest as ye are bold; I am a dwarf, or little better; but for all that—come, tell me!—for all that, passably fair to look upon; is't not so?"

"Nay, madam, exceedingly fair," said the distressed knight, pitifully trying to seem easy.

"And a man would be right glad to wed me?" she pursued.

"O, madam, right glad!" agreed Dick.

"Call me Alicia," said she.

"Alicia," quoth Sir Richard.

"Well, then, lion-driver," she continued, "sith that ye slew my kinsman, and left me without stay, ye owe me, in honour, every reparation; do ye not?"

232

"I do, madam," said Dick. "Although, upon my heart, I do hold me but partially guilty of that brave knight's blood."

"Would ye evade me?" she cried.

"Madam, not so. I have told you; at your bidding, I will even turn me a monk," said Richard.

"Then, in honour, ye belong to me?" she concluded.

"In honour, madam, I suppose—" began the young man.

"Go to!" she interrupted; "ye are too full of catches. In honour do ye belong to me, till ye have paid the evil?"

"In honour, I do," said Dick.

"Hear, then," she continued. "Ye would make but a sad friar, methinks; and since I am to dispose of you at pleasure, I will even take you for my husband. Nay, now, no words!" cried she. "They will avail you nothing. For see how just it is, that you who deprived me of one home, should supply me with another. And as for Joanna, she will be the first, believe me, to commend the change; for, after all, as we be dear friends, what matters it with which of us ye wed? Not one whit!"

"Madam," said Dick, "I will go into a cloister, an ye please to bid me; but to wed with any one in this big world besides Joanna Sedley is what I will consent to neither for man's force nor yet for lady's pleasure. Pardon me if I speak my plain thoughts plainly; but where a maid is very bold, a poor man must even be the bolder."

"Dick," she said, "ye sweet boy, ye must come and kiss me for that word. Nay, fear not, ye shall kiss me for Joanna; and when we meet, I shall give it back to her, and say I stole it. And as for what ye owe me, why, dear simpleton, methinks ye were not alone in that great battle; and even if York be on the throne, it was not you that set him there. But for a good, sweet, honest heart, Dick, y'are all that; and if I could find it in my soul to envy your Joanna anything, I would even envy her your love."

CHAPTER VI. NIGHT IN THE WOODS (CONCLUDED): DICK AND JOAN

The horses had by this time finished the small store of provender, and fully breathed from their fatigues. At Dick's command, the fire was smothered in snow; and while his men got once more wearily to saddle, he himself, remembering, somewhat late, true woodland caution, chose a tall oak and nimbly clambered to the topmost fork. Hence he could look far abroad on the moonlit and snow-paven forest. On the south-west, dark against the horizon, stood those upland, heathy quarters where he and Joanna had met with the terrifying misadventure of the leper. And there his eye was caught by a spot of ruddy brightness no bigger than a needle's eye.

He blamed himself sharply for his previous neglect. Were that, as it appeared to be, the shining of Sir Daniel's camp-fire, he should long ago have seen and marched for it; above all, he should, for no consideration, have announced his neighbourhood by lighting a fire of his own. But now he must no longer squander valuable hours. The direct way to the uplands was about two miles in length; but it was crossed by a very deep, precipitous dingle, impassable to mounted men; and for the sake of speed, it seemed to Dick advisable to desert the horses and attempt the adventure on foot.

Ten men were left to guard the horses; signals were agreed upon by which they could communicate in case of need; and Dick set forth at the head of the remainder, Alicia Risingham walking stoutly by his side.

The men had freed themselves of heavy armour, and left behind their lances; and they now marched with a very good spirit in the frozen snow, and under the exhilarating lustre of the moon. The descent into the dingle, where a stream strained sobbing through the snow and ice, was effected with silence and order; and on the farther side, being then within a short half-mile of where Dick had seen the glimmer of the fire, the party halted to breathe before the attack.

In the vast silence of the wood, the lightest sounds were audible from far; and Alicia, who was keen of hearing, held up her finger warningly and stooped to listen. All followed her example; but besides the groans of the choked brook in the dingle close behind, and the barking of a fox at a distance of many miles among the forest, to Dick's acutest hearkening, not a breath was audible.

"But yet, for sure, I heard the clash of harness," whispered Alicia.

"Madam," returned Dick, who was more afraid of that young lady than of ten stout warriors, "I would not hint ye were mistaken; but it might well have come from either of the camps."

"It came not thence. It came from westward," she declared.

"It may be what it will," returned Dick; "and it must be as Heaven please. Reck we not a jot, but push on the livelier, and put it to the touch. Up, friends—enough breathed."

As they advanced, the snow became more and more trampled with hoof-marks, and it was plain that they were drawing near to the encampment of a considerable force of mounted men. Presently they could see the smoke pouring from among the trees, ruddily coloured on its lower edge and scattering bright sparks.

And here, pursuant to Dick's orders, his men began to open out, creeping stealthily in the covert, to surround on every side the camp of their opponents. He himself, placing Alicia in the shelter of a bulky oak, stole straight forth in the direction of the fire.

At last, through an opening of the wood, his eye embraced the scene of the encampment. The fire had been built upon a heathy hummock of the ground, surrounded on three sides by thicket, and it now burned very strong, roaring aloud and brandishing flames. Around it there sat not quite a dozen people, warmly cloaked; but though the neighbouring snow was trampled down as by a regiment, Dick looked in vain for any horse. He began to have a terrible misgiving that he was out-manœuvred. At the same time, in a tall man with a steel salet, who was spreading his hands before the blaze, he recognised his old friend and still kindly enemy, Bennet Hatch; and in two others, sitting a little back, he made out, even in their male disguise, Joanna Sedley and Sir Daniel's wife.

"Well," thought he to himself, "even if I lose my horses, let me get my Joanna, and why should I complain?"

And then, from the farther side of the encampment, there came a little whistle, announcing that his men had joined, and the investment was complete.

Bennet, at the sound, started to his feet; but ere he had time to spring upon his arms, Dick hailed him.

"Bennet," he said—"Bennet, old friend, yield ye. Ye will but spill men's lives in vain, if ye resist."

"'Tis Master Shelton, by St. Barbary!" cried Hatch. "Yield me? Ye ask much. What force have ye?"

"I tell you, Bennet, ye are both outnumbered and begirt," said Dick. "Cæsar and Charlemagne would cry for quarter. I have two-score men at my whistle, and with one shoot of arrows I could answer for you all."

"Master Dick," said Bennet, "it goes against my heart; but I must do my duty. The saints help you!" And therewith he raised a little tucket to his mouth and wound a rousing call.

Then followed a moment of confusion; for while Dick, fearing for the ladies, still hesitated to give the word to shoot, Hatch's little band sprang to their weapons and formed back to back as for a fierce resistance. In the hurry of their change of place, Joanna sprang from her seat and ran like an arrow to her lover's side.

"Here, Dick!" she cried, as she clasped his hand in hers.

But Dick still stood irresolute; he was yet young to the more deplorable necessities of war, and the thought of old Lady Brackley checked the command upon his tongue. His own men became restive. Some of them cried on him by name; others, of their own accord, began to shoot; and at the first discharge poor Bennet bit the dust. Then Dick awoke.

"On!" he cried. "Shoot, boys, and keep to cover. England and York!"

But just then the dull beat of many horses on the snow suddenly arose in the hollow ear of the night, and, with incredible swiftness, drew nearer and swelled louder. At the same time, answering tuckets repeated and repeated Hatch's call.

"Rally, rally!" cried Dick. "Rally upon me! Rally for your lives!"

But his men—afoot, scattered, taken in the hour when they had counted on an easy triumph—began instead to give ground severally, and either stood wavering or dispersed into the thickets. And when the first of the horsemen came charging through the open avenues and fiercely riding their steeds into the underwood, a few stragglers were overthrown or speared among the brush, but the bulk of Dick's command had simply melted at the rumour of their coming.

Dick stood for a moment, bitterly recognising the fruits of his precipitate and unwise valour. Sir Daniel had seen the fire; he had moved out with his main force, whether to attack his pursuers or to take them in the rear if they should venture the assault. His had been throughout the part of a sagacious captain; Dick's the conduct of an eager boy. And here was the young knight, his sweetheart, indeed, holding him tightly by the hand, but otherwise alone, his whole command of men and horses dispersed in the night and the wide forest, like a paper of pins in a hay barn.

"The saints enlighten me!" he thought. "It is well I was knighted for this morning's matter; this doth me little honour."

And thereupon, still holding Joanna, he began to run.

The silence of the night was now shattered by the shouts of the men of Tunstall, as they galloped hither and thither, hunting fugitives; and Dick broke boldly through the underwood and ran straight before him like a deer. The silver clearness of the moon upon the open snow increased, by contrast, the obscurity of the thickets; and the extreme dispersion of the vanquished led the pursuers into widely divergent paths. Hence, in but a little while, Dick and Joanna paused, in a close covert, and heard the sounds of the pursuit, scattering abroad, indeed, in all directions, but yet fainting already in the distance.

"An I had but kept a reserve of them together," Dick cried, bitterly, "I could have turned the tables yet! Well, we live and learn; next time it shall go better, by the rood."

"Nay, Dick," said Joanna, "what matters it? Here we are together once again."

He looked at her, and there she was—John Matcham, as of yore, in hose and doublet. But now he knew her; now, even in that ungainly dress, she smiled upon him, bright with love; and his heart was transported with joy.

"Sweetheart," he said, "if ye forgive this blunderer, what care I? Make we direct for Holywood; there lieth your good guardian and my better friend, Lord Foxham. There shall we be wed; and whether poor or wealthy, famous or unknown, what matters it? This day, dear love, I won my spurs; I was commended by great men for my valour; I thought myself the goodliest man of war in all broad England. Then, first, I fell out of my favour with the great; and now have I been well thrashed, and clean lost my soldiers. There was a downfall for conceit! But, dear, I care not—dear, if ye still love me and will wed, I would have my knighthood done away, and mind it not a jot."

"My Dick!" she cried. "And did they knight you?"

"Ay, dear, ye are my lady now," he answered, fondly; "or ye shall, ere noon to-morrow—will ye not?"

"That will I, Dick, with a glad heart," she answered.

"Ay, sir? Methought ye were to be a monk!" said a voice in their ears.

"Alicia!" cried Joanna.

"Even so," replied the young lady, coming forward. "Alicia, whom ye left for dead, and whom your lion-driver found, and brought to life again, and, by my sooth, made love to, if ye want to know!"

"I'll not believe it," cried Joanna. "Dick!"

"Dick!" mimicked Alicia. "Dick, indeed! Ay, fair sir, and ye desert poor damsels in distress," she continued, turning to the young knight. "Ye leave them planted behind oaks. But they say true—the age of chivalry is dead."

"Madam," cried Dick, in despair, "upon my soul I had forgotten you outright. Madam, ye must try to pardon me. Ye see, I had new found Joanna!"

"I did not suppose that ye had done it o' purpose," she retorted. "But I will be cruelly avenged. I will tell a secret to my Lady Shelton—she that is to be," she added, curtseying. "Joanna," she continued, "I believe, upon my soul, your sweetheart is a bold fellow in a fight, but he is, let me tell you plainly, the softest-hearted simpleton in England. Go to—ye may do your pleasure with him! And now, fool children, first kiss me, either one of you, for luck and kindness; and then kiss each other just one minute by the glass, and not one second longer; and then let us all three set forth for Holywood as fast as we can stir; for these woods, methinks, are full of peril and exceeding cold."

"But did my Dick make love to you?" asked Joanna, clinging to her sweetheart's side.

"Nay, fool girl," returned Alicia; "It was I made love to him. I offered to marry him, indeed; but he bade me go marry with my likes. These were his words. Nay, that I will say: he is more plain than pleasant. But now, children, for the sake of sense, set forward. Shall we go once more over the dingle, or push straight for Holywood?"

"Why," said Dick, "I would like dearly to get upon a horse; for I have been sore mauled and beaten, one way and another, these last days, and my poor body is one bruise. But how think ye? If the men, upon the alarm of the fighting, had fled away, we should have gone about for nothing. 'Tis but some three short miles to Holywood direct; the bell hath not beat nine; the snow is pretty firm to walk upon, the moon clear; how if we went even as we are?"

"Agreed," cried Alicia; but Joanna only pressed upon Dick's arm.

Forth, then, they went, through open leafless groves and down snow-clad alleys, under the white face of the winter moon; Dick and Joanna walking hand in hand and in a heaven of pleasure; and their light-minded companion, her own bereavements heartily forgotten, followed a pace or two behind, now rallying them upon their silence, and now drawing happy pictures of their future and united lives.

Still, indeed, in the distance of the wood, the riders of Tunstall might be heard urging their pursuit; and from time to time cries or the clash of steel announced the shock of enemies. But in these young folk, bred among the alarms of war, and fresh from such a multiplicity of dangers, neither fear nor pity could be lightly wakened. Content to find the sounds still drawing farther and farther away, they gave up their hearts to the enjoyment of the hour, walking already, as Alicia put it, in a wedding procession; and neither the rude solitude of the forest, nor the cold of the freezing night, had any force to shadow or distract their happiness.

At length, from a rising hill, they looked below them on the dell of Holywood. The great windows of the forest abbey shone with torch and candle; its high pinnacles and spires arose very clear and silent, and the gold rood upon the topmost summit glittered brightly in the moon. All about it, in the open glade, camp-fires were burning, and the ground was thick with huts; and across the midst of the picture the frozen river curved.

"By the mass," said Richard, "there are Lord Foxham's fellows still encamped. The messenger hath certainly miscarried. Well, then, so better. We have power at hand to face Sir Daniel."

But if Lord Foxham's men still lay encamped in the long holm at Holywood, it was from a different reason from the one supposed by Dick. They had marched, indeed, for Shoreby; but ere they were half-way thither, a second messenger met them, and bade them return to their morning's camp, to bar the road against Lancastrian fugitives, and to be so much nearer to the main army of York. For Richard of Gloucester, having finished the battle and stamped out his foes in that district, was already on the march to rejoin his brother; and not long after the return of my Lord Foxham's retainers,

Crookback himself drew rein before the abbey door. It was in honour of this august visitor that the windows shone with lights; and at the hour of Dick's arrival with his sweetheart and her friend, the whole ducal party was being entertained in the refectory with the splendour of that powerful and luxurious monastery.

Dick, not quite with his good-will, was brought before them. Gloucester, sick with fatigue, sat leaning upon one hand his white and terrifying countenance; Lord Foxham, half recovered from his wound, was in a place of honour on his left.

"How, sir?" asked Richard. "Have ye brought me Sir Daniel's head?"

"My lord duke," replied Dick, stoutly enough, but with a qualm at heart, "I have not even the good fortune to return with my command. I have been, so please your grace, well beaten."

Gloucester looked upon him with a formidable frown.

"I gave you fifty lances,[3] sir," he said.

"My lord duke, I had but fifty men-at-arms," replied the young knight.

"How is this?" said Gloucester. "He did ask me fifty lances."

"May it please your grace," replied Catesby, smoothly, "for a pursuit we gave him but the horsemen."

"It is well," replied Richard, adding, "Shelton, ye may go."

"Stay!" said Lord Foxham. "This young man likewise had a charge from me. It may be he hath better sped. Say, Master Shelton, have ye found the maid?"

"I praise the saints, my lord," said Dick, "she is in this house."

"Is it even so? Well, then, my lord the duke," resumed Lord Foxham, "with your good-will, to-morrow, before the army march, I do propose a marriage. This young squire——"

"Young knight," interrupted Catesby.

"Say ye so, Sir William?" cried Lord Foxham.

"I did myself, and for good service, dub him knight," said Gloucester. "He hath twice manfully served me. It is not valour of hands, it is a man's mind of iron, that he lacks. He will not rise, Lord Foxham. 'Tis a fellow that will fight indeed bravely in a mellay, but hath a capon's heart. Howbeit, if he is to marry, marry him in the name of Mary, and be done!"

"Nay, he is a brave lad—I know it," said Lord Foxham. "Content ye, then, Sir Richard. I have compounded this affair with Master Hamley, and to-morrow ye shall wed."

Whereupon Dick judged it prudent to withdraw; but he was not yet clear of the refectory, when a man, but newly alighted at the gate, came running four stairs at a bound, and, brushing through the abbey servants, threw himself on one knee before the duke.

"Victory, my lord," he cried.

And before Dick had got to the chamber set apart for him as Lord Foxham's guest, the troops in the holm were cheering around their fires; for upon that same day, not twenty miles away, a second crushing blow had been dealt to the power of Lancaster.

CHAPTER VII. DICK'S REVENGE

The next morning Dick was afoot before the sun, and having dressed himself to the best advantage with the aid of the Lord Foxham's baggage, and got good reports of Joan, he set forth on foot to walk away his impatience.

For some while he made rounds among the soldiery, who were getting to arms in the wintry twilight of the dawn and by the red glow of torches; but gradually he strolled farther afield, and at length passed clean beyond the outposts, and walked alone in the frozen forest, waiting for the sun.

His thoughts were both quiet and happy. His brief favour with the duke he could not find it in his heart to mourn; with Joan to wife, and my Lord Foxham for a faithful patron, he looked most happily upon the future; and in the past he found but little to regret.

As he thus strolled and pondered, the solemn light of the morning grew more clear, the east was already coloured by the sun, and a little scathing wind blew up the frozen snow. He turned to go home; but even as he turned, his eye lit upon a figure behind a tree.

"Stand!" he cried. "Who goes?"

The figure stepped forth and waved its hand like a dumb person. It was arrayed like a pilgrim, the hood lowered over the face, but Dick, in an instant, recognised Sir Daniel.

He strode up to him, drawing his sword; and the knight, putting his hand in his bosom, as if to seize a hidden weapon, steadfastly awaited his approach.

"Well, Dickon," said Sir Daniel, "how is it to be? Do ye make war upon the fallen?"

"I made no war upon your life," replied the lad; "I was your true friend until ye sought for mine; but ye have sought for it greedily."

"Nay—self-defence," replied the knight. "And now, boy, the news of this battle, and the presence of yon crooked devil here in mine own wood, have broken me beyond all help. I go to Holywood for sanctuary; thence overseas, with what I can carry, and to begin life again in Burgundy or France."

"Ye may not go to Holywood," said Dick.

"How! May not?" asked the knight.

"Look ye, Sir Daniel, this is my marriage morn," said Dick; "and yon sun that is to rise will make the brightest day that ever shone for me. Your life is forfeit—doubly forfeit, for my father's death and your own practices to meward. But I myself have done amiss; I have brought about men's deaths; and upon this glad day I will be neither judge nor hangman. An ye were the devil, I would not lay a hand on you. An ye were the devil, ye might go where ye will for me. Seek God's forgiveness; mine ye have freely. But to go on to Holywood is different. I carry arms for York, and I will suffer no spy within their lines. Hold it, then, for certain, if ye set one foot before another, I will uplift my voice and call the nearest post to seize you."

"Ye mock me," said Sir Daniel. "I have no safety out of Holywood."

"I care no more," returned Richard. "I let you go east, west, or south; north I will not. Holywood is shut against you. Go, and seek not to return. For, once ye are gone, I will warn every post about this army, and there will be so shrewd a watch upon all pilgrims that, once again, were ye the very devil, ye would find it ruin to make the essay."

"Ye doom me," said Sir Daniel, gloomily.

"I doom you not," returned Richard. "If it so please you to set your valour against mine, come on; and though I fear it be disloyal to my party, I will take the challenge openly and fully, fight you with mine own single strength, and call for none to help me. So shall I avenge my father, with a perfect conscience."

"Ay," said Sir Daniel, "y' have a long sword against my dagger."

"I rely upon Heaven only," answered Dick, casting his sword some way behind him on the snow. "Now, if your ill-fate bids you, come; and, under the pleasure of the Almighty, I make myself bold to feed your bones to foxes."

"I did but try you, Dickon," returned the knight, with an uneasy semblance of a laugh. "I would not spill your blood."

"Go, then, ere it be too late," replied Shelton. "In five minutes I will call the post. I do perceive that I am too long-suffering. Had but our places been reversed, I should have been bound hand and foot some minutes past."

"Well, Dickon, I will go," replied Sir Daniel. "When we next meet, it shall repent you that ye were so harsh."

And with these words, the knight turned and began to move off under the trees. Dick watched him with strangely-mingled feelings, as he went, swiftly and warily, and ever and again turning a wicked eye upon the lad who had spared him, and whom he still suspected.

There was upon one side of where he went a thicket, strongly matted with green ivy, and, even in its winter state, impervious to the eye. Herein, all of a sudden, a bow sounded like a note of music. An arrow flew, and with a great, choked cry of agony and anger, the Knight of Tunstall threw up his hands and fell forward in the snow.

Dick bounded to his side and raised him. His face desperately worked; his whole body was shaken by contorting spasms.

"Is the arrow black?" he gasped.

"It is black," replied Dick, gravely.

And then, before he could add one word, a desperate seizure of pain shook the wounded man from head to foot, so that his body leaped in Dick's supporting arms, and with the extremity of that pang his spirit fled in silence.

The young man laid him back gently on the snow and prayed for that unprepared and guilty spirit, and as he prayed the sun came up at a bound, and the robins began chirping in the ivy.

When he rose to his feet, he found another man upon his knees but a few steps behind him, and, still with uncovered head, he waited until that prayer also should be over. It took long; the man, with his head bowed and his face covered with his hands, prayed like one in a great disorder or distress of mind; and by the bow that lay beside him, Dick judged that he was no other than the archer who had laid Sir Daniel low.

At length he, also, rose, and showed the countenance of Ellis Duckworth.

"Richard," he said, very gravely, "I heard you. Ye took the better part and pardoned; I took the worse, and there lies the clay of mine enemy. Pray for me."

And he wrung him by the hand.

"Sir," said Richard, "I will pray for you, indeed; though how I may prevail I wot not. But if ye have so long pursued revenge, and find it now of such a sorry flavour, bethink ye, were it not well to pardon others? Hatch—he is dead, poor shrew! I would have spared a better; and for Sir Daniel, here lies his body. But for the priest, if I might anywise prevail, I would have you let him go."

A flash came into the eyes of Ellis Duckworth.

"Nay," he said, "the devil is still strong within me. But be at rest; the Black Arrow flieth nevermore—the fellowship is broken. They that still live shall come to their quiet and ripe end, in Heaven's good time, for me; and for yourself, go where your better fortune calls you, and think no more of Ellis."

CHAPTER VIII. CONCLUSION

About nine in the morning, Lord Foxham was leading his ward, once more dressed as befitted her sex, and followed by Alicia Risingham, to the church of Holywood, when Richard Crookback, his brow already heavy with cares, crossed their path and paused.

"Is this the maid?" he asked; and when Lord Foxham had replied in the affirmative, "Minion," he added, "hold up your face until I see its favour."

He looked upon her sourly for a little.

"Ye are fair," he said at last, "and, as they tell me, dowered. How if I offered you a brave marriage, as became your face and parentage?"

"My lord duke," replied Joanna, "may it please your grace, I had rather wed with Sir Richard."

"How so?" he asked, harshly. "Marry but the man I name to you, and he shall be my lord, and you my lady, before night. For Sir Richard, let me tell you plainly, he will die Sir Richard."

"I ask no more of Heaven, my lord, than but to die Sir Richard's wife," returned Joanna.

"Look ye at that, my lord," said Gloucester, turning to Lord Foxham. "Here be a pair for you. The lad, when for good services I gave him his choice of my favour, chose but the grace of an old, drunken shipman. I did warn him freely, but he was stout in his besottedness. 'Here dieth your favour,' said I; and he, my lord, with a most assured impertinence, 'Mine be the loss,' quoth he. It shall be so, by the rood!"

"Said he so?" cried Alicia. "Then well said, lion-driver!"

"Who is this?" asked the duke.

"A prisoner of Sir Richard's," answered Lord Foxham; "Mistress Alicia Risingham."

"See that she be married to a sure man," said the duke.

"I had thought of my kinsman, Hamley, an it like your grace," returned Lord Foxham. "He hath well served the cause."

"It likes me well," said Richard. "Let them be wedded speedily. Say, fair maid, will you wed?"

"My lord duke," said Alicia, "so as the man is straight—" And there, in a perfect consternation, the voice died on her tongue.

"He is straight, my mistress," replied Richard, calmly. "I am the only crookback of my party; we are else passably well shapen. Ladies, and you, my lord," he added, with a sudden change to grave courtesy, "judge me not too churlish if I leave you. A captain, in the time of war, hath not the ordering of his hours."

And with a very handsome salutation he passed on, followed by his officers.

"Alack," cried Alicia, "I am shent!"

"Ye know him not," replied Lord Foxham. "It is but a trifle; he hath already clean forgot your words."

"He is, then, the very flower of knighthood," said Alicia.

"Nay, he but mindeth other things," returned Lord Foxham. "Tarry we no more."

In the chancel they found Dick waiting, attended by a few young men; and there were he and Joan united. When they came forth again, happy and yet serious, into the frosty air and sunlight, the long files of the army were already winding forward up the road; already the Duke of Gloucester's banner was unfolded and began to move from before the abbey in a clump of spears; and behind it, girt by steel-clad knights, the bold, black-hearted, and ambitious hunchback moved on towards his brief kingdom and his lasting infamy. But the wedding party turned upon the other side, and sat down, with sober merriment, to breakfast. The father cellarer attended on their wants, and sat with them at table. Hamley, all jealousy forgotten, began to ply the nowise loth Alicia with courtship. And there, amid the sounding of tuckets and the clash of armoured soldiery and horses continually moving forth, Dick and Joan sat side by side, tenderly held hands, and looked, with ever growing affection, in each other's eyes.

Thenceforth the dust and blood of that unruly epoch passed them by. They dwelt apart from alarms in the green forest where their love began.

Two old men in the meanwhile enjoyed pensions in great prosperity and peace, and with perhaps a superfluity of ale and wine, in Tunstall hamlet. One had been all his life a shipman, and continued to the last to lament his man Tom. The other, who had been a bit of everything, turned in the end towards piety, and made a most religious death under the name of Brother Honestus in the neighbouring abbey. So Lawless had his will, and died a friar.

Footnotes

[1] At the date of this story, Richard Crookback could not have been created Duke of Gloucester; but for clearness, with the reader's leave, he shall so be called.

[2] Richard Crookback would have been really far younger at this date.

[3] Technically, the term "lance" included a not quite certain number of foot soldiers attached to the man-at-arms.

MEMORIES AND PORTRAITS

TO

MY MOTHER

IN THE

NAME OF PAST JOY AND PRESENT SORROW

I DEDICATE

THESE MEMORIES AND PORTRAITS

S.S. "Ludgate Hill"

within sight of Cape Race

NOTE

This volume of papers, unconnected as they are, it will be better to read through from the beginning, rather than dip into at random. A certain thread of meaning binds them. Memories of childhood and youth, portraits of those who have gone before us in the battle—taken together, they build up a face that "I have loved long since and lost awhile," the face of what was once myself. This has come by accident; I had no design at first to be autobiographical; I was but led away by the charm of beloved memories and by regret for the irrevocable dead; and when my own young face (which is a face of the dead also) began to appear in the well as by a kind of magic, I was the first to be surprised at the occurrence.

My grandfather the pious child, my father the idle eager sentimental youth, I have thus unconsciously exposed. Of their descendant, the person of to-day, I wish to keep the secret: not because I love him better, but because, with him, I am still in a business partnership, and cannot divide interests.

Of the papers which make up the volume, some have appeared already in The Cornhill, Longman's, Scribner, The English Illustrated, The Magazine of Art, The Contemporary Review; three are here in print for the first time; and two others have enjoyed only what may he regarded as a private circulation.

R. L S.

CHAPTER I. THE FOREIGNER AT HOME

"This is no my ain house;

I ken by the biggin' o't."

Two recent books [1] one by Mr. Grant White on England, one on France by the diabolically clever Mr. Hillebrand, may well have set people thinking on the divisions of races and nations. Such thoughts should arise with particular congruity and force to inhabitants of that United Kingdom, peopled from so many different stocks, babbling so many different dialects, and offering in its extent such singular contrasts, from the busiest over-population to the unkindliest desert, from the Black Country to the Moor of Rannoch. It is not only when we cross the seas that we go abroad; there are foreign parts of England; and the race that has conquered so wide an empire has not yet managed to assimilate the islands whence she sprang. Ireland, Wales, and the Scottish mountains still cling, in part, to their old Gaelic speech. It was but the other day that English triumphed in Cornwall, and they still show in Mousehole, on St. Michael's Bay, the house of the last Cornish-speaking woman. English itself, which will now frank the traveller through the most of North America, through the greater South Sea Islands, in India, along much of the coast of Africa, and in the ports of China and Japan, is still to be heard, in its home country, in half a hundred varying stages of transition. You may go all over the States, and—setting aside the actual intrusion and influence of foreigners, negro, French, or Chinese—you shall scarce meet with so marked a difference of accent as in the forty miles between Edinburgh and Glasgow, or of dialect as in the hundred miles between Edinburgh and Aberdeen. Book English has gone round the world, but at home we still preserve the racy idioms of our fathers, and every county, in some parts every dale, has its own quality of speech, vocal or verbal. In like manner, local custom and prejudice, even local religion and local law, linger on into the latter end of the nineteenth century—imperia in imperio, foreign things at home.

In spite of these promptings to reflection, ignorance of his neighbours is the character of the typical John Bull. His is a domineering nature, steady in fight, imperious to command, but neither curious nor quick about the life of others. In French colonies, and still more in the Dutch, I have read that there is an immediate and lively contact between the dominant and the dominated race, that a certain sympathy is begotten, or at the least a transfusion of prejudices, making life easier for both. But the Englishman sits apart, bursting with pride and ignorance. He figures among his vassals in the hour of peace with the same disdainful air that led him on to victory. A passing enthusiasm for some foreign art or fashion may deceive the world, it cannot impose upon his intimates. He may be amused by a foreigner as by a monkey, but he will never condescend to study him with any patience. Miss Bird, an authoress with whom I profess myself in love, declares all the viands of Japan to be uneatable—a staggering pretension. So, when the Prince of Wales's marriage was celebrated at Mentone by a dinner to the Mentonese, it was proposed to give them solid English fare—roast beef and plum pudding, and no tomfoolery. Here we have either pole of the Britannic folly. We will not eat the food of any foreigner; nor, when we have the chance, will we suffer him to eat of it himself. The same spirit inspired Miss Bird's American missionaries, who had come thousands of miles to change the faith of Japan, and openly professed their ignorance of the religions they were trying to supplant.

I quote an American in this connection without scruple. Uncle Sam is better than John Bull, but he is tarred with the English stick. For Mr. Grant White the States are the New England States and nothing more. He wonders at the amount of drinking in London; let him try San Francisco. He wittily reproves English ignorance as to the status of women in America; but has he not himself forgotten Wyoming? The name Yankee, of which he is so tenacious, is used over the most of the great Union as a term of reproach. The Yankee States, of which he is so staunch a subject, are but a drop in the bucket. And we find in his book a vast virgin ignorance of the life and prospects of America; every view partial, parochial, not raised to the horizon; the moral feeling proper, at the largest, to a clique of states; and the whole scope and atmosphere not American, but merely Yankee. I will go far beyond him in reprobating the assumption and the incivility of my countryfolk to their cousins from beyond the sea; I grill in my blood over the silly rudeness of our newspaper articles; and I do not know where to look when I find myself in company with an American and see my countrymen unbending to him as to a performing dog. But in the case of Mr. Grant White example were better than precept. Wyoming is, after all, more readily accessible to Mr. White than Boston to the English, and the New England self-sufficiency no better justified than the Britannic.

It is so, perhaps, in all countries; perhaps in all, men are most ignorant of the foreigners at home. John Bull is ignorant of the States; he is probably ignorant of India; but considering his opportunities, he is far more ignorant of countries nearer his own door. There is one country, for instance—its frontier not so far from London, its people closely akin, its language the same in all essentials with the English—of which I will go bail he knows nothing. His ignorance of the sister kingdom cannot be described; it can only be illustrated by anecdote. I once travelled with a man of plausible manners and good intelligence—a University man, as the phrase goes—a man, besides, who had taken his degree in life and knew a thing or two about the age we live in. We were deep in talk, whirling between Peterborough and London; among other things, he began to describe some piece of legal injustice he had recently encountered, and I observed in my innocence that things were not so in Scotland. "I beg your pardon," said he, "this is a matter of law." He had never heard of the Scots law; nor did he choose to be informed. The law was the same for the whole country, he told me roundly; every child knew that. At last, to settle matters, I explained to him that I was a member of a Scottish legal body, and had stood the brunt of an examination in the very law in question. Thereupon he looked me for a moment full in the face and dropped the conversation. This is a monstrous instance, if you like, but it does not stand alone in the experience of Scots.

England and Scotland differ, indeed, in law, in history, in religion, in education, and in the very look of nature and men's faces, not always widely, but always trenchantly. Many particulars that struck Mr. Grant White, a Yankee, struck me, a Scot, no less forcibly; he and I felt ourselves foreigners on many common provocations. A Scotchman may tramp the better part of Europe and the United States, and never again receive so vivid an impression of foreign travel and strange lands and manners as on his first excursion into England. The change from a hilly to a level country strikes him with delighted wonder. Along the flat horizon there arise the frequent venerable towers of churches. He sees at the end of airy vistas the revolution of the windmill sails. He may go where he pleases in the future; he may see Alps, and Pyramids, and lions; but it will be hard to beat the pleasure of that moment. There are, indeed, few merrier spectacles than that of many windmills bickering together in a fresh breeze over a woody country; their halting alacrity of movement, their pleasant business, making bread all day with uncouth gesticulations, their air, gigantically human, as of a creature half alive, put a spirit of romance into the tamest landscape. When the Scotch child sees them first he falls immediately in love; and from that time forward windmills keep turning in his dreams. And so, in their degree, with every feature of the life and landscape. The warm, habitable age of towns and hamlets, the green, settled, ancient look of the country; the lush hedgerows, stiles, and privy path-ways in the fields; the sluggish, brimming rivers; chalk and smock-frocks; chimes of bells and the rapid, pertly-sounding English speech—they are all new to the curiosity; they are all set to English airs in the child's story that he tells himself at night. The sharp edge of novelty wears off; the feeling is scotched, but I doubt whether it is ever killed. Rather it keeps returning, ever the more rarely and strangely, and even in scenes to which you have been long accustomed suddenly awakes and gives a relish to enjoyment or heightens the sense of isolation.

One thing especially continues unfamiliar to the Scotchman's eye—the domestic architecture, the look of streets and buildings; the quaint, venerable age of many, and the thin walls and warm colouring of all. We have, in Scotland, far fewer ancient buildings, above all in country places; and those that we have are all of hewn or harled masonry. Wood has been sparingly used in their construction; the window-frames are sunken in the wall, not flat to the front, as in England; the roofs are steeper-pitched; even a hill farm will have a massy, square, cold and permanent appearance. English houses, in comparison, have the look of cardboard toys, such as a puff might shatter. And to this the Scotchman never becomes used. His eye can never rest consciously on one of these brick houses—rickles of brick, as he might call them—or on one of these flat-chested streets, but he is instantly reminded where he is, and instantly travels back in fancy to his home. "This is no my ain house; I ken by the biggin' o't." And yet perhaps it is his own, bought with his own money, the key of it long polished in his pocket; but it has not yet, and never will be, thoroughly adopted by his imagination; nor does he cease to remember that, in the whole length and breadth of his native country, there was no building even distantly resembling it.

But it is not alone in scenery and architecture that we count England foreign. The constitution of society, the very pillars of the empire, surprise and even pain us. The dull, neglected peasant, sunk in matter, insolent, gross and servile, makes a startling contrast with our own long-legged, long-headed, thoughtful, Bible-quoting ploughman. A week or two in such a place as Suffolk leaves the Scotchman gasping. It seems incredible that within the boundaries of his own island a class should have been thus forgotten. Even the educated and intelligent, who hold our own opinions and speak in our own words, yet seem to hold them with a difference or, from another reason, and to speak on all things with less interest and conviction. The first shock of English society is like a cold plunge. It is possible that the Scot comes looking for too much, and to be sure his first experiment will be in the wrong direction. Yet surely his complaint is grounded; surely the speech of Englishmen is too often lacking in generous ardour, the better part of the man too often withheld from the social commerce, and the contact of mind with mind evaded as with terror. A Scotch peasant will talk more liberally out of his own experience. He will not put you by with conversational counters and small jests; he will give you the best of himself, like one interested in life and man's chief end. A Scotchman is vain, interested in himself and others, eager for sympathy, setting forth his thoughts and experience in the best light. The egoism of the Englishman is self-contained. He does not seek to proselytise. He takes no interest in Scotland or the Scotch, and, what is the unkindest cut of all, he does not care to justify his indifference. Give him the wages of going on and being an Englishman, that is all he asks; and in the meantime, while you continue to associate, he would rather not be reminded of your baser origin. Compared with the grand, tree-like self-sufficiency of his demeanour, the vanity and curiosity of the Scot seem uneasy, vulgar, and immodest. That you should continually try to establish human and serious relations, that you should actually feel an interest in John Bull, and desire and invite a return of interest from him, may argue something more awake and lively in your mind, but it still puts you in the attitude of a suitor and a poor relation. Thus even the lowest class of the educated English towers over a Scotchman by the head and shoulders.

Different indeed is the atmosphere in which Scotch and English youth begin to look about them, come to themselves in life, and gather up those first apprehensions which are the material of future thought and, to a great extent, the rule of future conduct. I have been to school in both countries, and I found, in the boys of the North, something at once rougher and more tender, at once more reserve and more expansion, a greater habitual distance chequered by glimpses of a nearer intimacy, and on the whole wider extremes of temperament and sensibility. The boy of the South seems more wholesome, but less thoughtful; he gives himself to games as to a business, striving to excel, but is not readily transported by imagination; the type remains with me as cleaner in mind and body, more active, fonder of eating, endowed with a lesser and a less romantic sense of life and of the future, and more immersed in present circumstances. And certainly, for one thing, English boys are younger for their age. Sabbath observance makes a series of grim, and perhaps serviceable, pauses in the tenor of Scotch boyhood—days of great stillness and solitude for the rebellious mind, when in the dearth of books and play, and in the intervals of studying the Shorter Catechism, the intellect and senses prey upon and test each other. The typical English Sunday, with the huge midday dinner and the plethoric afternoon, leads perhaps to different results. About the very cradle of the Scot there goes a hum of metaphysical divinity; and the whole of two divergent systems is summed up, not merely speciously, in the two first questions of the rival catechisms, the English tritely inquiring, "What is your name?" the Scottish striking at the very roots of life with, "What is the chief end of man?" and answering nobly, if obscurely, "To glorify God and to enjoy Him for ever." I do not wish to make an idol of the Shorter Catechism; but the fact of such a question being asked opens to us Scotch a great field of speculation; and the fact that it is asked of all of us, from the peer to the ploughboy, binds us more nearly together. No Englishman of Byron's age, character, and history would have had patience for long theological discussions on the way to fight for Greece; but the daft Gordon blood and the Aberdonian school-days kept their influence to the end. We have spoken of the material conditions; nor need much more be said of these: of the land lying everywhere more exposed, of the wind always louder and bleaker, of the black, roaring winters, of the gloom of high-lying, old stone cities, imminent on the windy seaboard; compared with the level streets, the warm colouring of the brick, the domestic quaintness of the architecture, among which English children begin to grow up and come to themselves in life. As the stage of the University approaches, the contrast becomes more express. The English lad goes to Oxford or Cambridge; there, in an ideal world of gardens, to lead a semi-scenic life, costumed, disciplined and drilled by proctors. Nor is this to be regarded merely as a stage of education; it is a piece of privilege besides, and a step that separates him further from the bulk of his compatriots. At an earlier age the Scottish lad begins his greatly different experience of crowded class-rooms, of a gaunt quadrangle, of a bell hourly booming over the traffic of the city to recall him from the public-house where he has been lunching, or the streets where he has been wandering fancy-free. His college life has little of restraint, and nothing of necessary gentility. He will find no quiet clique of the exclusive, studious and cultured; no rotten borough of the arts. All classes rub shoulders on the greasy benches. The raffish young gentleman in gloves must measure his scholarship with the plain, clownish laddie from the parish school. They separate, at the session's end, one to smoke cigars about a watering-place, the other to resume the labours of the field beside his peasant family. The first muster of a college class in Scotland is a scene of curious and painful interest; so many lads, fresh from the heather, hang round the stove in cloddish embarrassment, ruffled by the presence of their smarter comrades, and afraid of the sound of their own rustic voices. It was in these early days, I think, that Professor Blackie won the affection of his pupils, putting these uncouth, umbrageous students at their ease with ready human geniality. Thus, at least, we have a healthy democratic atmosphere to breathe in while at work; even when there is no cordiality there is always a juxtaposition of the different classes, and in the competition of study the intellectual power of each is plainly demonstrated to the other. Our tasks ended, we of the North go forth as freemen into the humming, lamplit city. At five o'clock you may see the last of us hiving from the college gates, in the glare of the shop windows, under the green glimmer of the winter sunset. The frost tingles in our blood; no proctor lies in wait to intercept us; till the bell sounds again, we are the masters of the world; and some portion of our lives is always Saturday, la trêve de Dieu.

Nor must we omit the sense of the nature of his country and his country's history gradually growing in the child's mind from story and from observation. A Scottish child hears much of shipwreck, outlying iron skerries, pitiless breakers, and great sea-lights; much of heathery mountains, wild clans, and hunted Covenanters. Breaths come to him in song of the distant Cheviots and the ring of foraying hoofs. He glories in his hard-fisted forefathers, of the iron girdle and the handful of oat-meal, who rode so swiftly and lived so sparely on their raids. Poverty, ill-luck, enterprise, and constant resolution are the fibres of the legend of his country's history. The heroes and kings of Scotland have been tragically fated; the most marking incidents in Scottish history—Flodden, Darien, or the Forty-five—were still either failures or defeats; and the fall of Wallace and the repeated reverses of the Bruce combine with the very smallness of the country to teach rather a moral than a material criterion for life. Britain is altogether small, the mere taproot of her extended empire: Scotland, again, which alone the Scottish boy adopts in his imagination, is but a little part of that, and avowedly cold, sterile and unpopulous. It is not so for nothing. I once seemed to have perceived in an American boy a greater readiness of sympathy for lands that are great, and rich, and growing, like his own. It proved to be quite otherwise: a mere dumb piece of boyish romance, that I had lacked penetration to divine. But the error serves the purpose of my argument; for I am sure, at least, that the heart of young Scotland will be always touched more nearly by paucity of number and Spartan poverty of life.

So we may argue, and yet the difference is not explained. That Shorter Catechism which I took as being so typical of Scotland, was yet composed in the city of Westminster. The division of races is more sharply marked within the borders of Scotland itself than between the countries. Galloway and Buchan, Lothian and Lochaber, are like foreign parts; yet you may choose a man from any of them, and, ten to one, he shall prove to have the headmark of a Scot. A century and a half ago the Highlander wore a different costume, spoke a different language, worshipped in another church, held different morals, and obeyed a different social constitution from his fellow-countrymen either of the south or north. Even the English, it is recorded, did not loathe the Highlander and the Highland costume as they were loathed by the remainder of the Scotch. Yet the Highlander felt himself a Scot. He would willingly raid into the Scotch lowlands; but his courage failed him at the border, and he regarded England as a perilous, unhomely land. When the Black Watch, after years of foreign service, returned to Scotland, veterans leaped out and kissed the earth at Port Patrick. They had been in Ireland, stationed among men of their own race and language, where they were well liked and treated with affection; but it was the soil of Galloway that they kissed at the extreme end of the hostile lowlands, among a people who did not understand their speech, and who had hated, harried, and hanged them since the dawn of history. Last, and perhaps most curious, the sons of chieftains were often educated on the continent of Europe. They went abroad speaking Gaelic; they returned speaking, not English, but the broad dialect of Scotland. Now, what idea had they in their minds when they thus, in thought, identified themselves with their ancestral enemies? What was the sense in which they were Scotch and not English, or Scotch and not Irish? Can a bare name be thus influential on the minds and affections of men, and a political aggregation blind them to the nature of facts? The story of the Austrian Empire would seem to answer, No; the far more galling business of Ireland clenches the negative from nearer home. Is it common education, common morals, a common language or a common faith, that join men into nations? There were practically none of these in the case we are considering.

The fact remains: in spite of the difference of blood and language, the Lowlander feels himself the sentimental countryman of the Highlander. When they meet abroad, they fall upon each other's necks in spirit; even at home there is a kind of clannish intimacy in their talk. But from his compatriot in the south the Lowlander stands consciously apart. He has had a different training; he obeys different laws; he makes his will in other terms, is otherwise divorced and married; his eyes are not at home in an English landscape or with English houses; his ear continues to remark the English speech; and even though his tongue acquire the Southern knack, he will still have a strong Scotch accent of the mind.

CHAPTER II. SOME COLLEGE MEMORIES [15]

I am asked to write something (it is not specifically stated what) to the profit and glory of my Alma Mater; and the fact is I seem to be in very nearly the same case with those who addressed me, for while I am willing enough to write something, I know not what to write. Only one point I see, that if I am to write at all, it should be of the University itself and my own days under its shadow; of the things that are still the same and of those that are already changed: such talk, in short, as would pass naturally between a student of to-day and one of yesterday, supposing them to meet and grow confidential.

The generations pass away swiftly enough on the high seas of life; more swiftly still in the little bubbling back-water of the quadrangle; so that we see there, on a scale startlingly diminished, the flight of time and the succession of men. I looked for my name the other day in last year's case-book of the Speculative. Naturally enough I looked for it near the end; it was not there, nor yet in the next column, so that I began to think it had been dropped at press; and when at last I found it, mounted on the shoulders of so many successors, and looking in that posture like the name of a man of ninety, I was conscious of some of the dignity of years. This kind of dignity of temporal precession is likely, with prolonged life, to become more familiar, possibly less welcome; but I felt it strongly then, it is strongly on me now, and I am the more emboldened to speak with my successors in the tone of a parent and a praiser of things past.

For, indeed, that which they attend is but a fallen University; it has doubtless some remains of good, for human institutions decline by gradual stages; but decline, in spite of all seeming embellishments, it does; and what is perhaps more singular, began to do so when I ceased to be a student. Thus, by an odd chance, I had the very last of the very best of Alma Mater; the same thing, I hear (which makes it the more strange), had previously happened to my father; and if they are good and do not die, something not at all unsimilar will be found in time to have befallen my successors of to-day. Of the specific points of change, of advantage in the past, of shortcoming in the present, I must own that, on a near examination, they look wondrous cloudy. The chief and far the most lamentable change is the absence of a certain lean, ugly, idle, unpopular student, whose presence was for me the gist and heart of the whole matter; whose changing humours, fine occasional purposes of good, flinching acceptance of evil, shiverings on wet, east-windy, morning journeys up to class, infinite yawnings during lecture and unquenchable gusto in the delights of truantry, made up the sunshine and shadow of my college life. You cannot fancy what you missed in missing him; his virtues, I make sure, are inconceivable to his successors, just as they were apparently concealed from his contemporaries, for I was practically alone in the pleasure I had in his society. Poor soul, I remember how much he was cast down at times, and how life (which had not yet begun) seemed to be already at an end, and hope quite dead, and misfortune and dishonour, like physical presences, dogging him as he went. And it may be worth while to add that these clouds rolled away in their season, and that all clouds roll away at last, and the troubles of youth in particular are things but of a moment. So this student, whom I have in my eye, took his full share of these concerns, and that very largely by his own fault; but he still clung to his fortune, and in the midst of much misconduct, kept on in his own way learning how to work; and at last, to his wonder, escaped out of the stage of studentship not openly shamed; leaving behind him the University of Edinburgh shorn of a good deal of its interest for myself.

But while he is (in more senses than one) the first person, he is by no means the only one whom I regret, or whom the students of to-day, if they knew what they had lost, would regret also. They have still Tait, to be sure—long may they have him!—and they have still Tait's class-room, cupola and all; but think of what a different place it was when this youth of mine (at least on roll days) would be present on the benches, and, at the near end of the platform, Lindsay senior [17] was airing his robust old age. It is possible my successors may have never even heard of Old Lindsay; but when he went, a link snapped with the last century. He had something of a rustic air, sturdy and fresh and plain; he spoke with a ripe east-country accent, which I used to admire; his reminiscences were all of journeys on foot or highways busy with post-chaises—a Scotland before steam; he had seen the coal fire on the Isle of May, and he regaled me with tales of my own grandfather. Thus he was for me a mirror of things perished; it was only in his memory that I could see the huge shock of flames of the May beacon stream to leeward, and the watchers, as they fed the fire, lay hold unscorched of the windward bars of the furnace; it was only thus that I could see my grandfather driving swiftly in a gig along the seaboard road from Pittenweem to Crail, and for all his business hurry, drawing up to speak good-humouredly with those he met. And now, in his turn, Lindsay is gone also; inhabits only the memories of other men, till these shall follow him; and figures in my reminiscences as my grandfather figured in his.

To-day, again, they have Professor Butcher, and I hear he has a prodigious deal of Greek; and they have Professor Chrystal, who is a man filled with the mathematics. And doubtless these are set-offs. But they cannot change the fact that Professor Blackie has retired, and that Professor Kelland is dead. No man's education is complete or truly liberal who knew not Kelland. There were unutterable lessons in the mere sight of that frail old clerical gentleman, lively as a boy, kind like a fairy godfather, and keeping perfect order in his class by the spell of that very kindness. I have heard him drift into reminiscences in class time, though not for long, and give us glimpses of old-world life in out-of-the-way English parishes when he was young; thus playing the same part as Lindsay—the part of the surviving memory, signalling out of the dark backward and abysm of time the images of perished things. But it was a part that scarce became him; he somehow lacked the means: for all his silver hair and worn face, he was not truly old; and he had too much of the unrest and petulant fire of youth, and too much invincible innocence of mind, to play the veteran well. The time to measure him best, to taste (in the old phrase) his gracious nature, was when he received his class at home. What a pretty simplicity would he then show, trying to amuse us like children with toys; and what an engaging nervousness of manner, as fearing that his efforts might not succeed! Truly he made us all feel like children, and like children embarrassed, but at the same time filled with sympathy for the conscientious, troubled elder-boy who was working so hard to entertain us. A theorist has held the view that there is no feature in man so tell-tale as his spectacles;

that the mouth may be compressed and the brow smoothed artificially, but the sheen of the barnacles is diagnostic. And truly it must have been thus with Kelland; for as I still fancy I behold him frisking actively about the platform, pointer in hand, that which I seem to see most clearly is the way his glasses glittered with affection. I never knew but one other man who had (if you will permit the phrase) so kind a spectacle; and that was Dr. Appleton. But the light in his case was tempered and passive; in Kelland's it danced, and changed, and flashed vivaciously among the students, like a perpetual challenge to goodwill.

I cannot say so much about Professor Blackie, for a good reason. Kelland's class I attended, once even gained there a certificate of merit, the only distinction of my University career. But although I am the holder of a certificate of attendance in the professor's own hand, I cannot remember to have been present in the Greek class above a dozen times. Professor Blackie was even kind enough to remark (more than once) while in the very act of writing the document above referred to, that he did not know my face. Indeed, I denied myself many opportunities; acting upon an extensive and highly rational system of truantry, which cost me a great deal of trouble to put in exercise—perhaps as much as would have taught me Greek—and sent me forth into the world and the profession of letters with the merest shadow of an education. But they say it is always a good thing to have taken pains, and that success is its own reward, whatever be its nature; so that, perhaps, even upon this I should plume myself, that no one ever played the truant with more deliberate care, and none ever had more certificates for less education. One consequence, however, of my system is that I have much less to say of Professor Blackie than I had of Professor Kelland; and as he is still alive, and will long, I hope, continue to be so, it will not surprise you very much that I have no intention of saying it.

Meanwhile, how many others have gone—Jenkin, Hodgson, and I know not who besides; and of that tide of students that used to throng the arch and blacken the quadrangle, how many are scattered into the remotest parts of the earth, and how many more have lain down beside their fathers in their "resting-graves"! And again, how many of these last have not found their way there, all too early, through the stress of education! That was one thing, at least, from which my truantry protected me. I am sorry indeed that I have no Greek, but I should be sorrier still if I were dead; nor do I know the name of that branch of knowledge which is worth acquiring at the price of a brain fever. There are many sordid tragedies in the life of the student, above all if he be poor, or drunken, or both; but nothing more moves a wise man's pity than the case of the lad who is in too much hurry to be learned. And so, for the sake of a moral at the end, I will call up one more figure, and have done. A student, ambitious of success by that hot, intemperate manner of study that now grows so common, read night and day for an examination. As he went on, the task became more easy to him, sleep was more easily banished, his brain grew hot and clear and more capacious, the necessary knowledge daily fuller and more orderly. It came to the eve of the trial and he watched all night in his high chamber, reviewing what he knew, and already secure of success. His window looked eastward, and being (as I said) high up, and the house itself standing on a hill, commanded a view over dwindling suburbs to a country horizon. At last my student drew up his blind, and still in quite a jocund humour, looked abroad. Day was breaking, the east was tinging with strange fires, the clouds breaking up for the coming of the sun; and at the sight, nameless terror seized upon his mind. He was sane, his senses were undisturbed; he saw clearly, and knew what he was seeing, and knew that it was normal; but he could neither bear to see it nor find the strength to look away, and fled in panic from his chamber into the enclosure of the street. In the cool air and silence, and among the sleeping houses, his strength was renewed. Nothing troubled him but the memory of what had passed, and an abject fear of its return.

> "Gallo canente, spes redit,
>
> Aegris salus refunditur,
>
> Lapsis fides revertitur,"

as they sang of old in Portugal in the Morning Office. But to him that good hour of cockcrow, and the changes of the dawn, had brought panic, and lasting doubt, and such terror as he still shook to think of. He dared not

271

return to his lodging; he could not eat; he sat down, he rose up, he wandered; the city woke about him with its cheerful bustle, the sun climbed overhead; and still he grew but the more absorbed in the distress of his recollection and the fear of his past fear. At the appointed hour, he came to the door of the place of examination; but when he was asked, he had forgotten his name. Seeing him so disordered, they had not the heart to send him away, but gave him a paper and admitted him, still nameless, to the Hall. Vain kindness, vain efforts. He could only sit in a still growing horror, writing nothing, ignorant of all, his mind filled with a single memory of the breaking day and his own intolerable fear. And that same night he was tossing in a brain fever.

People are afraid of war and wounds and dentists, all with excellent reason; but these are not to be compared with such chaotic terrors of the mind as fell on this young man, and made him cover his eyes from the innocent morning. We all have by our bedsides the box of the Merchant Abudah, thank God, securely enough shut; but when a young man sacrifices sleep to labour, let him have a care, for he is playing with the lock.

CHAPTER III. OLD MORTALITY

I

There is a certain graveyard, looked upon on the one side by a prison, on the other by the windows of a quiet hotel; below, under a steep cliff, it beholds the traffic of many lines of rail, and the scream of the engine and the shock of meeting buffers mount to it all day long. The aisles are lined with the inclosed sepulchres of families, door beyond door, like houses in a street; and in the morning the shadow of the prison turrets, and of many tall memorials, fall upon the graves. There, in the hot fits of youth, I came to be unhappy. Pleasant incidents are woven with my memory of the place. I here made friends with a plain old gentleman, a visitor on sunny mornings, gravely cheerful, who, with one eye upon the place that awaited him, chirped about his youth like winter sparrows; a beautiful housemaid of the hotel once, for some days together, dumbly flirted with me from a window and kept my wild heart flying; and once—she possibly remembers—the wise Eugenia followed me to that austere inclosure. Her hair came down, and in the shelter of the tomb my trembling fingers helped her to repair the braid. But for the most part I went there solitary and, with irrevocable emotion, pored on the names of the forgotten. Name after name, and to each the conventional attributions and the idle dates: a regiment of the unknown that had been the joy of mothers, and had thrilled with the illusions of youth, and at last, in the dim sick-room, wrestled with the pangs of old mortality. In that whole crew of the silenced there was but one of whom my fancy had received a picture; and he, with his comely, florid countenance, bewigged and habited in scarlet, and in his day combining fame and popularity, stood forth, like a taunt, among that company of phantom appellations. It was then possible to leave behind us something more explicit than these severe, monotonous and lying epitaphs; and the thing left, the memory of a painted picture and what we call the immortality of a name, was hardly more desirable than mere oblivion. Even David Hume, as he lay composed beneath that "circular idea," was fainter than a dream; and when the housemaid, broom in hand, smiled and beckoned from the open window, the fame of that bewigged philosopher melted like a raindrop in the sea.

And yet in soberness I cared as little for the housemaid as for David Hume. The interests of youth are rarely frank; his passions, like Noah's dove, come home to roost. The fire, sensibility, and volume of his own nature, that is all that he has learned to recognise. The tumultuary and gray tide of life, the empire of routine, the unrejoicing faces of his elders, fill him with contemptuous surprise; there also he seems to walk among the tombs of spirits; and it is only in the course of years, and after much rubbing with his fellow-men, that he begins by glimpses to see himself from without and his fellows from within: to know his own for one among the thousand undenoted countenances of the city street, and to divine in others the throb of human agony and hope. In the meantime he will avoid the hospital doors, the pale faces, the cripple, the sweet whiff of chloroform—for there, on the most thoughtless, the pains of others are burned home; but he will continue to walk, in a divine self-pity, the aisles of the forgotten graveyard. The length of man's life, which is endless to the brave and busy, is scorned by his ambitious thought. He cannot bear to have come for so little, and to go again so wholly. He cannot bear, above all, in that brief scene, to be still idle, and by way of cure, neglects the little that he has to do. The parable of the talent is the brief epitome of youth. To believe in immortality is one thing, but it is first needful to believe in life. Denunciatory preachers seem not to suspect that they may be taken gravely and in evil part; that young men may come to think of time as of a moment, and with the pride of Satan wave back the inadequate gift. Yet here is a true peril; this it is that sets them to pace the graveyard alleys and to read, with strange extremes of pity and derision, the memorials of the dead.

Books were the proper remedy: books of vivid human import, forcing upon their minds the issues, pleasures, busyness, importance and immediacy of that life in which they stand; books of smiling or heroic temper, to excite or to console; books of a large design, shadowing the complexity of that game of consequences to which we all sit down, the hanger-back not least. But the average sermon flees the point, disporting itself in that eternity of which we know, and need to know, so little; avoiding the bright, crowded, and momentous fields of life where destiny awaits us. Upon the average book a writer may be silent; he may set it down to his ill-hap that when his own youth was in the acrid fermentation, he should have fallen and fed upon the cheerless fields of Obermann. Yet to Mr. Arnold, who led him to these pastures, he still bears a grudge. The day is perhaps not far off when people will begin to count Moll Flanders, ay, or The Country Wife, more wholesome and more pious diet than these guide-books to consistent egoism.

But the most inhuman of boys soon wearies of the inhumanity of Obermann. And even while I still continued to be a haunter of the graveyard, I began insensibly to turn my attention to the grave-diggers, and was weaned out of myself to observe the conduct of visitors. This was dayspring, indeed, to a lad in such great darkness. Not that I began to see men, or to try to see them, from within, nor to learn charity and modesty and justice from the sight; but still stared at them externally from the prison windows of my affection. Once I remember to have observed two working-women with a baby halting by a grave; there was something monumental in the grouping, one upright carrying the child, the other with bowed face crouching by her side. A wreath of immortelles under a glass dome had thus attracted them; and, drawing near, I overheard their judgment on that wonder. "Eh! what extravagance!" To a youth afflicted with the callosity of sentiment, this quaint and pregnant saying appeared merely base.

My acquaintance with grave-diggers, considering its length, was unremarkable. One, indeed, whom I found plying his spade in the red evening, high above Allan Water and in the shadow of Dunblane Cathedral, told me of his acquaintance with the birds that still attended on his labours; how some would even perch about him, waiting for their prey; and in a true Sexton's Calendar, how the species varied with the season of the year. But this was the very poetry of the profession. The others whom I knew were somewhat dry. A faint flavour of the gardener hung about them, but sophisticated and dis-bloomed. They had engagements to keep, not alone with the deliberate series of the seasons, but with man-kind's clocks and hour-long measurement of time. And thus there was no leisure for the relishing pinch, or the hour-long gossip, foot on spade. They were men wrapped up in their grim business; they liked well to open long-closed family vaults, blowing in the key and throwing wide the grating; and they carried in their minds a calendar of names and dates. It would be "in fifty-twa" that such a tomb was last opened for "Miss Jemimy." It was thus they spoke of their past patients—familiarly but not without respect, like old family servants. Here is indeed a servant, whom we forget that we possess; who does not wait at the bright table, or run at the bell's summons, but patiently smokes his pipe beside the mortuary fire, and in his faithful memory notches the burials of our race. To suspect Shakespeare in his maturity of a superficial touch savours of paradox; yet he was surely in error when he attributed insensibility to the digger of the grave. But perhaps it is on Hamlet that the charge should lie; or perhaps the English sexton differs from the Scotch. The "goodman delver," reckoning up his years of office, might have at least suggested other thoughts. It is a pride common among sextons. A cabinet-maker does not count his cabinets, nor even an author his volumes, save when they stare upon him from the shelves; but the grave-digger numbers his graves. He would indeed be something different from human if his solitary open-air and tragic labours left not a broad mark upon his mind. There, in his tranquil aisle, apart from city clamour, among the cats and robins and the ancient effigies and legends of the tomb, he waits the continual passage of his contemporaries, falling like minute drops into eternity. As they fall, he counts them; and this enumeration, which was at first perhaps appalling to his soul, in the process of years and by the kindly influence of habit grows to be his pride and pleasure. There are many common stories telling how he piques himself on crowded cemeteries. But I will rather tell of the old grave-digger of Monkton, to whose unsuffering bedside the minister was summoned. He dwelt in a cottage built into the wall of the church-yard; and through a bull's-eye pane above his bed he could see, as he lay dying, the rank grasses and the upright and recumbent stones. Dr. Laurie was, I think, a Moderate: 'tis certain, at least, that he took a very Roman view of deathbed dispositions; for he told the old man that he had lived beyond man's natural years, that his life had been easy and reputable, that his family had all grown up and been a credit to his care, and that it now behoved him unregretfully to gird his loins and follow the majority. The grave-digger heard him out; then he raised himself upon one elbow, and with the other hand pointed through the window to the scene of his life-long labours. "Doctor," he said, "I ha'e laid three hunner and fower-score in that kirkyaird; an it had been His wull," indicating Heaven, "I would ha'e likit weel to ha'e made out the fower hunner." But it was not to be; this tragedian of the fifth act had now another part to play; and the time had come when others were to gird and carry him.

II

I would fain strike a note that should be more heroical; but the ground of all youth's suffering, solitude, hysteria, and haunting of the grave, is nothing else than naked, ignorant selfishness. It is himself that he sees dead; those are his virtues that are forgotten; his is the vague epitaph. Pity him but the more, if pity be your cue; for where a man is all pride, vanity, and personal aspiration, he goes through fire unshielded. In every part and corner of our life, to lose oneself is to be gainer; to forget oneself is to be happy; and this poor, laughable and tragic fool has not yet learned the rudiments; himself, giant Prometheus, is still ironed on the peaks of Caucasus. But by-and-by his truant interests will leave that tortured body, slip abroad and gather flowers. Then shall death appear before him in an altered guise; no longer as a doom peculiar to himself, whether fate's crowning injustice or his own last vengeance upon those who fail to value him; but now as a power that wounds him far more tenderly, not without solemn compensations, taking and giving, bereaving and yet storing up.

The first step for all is to learn to the dregs our own ignoble fallibility. When we have fallen through storey after storey of our vanity and aspiration, and sit rueful among the ruins, then it is that we begin to measure the stature of our friends: how they stand between us and our own contempt, believing in our best; how, linking us with others, and still spreading wide the influential circle, they weave us in and in with the fabric of contemporary life; and to what petty size they dwarf the virtues and the vices that appeared gigantic in our youth. So that at the last, when such a pin falls out—when there vanishes in the least breath of time one of those rich magazines of life on which we drew for our supply—when he who had first dawned upon us as a face among the faces of the city, and, still growing, came to bulk on our regard with those clear features of the loved and living man, falls in a breath to memory and shadow, there falls along with him a whole wing of the palace of our life.

III

One such face I now remember; one such blank some half-a-dozen of us labour to dissemble. In his youth he was most beautiful in person, most serene and genial by disposition; full of racy words and quaint thoughts. Laughter attended on his coming. He had the air of a great gentleman, jovial and royal with his equals, and to the poorest student gentle and attentive. Power seemed to reside in him exhaustless; we saw him stoop to play with us, but held him marked for higher destinies; we loved his notice; and I have rarely had my pride more gratified than when he sat at my father's table, my acknowledged friend. So he walked among us, both hands full of gifts, carrying with nonchalance the seeds of a most influential life.

The powers and the ground of friendship is a mystery; but, looking back, I can discern that, in part, we loved the thing he was, for some shadow of what he was to be. For with all his beauty, power, breeding, urbanity and mirth, there was in those days something soulless in our friend. He would astonish us by sallies, witty, innocent and inhumane; and by a misapplied Johnsonian pleasantry, demolish honest sentiment. I can still see and hear him, as he went his way along the lamplit streets, Là ci darem la mano on his lips, a noble figure of a youth, but following vanity and incredulous of good; and sure enough, somewhere on the high seas of life, with his health, his hopes, his patrimony and his self-respect, miserably went down.

From this disaster, like a spent swimmer, he came desperately ashore, bankrupt of money and consideration; creeping to the family he had deserted; with broken wing, never more to rise. But in his face there was a light of knowledge that was new to it. Of the wounds of his body he was never healed; died of them gradually, with clear-eyed resignation; of his wounded pride, we knew only from his silence. He returned to that city where he had lorded it in his ambitious youth; lived there alone, seeing few; striving to retrieve the irretrievable; at times still grappling with that mortal frailty that had brought him down; still joying in his friend's successes; his laugh still ready but with kindlier music; and over all his thoughts the shadow of that unalterable law which he had disavowed and which had brought him low. Lastly, when his bodily evils had quite disabled him, he lay a great while dying, still without complaint, still finding interests; to his last step gentle, urbane and with the will to smile.

The tale of this great failure is, to those who remained true to him, the tale of a success. In his youth he took thought for no one but himself; when he came ashore again, his whole armada lost, he seemed to think of none but others. Such was his tenderness for others, such his instinct of fine courtesy and pride, that of that impure passion of remorse he never breathed a syllable; even regret was rare with him, and pointed with a jest. You would not have dreamed, if you had known him then, that this was that great failure, that beacon to young men, over whose fall a whole society had hissed and pointed fingers. Often have we gone to him, red-hot with our own hopeful sorrows, railing on the rose-leaves in our princely bed of life, and he would patiently give ear and wisely counsel; and it was only upon some return of our own thoughts that we were reminded what manner of man this was to whom we disembosomed: a man, by his own fault, ruined; shut out of the garden of his gifts; his whole city of hope both ploughed and salted; silently awaiting the deliverer. Then something took us by the throat; and to see him there, so gentle, patient, brave and pious, oppressed but not cast down, sorrow was so swallowed up in admiration that we could not dare to pity him. Even if the old fault flashed out again, it but awoke our wonder that, in that lost battle, he should have still the energy to fight. He had gone to ruin with a kind of kingly abandon, like one who condescended; but once ruined, with the lights all out, he fought as for a kingdom. Most men, finding themselves the authors of their own disgrace, rail the louder against God or destiny. Most men, when they repent, oblige their friends to share the bitterness of that repentance. But he had held an inquest and passed sentence: mene, mene; and condemned himself to smiling silence. He had given trouble enough; had earned misfortune amply, and foregone the right to murmur.

Thus was our old comrade, like Samson, careless in his days of strength; but on the coming of adversity, and when that strength was gone that had betrayed him—"for our strength is weakness"—he began to blossom and bring forth. Well, now, he is out of the fight: the burden that he bore thrown down before the great deliverer. We

"In the vast cathedral leave him;

God accept him,

Christ receive him!"

IV

If we go now and look on these innumerable epitaphs, the pathos and the irony are strangely fled. They do not stand merely to the dead, these foolish monuments; they are pillars and legends set up to glorify the difficult but not desperate life of man. This ground is hallowed by the heroes of defeat.

I see the indifferent pass before my friend's last resting-place; pause, with a shrug of pity, marvelling that so rich an argosy had sunk. A pity, now that he is done with suffering, a pity most uncalled for, and an ignorant wonder. Before those who loved him, his memory shines like a reproach; they honour him for silent lessons; they cherish his example; and in what remains before them of their toil, fear to be unworthy of the dead. For this proud man was one of those who prospered in the valley of humiliation;—of whom Bunyan wrote that, "Though Christian had the hard hap to meet in the valley with Apollyon, yet I must tell you, that in former times men have met with angels here; have found pearls here; and have in this place found the words of life."

CHAPTER IV. A COLLEGE MAGAZINE

I

All through my boyhood and youth, I was known and pointed out for the pattern of an idler; and yet I was always busy on my own private end, which was to learn to write. I kept always two books in my pocket, one to read, one to write in. As I walked, my mind was busy fitting what I saw with appropriate words; when I sat by the roadside, I would either read, or a pencil and a penny version-book would be in my hand, to note down the features of the scene or commemorate some halting stanzas. Thus I lived with words. And what I thus wrote was for no ulterior use, it was written consciously for practice. It was not so much that I wished to be an author (though I wished that too) as that I had vowed that I would learn to write. That was a proficiency that tempted me; and I practised to acquire it, as men learn to whittle, in a wager with myself. Description was the principal field of my exercise; for to any one with senses there is always something worth describing, and town and country are but one continuous subject. But I worked in other ways also; often accompanied my walks with dramatic dialogues, in which I played many parts; and often exercised myself in writing down conversations from memory.

This was all excellent, no doubt; so were the diaries I sometimes tried to keep, but always and very speedily discarded, finding them a school of posturing and melancholy self-deception. And yet this was not the most efficient part of my training. Good though it was, it only taught me (so far as I have learned them at all) the lower and less intellectual elements of the art, the choice of the essential note and the right word: things that to a happier constitution had perhaps come by nature. And regarded as training, it had one grave defect; for it set me no standard of achievement. So that there was perhaps more profit, as there was certainly more effort, in my secret labours at home. Whenever I read a book or a passage that particularly pleased me, in which a thing was said or an effect rendered with propriety, in which there was either some conspicuous force or some happy distinction in the style, I must sit down at once and set myself to ape that quality. I was unsuccessful, and I knew it; and tried again, and was again unsuccessful and always unsuccessful; but at least in these vain bouts, I got some practice in rhythm, in harmony, in construction and the co-ordination of parts. I have thus played the sedulous ape to Hazlitt, to Lamb, to Wordsworth, to Sir Thomas Browne, to Defoe, to Hawthorne, to Montaigne, to Baudelaire and to Obermann. I remember one of these monkey tricks, which was called The Vanity of Morals: it was to have had a second part, The Vanity of Knowledge; and as I had neither morality nor scholarship, the names were apt; but the second part was never attempted, and the first part was written (which is my reason for recalling it, ghost-like, from its ashes) no less than three times: first in the manner of Hazlitt, second in the manner of Ruskin, who had cast on me a passing spell, and third, in a laborious pasticcio of Sir Thomas Browne. So with my other works: Cain, an epic, was (save the mark!) an imitation of Sordello: Robin Hood, a tale in verse, took an eclectic middle course among the fields of Keats, Chaucer and Morris: in Monmouth, a tragedy, I reclined on the bosom of Mr. Swinburne; in my innumerable gouty-footed lyrics, I followed many masters; in the first draft of The King's Pardon, a tragedy, I was on the trail of no lesser man than John Webster; in the second draft of the same piece, with staggering versatility, I had shifted my allegiance to Congreve, and of course conceived my fable in a less serious vein—for it was not Congreve's verse, it was his exquisite prose, that I admired and sought to copy. Even at the age of thirteen I had tried to do justice to the inhabitants of the famous city of Peebles in the style of the Book of Snobs. So I might go on for ever, through all my abortive novels, and down to my later plays, of which I think more tenderly, for they were not only conceived at first under the bracing influence of old Dumas, but have met with resurrection: one, strangely bettered by another hand, came on the stage itself and was played by bodily actors; the other, originally known as Semiramis: a Tragedy, I have observed on bookstalls under the alias of Prince Otto. But enough has been said to show by what arts of impersonation, and in what purely ventriloquial efforts I first saw my words on paper.

That, like it or not, is the way to learn to write whether I have profited or not, that is the way. It was so Keats learned, and there was never a finer temperament for literature than Keats's; it was so, if we could trace it out, that all men have learned; and that is why a revival of letters is always accompanied or heralded by a cast back to earlier and fresher models. Perhaps I hear some one cry out: But this is not the way to be original! It is not; nor is there any way but to be born so. Nor yet, if you are born original, is there anything in this training that shall clip the wings of your originality. There can be none more original than Montaigne, neither could any be more unlike Cicero; yet no craftsman can fail to see how much the one must have tried in his time to imitate the other. Burns is the very type of a prime force in letters: he was of all men the most imitative. Shakespeare himself, the imperial, proceeds directly from a school. It is only from a school that we can expect to have good writers; it is almost invariably from a school that great writers, these lawless exceptions, issue. Nor is there anything here that should astonish the considerate. Before he can tell what cadences he truly prefers, the student should have tried all that are possible; before he can choose and preserve a fitting key of words, he should long have practised the literary scales; and it is only after years of such gymnastic that he can sit down at last, legions of words swarming to his call, dozens of turns of phrase simultaneously bidding for his choice, and he himself knowing what he wants to do and (within the narrow limit of a man's ability) able to do it.

And it is the great point of these imitations that there still shines beyond the student's reach his inimitable model. Let him try as he please, he is still sure of failure; and it is a very old and a very true saying that failure is the only highroad to success. I must have had some disposition to learn; for I clear-sightedly condemned my own performances. I liked doing them indeed; but when they were done, I could see they were rubbish. In consequence, I very rarely showed them even to my friends; and such friends as I chose to be my confidants I must have chosen well, for they had the friendliness to be quite plain with me, "Padding," said one. Another wrote: "I cannot understand why you do lyrics so badly." No more could I! Thrice I put myself in the way of a more authoritative rebuff, by sending a paper to a magazine. These were returned; and I was not surprised nor even pained. If they had not been looked at, as (like all amateurs) I suspected was the case, there was no good in repeating the experiment; if they had been looked at—well, then I had not yet learned to write, and I must keep on learning and living. Lastly, I had a piece of good fortune which is the occasion of this paper, and by which I was able to see my literature in print, and to measure experimentally how far I stood from the favour of the public.

II

The Speculative Society is a body of some antiquity, and has counted among its members Scott, Brougham, Jeffrey, Horner, Benjamin Constant, Robert Emmet, and many a legal and local celebrity besides. By an accident, variously explained, it has its rooms in the very buildings of the University of Edinburgh: a hall, Turkey-carpeted, hung with pictures, looking, when lighted up at night with fire and candle, like some goodly dining-room; a passage-like library, walled with books in their wire cages; and a corridor with a fireplace, benches, a table, many prints of famous members, and a mural tablet to the virtues of a former secretary. Here a member can warm himself and loaf and read; here, in defiance of Senatus-consults, he can smoke. The Senatus looks askance at these privileges; looks even with a somewhat vinegar aspect on the whole society; which argues a lack of proportion in the learned mind, for the world, we may be sure, will prize far higher this haunt of dead lions than all the living dogs of the professorate.

I sat one December morning in the library of the Speculative; a very humble-minded youth, though it was a virtue I never had much credit for; yet proud of my privileges as a member of the Spec.; proud of the pipe I was smoking in the teeth of the Senatus; and in particular, proud of being in the next room to three very distinguished students, who were then conversing beside the corridor fire. One of these has now his name on the back of several volumes, and his voice, I learn, is influential in the law courts. Of the death of the second, you have just been reading what I had to say. And the third also has escaped out of that battle of life in which he fought so hard, it may be so unwisely. They were all three, as I have said, notable students; but this was the most conspicuous. Wealthy, handsome, ambitious, adventurous, diplomatic, a reader of Balzac, and of all men that I have known, the most like to one of Balzac's characters, he led a life, and was attended by an ill fortune, that could be properly set forth only in the Comédie Humaine. He had then his eye on Parliament; and soon after the time of which I write, he made a showy speech at a political dinner, was cried up to heaven next day in the Courant, and the day after was dashed lower than earth with a charge of plagiarism in the Scotsman. Report would have it (I daresay, very wrongly) that he was betrayed by one in whom he particularly trusted, and that the author of the charge had learned its truth from his own lips. Thus, at least, he was up one day on a pinnacle, admired and envied by all; and the next, though still but a boy, he was publicly disgraced. The blow would have broken a less finely tempered spirit; and even him I suppose it rendered reckless; for he took flight to London, and there, in a fast club, disposed of the bulk of his considerable patrimony in the space of one winter. For years thereafter he lived I know not how; always well dressed, always in good hotels and good society, always with empty pockets. The charm of his manner may have stood him in good stead; but though my own manners are very agreeable, I have never found in them a source of livelihood; and to explain the miracle of his continued existence, I must fall back upon the theory of the philosopher, that in his case, as in all of the same kind, "there was a suffering relative in the background." From this genteel eclipse he reappeared upon the scene, and presently sought me out in the character of a generous editor. It is in this part that I best remember him; tall, slender, with a not ungraceful stoop; looking quite like a refined gentleman, and quite like an urbane adventurer; smiling with an engaging ambiguity; cocking at you one peaked eyebrow with a great appearance of finesse; speaking low and sweet and thick, with a touch of burr; telling strange tales with singular deliberation and, to a patient listener, excellent effect. After all these ups and downs, he seemed still, like the rich student that he was of yore, to breathe of money; seemed still perfectly sure of himself and certain of his end. Yet he was then upon the brink of his last overthrow. He had set himself to found the strangest thing in our society: one of those periodical sheets from which men suppose themselves to learn opinions; in which young gentlemen from the universities are encouraged, at so much a line, to garble facts, insult foreign nations and calumniate private individuals; and which are now the source of glory, so that if a man's name be often enough printed there, he becomes a kind of demigod; and people will pardon him when he talks back and forth, as they do for Mr. Gladstone; and crowd him to suffocation on railway platforms, as they did the other day to General Boulanger; and buy his literary works, as I hope you have just done for me. Our fathers, when they were upon some great enterprise, would sacrifice a life; building, it may be, a favourite slave into the foundations of their palace. It was with his own life that my companion disarmed the envy of the gods. He fought his paper single-handed; trusting no one, for he was something of a cynic; up early and down late, for he was nothing of a sluggard; daily ear-wigging influential men, for he was a master of ingratiation. In that slender and silken fellow there must have been a rare vein of courage, that he should thus have died at his employment; and doubtless ambition spoke loudly in his ear, and doubtless love also, for it seems there was a marriage in his view had he succeeded. But he died, and his paper died after him; and of all this grace, and tact, and courage, it must seem to our blind eyes as if there had come literally nothing.

These three students sat, as I was saying, in the corridor, under the mural tablet that records the virtues of Macbean, the former secretary. We would often smile at that ineloquent memorial and thought it a poor thing to come into the world at all and have no more behind one than Macbean. And yet of these three, two are gone and have left less; and this book, perhaps, when it is old and foxy, and some one picks it up in a corner of a book-shop, and glances through it, smiling at the old, graceless turns of speech, and perhaps for the love of Alma Mater (which may be still extant and flourishing) buys it, not without haggling, for some pence—this book may alone preserve a memory of James Walter Ferrier and Robert Glasgow Brown.

Their thoughts ran very differently on that December morning; they were all on fire with ambition; and when they had called me in to them, and made me a sharer in their design, I too became drunken with pride and hope. We were to found a University magazine. A pair of little, active brothers—Livingstone by name, great skippers on the foot, great rubbers of the hands, who kept a book-shop over against the University building—had been debauched to play the part of publishers. We four were to be conjunct editors and, what was the main point of the concern, to print our own works; while, by every rule of arithmetic—that flatterer of credulity—the adventure must succeed and bring great profit. Well, well: it was a bright vision. I went home that morning walking upon air. To have been chosen by these three distinguished students was to me the most unspeakable advance; it was my first draught of consideration; it reconciled me to myself and to my fellow-men; and as I steered round the railings at the Tron, I could not withhold my lips from smiling publicly. Yet, in the bottom of my heart, I knew that magazine would be a grim fiasco; I knew it would not be worth reading; I knew, even if it were, that nobody would read it; and I kept wondering how I should be able, upon my compact income of twelve pounds per annum, payable monthly, to meet my share in the expense. It was a comfortable thought to me that I had a father.

The magazine appeared, in a yellow cover, which was the best part of it, for at least it was unassuming; it ran four months in undisturbed obscurity, and died without a gasp. The first number was edited by all four of us with prodigious bustle; the second fell principally into the hands of Ferrier and me; the third I edited alone; and it has long been a solemn question who it was that edited the fourth. It would perhaps be still more difficult to say who read it. Poor yellow sheet, that looked so hopefully Livingtones' window! Poor, harmless paper, that might have gone to print a Shakespeare on, and was instead so clumsily defaced with nonsense; And, shall I say, Poor Editors? I cannot pity myself, to whom it was all pure gain. It was no news to me, but only the wholesome confirmation of my judgment, when the magazine struggled into half-birth, and instantly sickened and subsided into night. I had sent a copy to the lady with whom my heart was at that time somewhat engaged, and who did all that in her lay to break it; and she, with some tact, passed over the gift and my cherished contributions in silence. I will not say that I was pleased at this; but I will tell her now, if by any chance she takes up the work of her former servant, that I thought the better of her taste. I cleared the decks after this lost engagement; had the necessary interview with my father, which passed off not amiss; paid over my share of the expense to the two little, active brothers, who rubbed their hands as much, but methought skipped rather less than formerly, having perhaps, these two also, embarked upon the enterprise with some graceful illusions; and then, reviewing the whole episode, I told myself that the time was not yet ripe, nor the man ready; and to work I went again with my penny version-books, having fallen back in one day from the printed author to the manuscript student.

III

From this defunct periodical I am going to reprint one of my own papers. The poor little piece is all tail-foremost. I have done my best to straighten its array, I have pruned it fearlessly, and it remains invertebrate and wordy. No self-respecting magazine would print the thing; and here you behold it in a bound volume, not for any worth of its own, but for the sake of the man whom it purports dimly to represent and some of whose sayings it preserves; so that in this volume of Memories and Portraits, Robert Young, the Swanston gardener, may stand alongside of John Todd, the Swanston shepherd. Not that John and Robert drew very close together in their lives; for John was rough, he smelt of the windy brae; and Robert was gentle, and smacked of the garden in the hollow. Perhaps it is to my shame that I liked John the better of the two; he had grit and dash, and that salt of the Old Adam that pleases men with any savage inheritance of blood; and he was a way-farer besides, and took my gipsy fancy. But however that may be, and however Robert's profile may be blurred in the boyish sketch that follows, he was a man of a most quaint and beautiful nature, whom, if it were possible to recast a piece of work so old, I should like well to draw again with a maturer touch. And as I think of him and of John, I wonder in what other country two such men would be found dwelling together, in a hamlet of some twenty cottages, in the woody fold of a green hill.

CHAPTER V. AN OLD SCOTCH GARDENER

I think I might almost have said the last: somewhere, indeed, in the uttermost glens of the Lammermuir or among the southwestern hills there may yet linger a decrepid representative of this bygone good fellowship; but as far as actual experience goes, I have only met one man in my life who might fitly be quoted in the same breath with Andrew Fairservice,—though without his vices. He was a man whose very presence could impart a savour of quaint antiquity to the baldest and most modern flower-plots. There was a dignity about his tall stooping form, and an earnestness in his wrinkled face that recalled Don Quixote; but a Don Quixote who had come through the training of the Covenant, and been nourished in his youth on Walker's Lives and The Hind let Loose.

Now, as I could not bear to let such a man pass away with no sketch preserved of his old-fashioned virtues, I hope the reader will take this as an excuse for the present paper, and judge as kindly as he can the infirmities of my description. To me, who find it so difficult to tell the little that I know, he stands essentially as a genius loci. It is impossible to separate his spare form and old straw hat from the garden in the lap of the hill, with its rocks overgrown with clematis, its shadowy walks, and the splendid breadth of champaign that one saw from the north-west corner. The garden and gardener seem part and parcel of each other. When I take him from his right surroundings and try to make him appear for me on paper, he looks unreal and phantasmal: the best that I can say may convey some notion to those that never saw him, but to me it will be ever impotent.

The first time that I saw him, I fancy Robert was pretty old already: he had certainly begun to use his years as a stalking horse. Latterly he was beyond all the impudencies of logic, considering a reference to the parish register worth all the reasons in the world, "I am old and well stricken in years," he was wont to say; and I never found any one bold enough to answer the argument. Apart from this vantage that he kept over all who were not yet octogenarian, he had some other drawbacks as a gardener. He shrank the very place he cultivated. The dignity and reduced gentility of his appearance made the small garden cut a sorry figure. He was full of tales of greater situations in his younger days. He spoke of castles and parks with a humbling familiarity. He told of places where under-gardeners had trembled at his looks, where there were meres and swanneries, labyrinths of walk and wildernesses of sad shrubbery in his control, till you could not help feeling that it was condescension on his part to dress your humbler garden plots. You were thrown at once into an invidious position. You felt that you were profiting by the needs of dignity, and that his poverty and not his will consented to your vulgar rule. Involuntarily you compared yourself with the swineherd that made Alfred watch his cakes, or some bloated citizen who may have given his sons and his condescension to the fallen Dionysius. Nor were the disagreeables purely fanciful and metaphysical, for the sway that he exercised over your feelings he extended to your garden, and, through the garden, to your diet. He would trim a hedge, throw away a favourite plant, or fill the most favoured and fertile section of the garden with a vegetable that none of us could eat, in supreme contempt for our opinion. If you asked him to send you in one of your own artichokes, "That I wull, mem," he would say, "with pleasure, for it is mair blessed to give than to receive." Ay, and even when, by extra twisting of the screw, we prevailed on him to prefer our commands to his own inclination, and he went away, stately and sad, professing that "our wull was his pleasure," but yet reminding us that he would do it "with feelin's,"—even then, I say, the triumphant master felt humbled in his triumph, felt that he ruled on sufferance only, that he was taking a mean advantage of the other's low estate, and that the whole scene had been one of those "slights that patient merit of the unworthy takes."

In flowers his taste was old-fashioned and catholic; affecting sunflowers and dahlias, wallflowers and roses and holding in supreme aversion whatsoever was fantastic, new-fashioned or wild. There was one exception to this sweeping ban. Foxgloves, though undoubtedly guilty on the last count, he not only spared, but loved; and when the shrubbery was being thinned, he stayed his hand and dexterously manipulated his bill in order to save every stately stem. In boyhood, as he told me once, speaking in that tone that only actors and the old-fashioned common folk can use nowadays, his heart grew "proud" within him when he came on a burn-course among the braes of Manor that shone purple with their graceful trophies; and not all his apprenticeship and practice for so many years of precise gardening had banished these boyish recollections from his heart. Indeed, he was a man keenly alive to the beauty of all that was bygone. He abounded in old stories of his boyhood, and kept pious account of all his former pleasures; and when he went (on a holiday) to visit one of the fabled great places of the earth where he had served before, he came back full of little pre-Raphaelite reminiscences that showed real passion for the past, such as might have shaken hands with Hazlitt or Jean-Jacques.

But however his sympathy with his old feelings might affect his liking for the foxgloves, the very truth was that he scorned all flowers together. They were but garnishings, childish toys, trifling ornaments for ladies' chimney-shelves. It was towards his cauliflowers and peas and cabbage that his heart grew warm. His preference for the more useful growths was such that cabbages were found invading the flower-pots, and an outpost of savoys was once discovered in the centre of the lawn. He would prelect over some thriving plant with wonderful enthusiasm, piling reminiscence on reminiscence of former and perhaps yet finer specimens. Yet even then he did not let the credit leave himself. He had, indeed, raised "finer o' them;" but it seemed that no one else had been favoured with a like success. All other gardeners, in fact, were mere foils to his own superior attainments; and he would recount, with perfect soberness of voice and visage, how so and so had wondered, and such another could scarcely give credit to his eyes. Nor was it with his rivals only that he parted praise and blame. If you remarked how well a plant was looking, he would gravely touch his hat and thank you with solemn unction; all credit in the matter falling to him. If, on the other hand, you called his attention to some back-going vegetable, he would quote Scripture: "Paul may plant and Apollos may water;" all blame being left to Providence, on the score of deficient rain or untimely frosts.

There was one thing in the garden that shared his preference with his favourite cabbages and rhubarb, and that other was the beehive. Their sound, their industry, perhaps their sweet product also, had taken hold of

291

his imagination and heart, whether by way of memory or no I cannot say, although perhaps the bees too were linked to him by some recollection of Manor braes and his country childhood. Nevertheless, he was too chary of his personal safety or (let me rather say) his personal dignity to mingle in any active office towards them. But he could stand by while one of the contemned rivals did the work for him, and protest that it was quite safe in spite of his own considerate distance and the cries of the distressed assistant. In regard to bees, he was rather a man of word than deed, and some of his most striking sentences had the bees for text. "They are indeed wonderfu' creatures, mem," he said once. "They just mind me o' what the Queen of Sheba said to Solomon—and I think she said it wi' a sigh,—'The half of it hath not been told unto me.'"

As far as the Bible goes, he was deeply read. Like the old Covenanters, of whom he was the worthy representative, his mouth was full of sacred quotations; it was the book that he had studied most and thought upon most deeply. To many people in his station the Bible, and perhaps Burns, are the only books of any vital literary merit that they read, feeding themselves, for the rest, on the draff of country newspapers, and the very instructive but not very palatable pabulum of some cheap educational series. This was Robert's position. All day long he had dreamed of the Hebrew stories, and his head had been full of Hebrew poetry and Gospel ethics; until they had struck deep root into his heart, and the very expressions had become a part of him; so that he rarely spoke without some antique idiom or Scripture mannerism that gave a raciness to the merest trivialities of talk. But the influence of the Bible did not stop here. There was more in Robert than quaint phrase and ready store of reference. He was imbued with a spirit of peace and love: he interposed between man and wife: he threw himself between the angry, touching his hat the while with all the ceremony of an usher: he protected the birds from everybody but himself, seeing, I suppose, a great difference between official execution and wanton sport. His mistress telling him one day to put some ferns into his master's particular corner, and adding, "Though, indeed, Robert, he doesn't deserve them, for he wouldn't help me to gather them," "Eh, mem," replies Robert, "But I wouldnae say that, for I think he's just a most deservin' gentleman." Again, two of our friends, who were on intimate terms, and accustomed to use language to each other, somewhat without the bounds of the parliamentary, happened to differ about the position of a seat in the garden. The discussion, as was usual when these two were at it, soon waxed tolerably insulting on both sides. Every one accustomed to such controversies several times a day was quietly enjoying this prize-fight of somewhat abusive wit—every one but Robert, to whom the perfect good faith of the whole quarrel seemed unquestionable, and who, after having waited till his conscience would suffer him to wait no more, and till he expected every moment that the disputants would fall to blows, cut suddenly in with tones of almost tearful entreaty: "Eh, but, gentlemen, I wad hae nae mair words about it!" One thing was noticeable about Robert's religion: it was neither dogmatic nor sectarian. He never expatiated (at least, in my hearing) on the doctrines of his creed, and he never condemned anybody else. I have no doubt that he held all Roman Catholics, Atheists, and Mahometans as considerably out of it; I don't believe he had any sympathy for Prelacy; and the natural feelings of man must have made him a little sore about Free-Churchism; but at least, he never talked about these views, never grew controversially noisy, and never openly aspersed the belief or practice of anybody. Now all this is not generally characteristic of Scotch piety; Scotch sects being churches militant with a vengeance, and Scotch believers perpetual crusaders the one against the other, and missionaries the one to the other. Perhaps Robert's originally tender heart was what made the difference; or, perhaps, his solitary and pleasant labour among fruits and flowers had taught him a more sunshiny creed than those whose work is among the tares of fallen humanity; and the soft influences of the garden had entered deep into his spirit,

"Annihilating all that's made

To a green thought in a green shade."

But I could go on for ever chronicling his golden sayings or telling of his innocent and living piety. I had meant to tell of his cottage, with the German pipe hung reverently above the fire, and the shell box that he had made for his son, and of which he would say pathetically: "He was real pleased wi' it at first, but I think he's got a kind o' tired o' it now"—the son being then a man of about forty. But I will let all these pass. "'Tis more significant: he's dead." The earth, that he had digged so much in his life, was dug out by another for himself; and the flowers that he had tended drew their life still from him, but in a new and nearer way. A bird flew about the open grave, as if it too wished to honour the obsequies of one who had so often quoted Scripture in favour of its kind. "Are not two sparrows sold for one farthing, and yet not one of them falleth to the ground."

Yes, he is dead. But the kings did not rise in the place of death to greet him "with taunting proverbs" as they rose to greet the haughty Babylonian; for in his life he was lowly, and a peacemaker and a servant of God.

CHAPTER VI. PASTORAL

To leave home in early life is to be stunned and quickened with novelties; but when years have come, it only casts a more endearing light upon the past. As in those composite photographs of Mr. Galton's, the image of each new sitter brings out but the more clearly the central features of the race; when once youth has flown, each new impression only deepens the sense of nationality and the desire of native places. So may some cadet of Royal Écossais or the Albany Regiment, as he mounted guard about French citadels, so may some officer marching his company of the Scots-Dutch among the polders, have felt the soft rains of the Hebrides upon his brow, or started in the ranks at the remembered aroma of peat-smoke. And the rivers of home are dear in particular to all men. This is as old as Naaman, who was jealous for Abana and Pharpar; it is confined to no race nor country, for I know one of Scottish blood but a child of Suffolk, whose fancy still lingers about the lilied lowland waters of that shire. But the streams of Scotland are incomparable in themselves—or I am only the more Scottish to suppose so—and their sound and colour dwell for ever in the memory. How often and willingly do I not look again in fancy on Tummel, or Manor, or the talking Airdle, or Dee swirling in its Lynn; on the bright burn of Kinnaird, or the golden burn that pours and sulks in the den behind Kingussie! I think shame to leave out one of these enchantresses, but the list would grow too long if I remembered all; only I may not forget Allan Water, nor birch-wetting Rogie, nor yet Almond; nor, for all its pollutions, that Water of Leith of the many and well-named mills—Bell's Mills, and Canon Mills, and Silver Mills; nor Redford Burn of pleasant memories; nor yet, for all its smallness, that nameless trickle that springs in the green bosom of Allermuir, and is fed from Halkerside with a perennial teacupful, and threads the moss under the Shearer's Knowe, and makes one pool there, overhung by a rock, where I loved to sit and make bad verses, and is then kidnapped in its infancy by subterranean pipes for the service of the sea-beholding city in the plain. From many points in the moss you may see at one glance its whole course and that of all its tributaries; the geographer of this Lilliput may visit all its corners without sitting down, and not yet begin to be breathed; Shearer's Knowe and Halkerside are but names of adjacent cantons on a single shoulder of a hill, as names are squandered (it would seem to the in-expert, in superfluity) upon these upland sheepwalks; a bucket would receive the whole discharge of the toy river; it would take it an appreciable time to fill your morning bath; for the most part, besides, it soaks unseen through the moss; and yet for the sake of auld lang syne, and the figure of a certain genius loci, I am condemned to linger awhile in fancy by its shores; and if the nymph (who cannot be above a span in stature) will but inspire my pen, I would gladly carry the reader along with me.

John Todd, when I knew him, was already "the oldest herd on the Pentlands," and had been all his days faithful to that curlew-scattering, sheep-collecting life. He remembered the droving days, when the drove roads, that now lie green and solitary through the heather, were thronged thoroughfares. He had himself often marched flocks into England, sleeping on the hillsides with his caravan; and by his account it was a rough business not without danger. The drove roads lay apart from habitation; the drovers met in the wilderness, as to-day the deep-sea fishers meet off the banks in the solitude of the Atlantic; and in the one as in the other case rough habits and fist-law were the rule. Crimes were committed, sheep filched, and drovers robbed and beaten; most of which offences had a moorland burial and were never heard of in the courts of justice. John, in those days, was at least once attacked,—by two men after his watch,—and at least once, betrayed by his habitual anger, fell under the danger of the law and was clapped into some rustic prison-house, the doors of which he burst in the night and was no more heard of in that quarter. When I knew him, his life had fallen in quieter places, and he had no cares beyond the dulness of his dogs and the inroads of pedestrians from town. But for a man of his propensity to wrath these were enough; he knew neither rest nor peace, except by snatches; in the gray of the summer morning, and already from far up the hill, he would wake the "toun" with the sound of his shoutings; and in the lambing time, his cries were not yet silenced late at night. This wrathful voice of a man unseen might be said to haunt that quarter of the Pentlands, an audible bogie; and no doubt it added to the fear in which men stood of John a touch of something legendary. For my own part, he was at first my enemy, and I, in my character of a rambling boy, his natural abhorrence. It was long before I saw him near at hand, knowing him only by some sudden blast of bellowing from far above, bidding me "c'way oot amang the sheep." The quietest recesses of the hill harboured this ogre; I skulked in my favourite wilderness like a Cameronian of the Killing Time, and John Todd was my Claverhouse, and his dogs my questing dragoons. Little by little we dropped into civilities; his hail at sight of me began to have less of the ring of a war-slogan; soon, we never met but he produced his snuff-box, which was with him, like the calumet with the Red Indian, a part of the heraldry of peace; and at length, in the ripeness of time, we grew to be a pair of friends, and when I lived alone in these parts in the winter, it was a settled thing for John to "give me a cry" over the garden wall as he set forth upon his evening round, and for me to overtake and bear him company.

That dread voice of his that shook the hills when he was angry, fell in ordinary talk very pleasantly upon the ear, with a kind of honied, friendly whine, not far off singing, that was eminently Scottish. He laughed not very often, and when he did, with a sudden, loud haw-haw, hearty but somehow joyless, like an echo from a rock. His face was permanently set and coloured; ruddy and stiff with weathering; more like a picture than a face; yet with a certain strain and a threat of latent anger in the expression, like that of a man trained too fine and harassed with perpetual vigilance. He spoke in the richest dialect of Scotch I ever heard; the words in themselves were a pleasure and often a surprise to me, so that I often came back from one of our patrols with new acquisitions; and this vocabulary he would handle like a master, stalking a little before me, "beard on shoulder," the plaid hanging loosely about him, the yellow staff clapped under his arm, and guiding me uphill by that devious, tactical ascent which seems peculiar to men of his trade. I might count him with the best talkers; only that talking Scotch and talking English seem incomparable acts. He touched on nothing at least, but he adorned it; when he narrated, the scene was before you; when he spoke (as he did mostly) of his own antique business, the thing took on a colour of romance and curiosity that was surprising. The clans of sheep with their particular territories on the hill, and how, in the yearly killings and purchases, each must be proportionally thinned and strengthened; the midnight busyness of

297

animals, the signs of the weather, the cares of the snowy season, the exquisite stupidity of sheep, the exquisite cunning of dogs: all these he could present so humanly, and with so much old experience and living gusto, that weariness was excluded. And in the midst he would suddenly straighten his bowed back, the stick would fly abroad in demonstration, and the sharp thunder of his voice roll out a long itinerary for the dogs, so that you saw at last the use of that great wealth of names for every knowe and howe upon the hillside; and the dogs, having hearkened with lowered tails and raised faces, would run up their flags again to the masthead and spread themselves upon the indicated circuit. It used to fill me with wonder how they could follow and retain so long a story. But John denied these creatures all intelligence; they were the constant butt of his passion and contempt; it was just possible to work with the like of them, he said,—not more than possible. And then he would expand upon the subject of the really good dogs that he had known, and the one really good dog that he had himself possessed. He had been offered forty pounds for it; but a good collie was worth more than that, more than anything, to a "herd;" he did the herd's work for him. "As for the like of them!" he would cry, and scornfully indicate the scouring tails of his assistants.

Once—I translate John's Lallan, for I cannot do it justice, being born Britannis in montibus, indeed, but alas! inerudito sæculo—once, in the days of his good dog, he had bought some sheep in Edinburgh, and on the way out, the road being crowded, two were lost. This was a reproach to John, and a slur upon the dog; and both were alive to their misfortune. Word came, after some days, that a farmer about Braid had found a pair of sheep; and thither went John and the dog to ask for restitution. But the farmer was a hard man and stood upon his rights. "How were they marked?" he asked; and since John had bought right and left from many sellers and had no notion of the marks—"Very well," said the farmer, "then it's only right that I should keep them."—"Well," said John, "it's a fact that I cannae tell the sheep; but if my dog can, will ye let me have them?" The farmer was honest as well as hard, and besides I daresay he had little fear of the ordeal; so he had all the sheep upon his farm into one large park, and turned John's dog into their midst. That hairy man of business knew his errand well; he knew that John and he had bought two sheep and (to their shame) lost them about Boroughmuirhead; he knew besides (the lord knows how, unless by listening) that they were come to Braid for their recovery; and without pause or blunder singled out, first one and then another, the two waifs. It was that afternoon the forty pounds were offered and refused. And the shepherd and his dog—what do I say? the true shepherd and his man—set off together by Fairmilehead in jocund humour, and "smiled to ither" all the way home, with the two recovered ones before them. So far, so good; but intelligence may be abused. The dog, as he is by little man's inferior in mind, is only by little his superior in virtue; and John had another collie tale of quite a different complexion. At the foot of the moss behind Kirk Yetton (Caer Ketton, wise men say) there is a scrog of low wood and a pool with a dam for washing sheep. John was one day lying under a bush in the scrog, when he was aware of a collie on the far hillside skulking down through the deepest of the heather with obtrusive stealth. He knew the dog; knew him for a clever, rising practitioner from quite a distant farm; one whom perhaps he had coveted as he saw him masterfully steering flocks to market. But what did the practitioner so far from home? and why this guilty and secret manoeuvring towards the pool?—for it was towards the pool that he was heading. John lay the closer under his bush, and presently saw the dog come forth upon the margin, look all about him to see if he were anywhere observed, plunge in and repeatedly wash himself over head and ears, and then (but now openly and with tail in air) strike homeward over the hills. That same night word was sent his master, and the rising practitioner, shaken up from where he lay, all innocence, before the fire, was had out to a dykeside and promptly shot; for alas! he was that foulest of criminals under trust, a sheep-eater; and it was from the maculation of sheep's blood that he had come so far to cleanse himself in the pool behind Kirk Yetton.

A trade that touches nature, one that lies at the foundations of life, in which we have all had ancestors employed, so that on a hint of it ancestral memories revive, lends itself to literary use, vocal or written. The fortune of a tale lies not alone in the skill of him that writes, but as much, perhaps, in the inherited experience of him who reads; and when I hear with a particular thrill of things that I have never done or seen, it is one of that innumerable army of my ancestors rejoicing in past deeds. Thus novels begin to touch not the fine dilettanti but the gross mass of mankind, when they leave off to speak of parlours and shades of manner and still-born niceties of motive, and begin to deal with fighting, sailoring, adventure, death or childbirth; and thus ancient outdoor crafts and occupations, whether Mr. Hardy wields the shepherd's crook or Count Tolstoi swings the scythe, lift romance into a near neighbourhood with epic. These aged things have on them the dew of man's morning; they lie near, not so much to us, the semi-artificial flowerets, as to the trunk and aboriginal taproot of the race. A thousand interests spring up in the process of the ages, and a thousand perish; that is now an eccentricity or a lost art which was once the fashion of an empire; and those only are perennial matters that rouse us to-day, and that roused men in all epochs of the past. There is a certain critic, not indeed of execution but of matter, whom I dare be known to set before the best: a certain low-browed, hairy gentleman, at first a percher in the fork of trees, next (as they relate) a dweller in caves, and whom I think I see squatting in cave-mouths, of a pleasant afternoon, to munch his berries—his wife, that accomplished lady, squatting by his side: his name I never heard, but he is often described as Probably Arboreal, which may serve for recognition. Each has his own tree of ancestors, but at the top of all sits Probably Arboreal; in all our veins there run some minims of his old, wild, tree-top blood; our civilised nerves still tingle with his rude terrors and pleasures; and to that which would have moved our common ancestor, all must obediently thrill.

We have not so far to climb to come to shepherds; and it may be I had one for an ascendant who has largely moulded me. But yet I think I owe my taste for that hillside business rather to the art and interest of John Todd. He it was that made it live for me, as the artist can make all things live. It was through him the simple strategy of massing sheep upon a snowy evening, with its attendant scampering of earnest, shaggy aides-de-camp, was an affair that I never wearied of seeing, and that I never weary of recalling to mind: the shadow of the night darkening on the hills, inscrutable black blots of snow shower moving here and there like night already come, huddles of yellow sheep and dartings of black dogs upon the snow, a bitter air that took you by the throat, unearthly harpings of the wind along the moors; and for centre piece to all these features and influences, John winding up the brae, keeping his captain's eye upon all sides, and breaking, ever and again, into a spasm of bellowing that seemed to make the evening bleaker. It is thus that I still see him in my mind's eye, perched on a hump of the declivity not far from Halkerside, his staff in airy flourish, his great voice taking hold upon the hills and echoing terror to the lowlands; I, meanwhile, standing somewhat back, until the fit should be over, and, with a pinch of snuff, my friend relapse into his easy, even conversation.

CHAPTER VII. THE MANSE

I have named, among many rivers that make music in my memory, that dirty Water of Leith. Often and often I desire to look upon it again; and the choice of a point of view is easy to me. It should be at a certain water-door, embowered in shrubbery. The river is there dammed back for the service of the flour-mill just below, so that it lies deep and darkling, and the sand slopes into brown obscurity with a glint of gold; and it has but newly been recruited by the borrowings of the snuff-mill just above, and these, tumbling merrily in, shake the pool to its black heart, fill it with drowsy eddies, and set the curded froth of many other mills solemnly steering to and fro upon the surface. Or so it was when I was young; for change, and the masons, and the pruning-knife, have been busy; and if I could hope to repeat a cherished experience, it must be on many and impossible conditions. I must choose, as well as the point of view, a certain moment in my growth, so that the scale may be exaggerated, and the trees on the steep opposite side may seem to climb to heaven, and the sand by the water-door, where I am standing, seem as low as Styx. And I must choose the season also, so that the valley may be brimmed like a cup with sunshine and the songs of birds;—and the year of grace, so that when I turn to leave the riverside I may find the old manse and its inhabitants unchanged.

It was a place in that time like no other: the garden cut into provinces by a great hedge of beech, and over-looked by the church and the terrace of the churchyard, where the tombstones were thick, and after nightfall "spunkies" might be seen to dance at least by children; flower-plots lying warm in sunshine; laurels and the great yew making elsewhere a pleasing horror of shade; the smell of water rising from all round, with an added tang of paper-mills; the sound of water everywhere, and the sound of mills—the wheel and the dam singing their alternate strain; the birds on every bush and from every corner of the overhanging woods pealing out their notes until the air throbbed with them; and in the midst of this, the manse. I see it, by the standard of my childish stature, as a great and roomy house. In truth, it was not so large as I supposed, nor yet so convenient, and, standing where it did, it is difficult to suppose that it was healthful. Yet a large family of stalwart sons and tall daughters were housed and reared, and came to man and womanhood in that nest of little chambers; so that the face of the earth was peppered with the children of the manse, and letters with outlandish stamps became familiar to the local postman, and the walls of the little chambers brightened with the wonders of the East. The dullest could see this was a house that had a pair of hands in divers foreign places: a well-beloved house—its image fondly dwelt on by many travellers.

Here lived an ancestor of mine, who was a herd of men. I read him, judging with older criticism the report of childish observation, as a man of singular simplicity of nature; unemotional, and hating the display of what he felt; standing contented on the old ways; a lover of his life and innocent habits to the end. We children admired him: partly for his beautiful face and silver hair, for none more than children are concerned for beauty and, above all, for beauty in the old; partly for the solemn light in which we beheld him once a week, the observed of all observers, in the pulpit. But his strictness and distance, the effect, I now fancy, of old age, slow blood, and settled habit, oppressed us with a kind of terror. When not abroad, he sat much alone, writing sermons or letters to his scattered family in a dark and cold room with a library of bloodless books—or so they seemed in those days, although I have some of them now on my own shelves and like well enough to read them; and these lonely hours wrapped him in the greater gloom for our imaginations. But the study had a redeeming grace in many Indian pictures, gaudily coloured and dear to young eyes. I cannot depict (for I have no such passions now) the greed with which I beheld them; and when I was once sent in to say a psalm to my grandfather, I went, quaking indeed with fear, but at the same time glowing with hope that, if I said it well, he might reward me with an Indian picture.

"Thy foot He'll not let slide, nor will

He slumber that thee keeps,"

it ran: a strange conglomerate of the unpronounceable, a sad model to set in childhood before one who was himself to be a versifier, and a task in recitation that really merited reward. And I must suppose the old man thought so too, and was either touched or amused by the performance; for he took me in his arms with most unwonted tenderness, and kissed me, and gave me a little kindly sermon for my psalm; so that, for that day, we were clerk and parson. I was struck by this reception into so tender a surprise that I forgot my disappointment. And indeed the hope was one of those that childhood forges for a pastime, and with no design upon reality. Nothing was more unlikely than that my grandfather should strip himself of one of those pictures, love-gifts and reminders of his absent sons; nothing more unlikely than that he should bestow it upon me. He had no idea of spoiling children, leaving all that to my aunt; he had fared hard himself, and blubbered under the rod in the last century; and his ways were still Spartan for the young. The last word I heard upon his lips was in this Spartan key. He had over-walked in the teeth of an east wind, and was now near the end of his many days. He sat by the dining-room fire, with his white hair, pale face and bloodshot eyes, a somewhat awful figure; and my aunt had given him a dose of our good old Scotch medicine, Dr. Gregory's powder. Now that remedy, as the work of a near kinsman of Rob Roy himself, may have a savour of romance for the imagination; but it comes uncouthly to the palate. The old gentleman had taken it with a wry face; and that being accomplished, sat with perfect simplicity, like a child's, munching a "barley-sugar kiss." But when my aunt, having the canister open in her hands, proposed to let me share in the sweets, he interfered at once. I had had no Gregory; then I should have no barley-sugar kiss: so he decided with a touch of irritation. And just then the phaeton coming opportunely to the kitchen door—for such was our unlordly fashion—I was taken for the last time from the presence of my grandfather.

Now I often wonder what I have inherited from this old minister. I must suppose, indeed, that he was fond of preaching sermons, and so am I, though I never heard it maintained that either of us loved to hear them. He sought health in his youth in the Isle of Wight, and I have sought it in both hemispheres; but whereas he found and kept it, I am still on the quest. He was a great lover of Shakespeare, whom he read aloud, I have been told, with taste; well, I love my Shakespeare also, and am persuaded I can read him well, though I own I never have been told so. He made embroidery, designing his own patterns; and in that kind of work I never made anything but a kettle-holder in Berlin wool, and an odd garter of knitting, which was as black as the chimney before I had done with it. He loved port, and nuts, and porter; and so do I, but they agreed better with my grandfather, which seems to me a breach of contract. He had chalk-stones in his fingers; and these, in good time, I may possibly inherit, but I would much rather have inherited his noble presence. Try as I please, I cannot join myself on with the reverend doctor; and all the while, no doubt, and even as I write the phrase, he moves in my blood, and whispers words to me, and sits efficient in the very knot and centre of my being. In his garden, as I played there, I learned the love of mills—or had I an ancestor a miller?—and a kindness for the neighbourhood of graves, as homely things not without their poetry—or had I an ancestor a sexton? But what of the garden where he played himself?—for that, too, was a scene of my education. Some part of me played there in the eighteenth century, and ran races under the green avenue at Pilrig; some part of me trudged up Leith Walk, which was still a country place, and sat on the High School benches, and was thrashed, perhaps, by Dr. Adam. The house where I spent my youth was not yet thought upon; but we made holiday parties among the cornfields on its site, and ate strawberries and cream near by at a gardener's. All this I had forgotten; only my grandfather remembered and once reminded me. I have forgotten, too, how we grew up, and took orders, and went to our first Ayrshire parish, and fell in love with and married a daughter of Burns's Dr. Smith—"Smith opens out his cauld harangues." I have forgotten, but I was there all the same, and heard stories of Burns at first hand.

And there is a thing stranger than all that; for this homunculus or part-man of mine that walked about the eighteenth century with Dr. Balfour in his youth, was in the way of meeting other homunculos or part-men, in the persons of my other ancestors. These were of a lower order, and doubtless we looked down upon them duly. But as I went to college with Dr. Balfour, I may have seen the lamp and oil man taking down the shutters from his shop beside the Tron;—we may have had a rabbit-hutch or a bookshelf made for us by a certain carpenter in I know not what wynd of the old, smoky city;

or, upon some holiday excursion, we may have looked into the windows of a cottage in a flower-garden and seen a certain weaver plying his shuttle. And these were all kinsmen of mine upon the other side; and from the eyes of the lamp and oil man one-half of my unborn father, and one-quarter of myself, looked out upon us as we went by to college. Nothing of all this would cross the mind of the young student, as he posted up the Bridges with trim, stockinged legs, in that city of cocked hats and good Scotch still unadulterated. It would not cross his mind that he should have a daughter; and the lamp and oil man, just then beginning, by a not unnatural metastasis, to bloom into a lighthouse-engineer, should have a grandson; and that these two, in the fulness of time, should wed; and some portion of that student himself should survive yet a year or two longer in the person of their child.

But our ancestral adventures are beyond even the arithmetic of fancy; and it is the chief recommendation of long pedigrees, that we can follow backward the careers of our homunculos and be reminded of our antenatal lives. Our conscious years are but a moment in the history of the elements that build us. Are you a bank-clerk, and do you live at Peckham? It was not always so. And though to-day I am only a man of letters, either tradition errs or I was present when there landed at St. Andrews a French barber-surgeon, to tend the health and the beard of the great Cardinal Beaton; I have shaken a spear in the Debateable Land and shouted the slogan of the Elliots; I was present when a skipper, plying from Dundee, smuggled Jacobites to France after the '15; I was in a West India merchant's office, perhaps next door to Bailie Nicol Jarvie's, and managed the business of a plantation in St. Kitt's; I was with my engineer-grandfather (the son-in-law of the lamp and oil man) when he sailed north about Scotland on the famous cruise that gave us the Pirate and the Lord of the Isles; I was with him, too, on the Bell Rock, in the fog, when the Smeaton had drifted from her moorings, and the Aberdeen men, pick in hand, had seized upon the only boats, and he must stoop and lap sea-water before his tongue could utter audible words; and once more with him when the Bell Rock beacon took a "thrawe," and his workmen fled into the tower, then nearly finished, and he sat unmoved reading in his Bible—or affecting to read—till one after another slunk back with confusion of countenance to their engineer. Yes, parts of me have seen life, and met adventures, and sometimes met them well. And away in the still cloudier past, the threads that make me up can be traced by fancy into the bosoms of thousands and millions of ascendants: Picts who rallied round Macbeth and the old (and highly preferable) system of descent by females, fleërs from before the legions of Agricola, marchers in Pannonian morasses, star-gazers on Chaldæan plateaus; and, furthest of all, what face is this that fancy can see peering through the disparted branches? What sleeper in green tree-tops, what muncher of nuts, concludes my pedigree? Probably arboreal in his habits. . . .

And I know not which is the more strange, that I should carry about with me some fibres of my minister-grandfather; or that in him, as he sat in his cool study, grave, reverend, contented gentleman, there was an aboriginal frisking of the blood that was not his; tree-top memories, like undeveloped negatives, lay dormant in his mind; tree-top instincts awoke and were trod down; and Probably Arboreal (scarce to be distinguished from a monkey) gambolled and chattered in the brain of the old divine.

CHAPTER VIII. MEMOIRS OF AN ISLET

Those who try to be artists use, time after time, the matter of their recollections, setting and resetting little coloured memories of men and scenes, rigging up (it may be) some especial friend in the attire of a buccaneer, and decreeing armies to manœuvre, or murder to be done, on the playground of their youth. But the memories are a fairy gift which cannot be worn out in using. After a dozen services in various tales, the little sunbright pictures of the past still shine in the mind's eye with not a lineament defaced, not a tint impaired. Glück und Unglück wird Gesang, if Goethe pleases; yet only by endless avatars, the original re-embodying after each. So that a writer, in time, begins to wonder at the perdurable life of these impressions; begins, perhaps, to fancy that he wrongs them when he weaves them in with fiction; and looking back on them with ever-growing kindness, puts them at last, substantive jewels, in a setting of their own.

One or two of these pleasant spectres I think I have laid. I used one but the other day: a little eyot of dense, freshwater sand, where I once waded deep in butterburrs, delighting to hear the song of the river on both sides, and to tell myself that I was indeed and at last upon an island. Two of my puppets lay there a summer's day, hearkening to the shearers at work in riverside fields and to the drums of the gray old garrison upon the neighbouring hill. And this was, I think, done rightly: the place was rightly peopled—and now belongs not to me but to my puppets—for a time at least. In time, perhaps, the puppets will grow faint; the original memory swim up instant as ever; and I shall once more lie in bed, and see the little sandy isle in Allan Water as it is in nature, and the child (that once was me) wading there in butterburrs; and wonder at the instancy and virgin freshness of that memory; and be pricked again, in season and out of season, by the desire to weave it into art.

There is another isle in my collection, the memory of which besieges me. I put a whole family there, in one of my tales; and later on, threw upon its shores, and condemned to several days of rain and shellfish on its tumbled boulders, the hero of another. The ink is not yet faded; the sound of the sentences is still in my mind's ear; and I am under a spell to write of that island again.

I

The little isle of Earraid lies close in to the south-west corner of the Ross of Mull: the sound of Iona on one side, across which you may see the isle and church of Columba; the open sea to the other, where you shall be able to mark, on a clear, surfy day, the breakers running white on many sunken rocks. I first saw it, or first remembered seeing it, framed in the round bull's-eye of a cabin port, the sea lying smooth along its shores like the waters of a lake, the colourless clear light of the early morning making plain its heathery and rocky hummocks. There stood upon it, in these days, a single rude house of uncemented stones, approached by a pier of wreckwood. It must have been very early, for it was then summer, and in summer, in that latitude, day scarcely withdraws; but even at that hour the house was making a sweet smoke of peats which came to me over the bay, and the bare-legged daughters of the cotter were wading by the pier. The same day we visited the shores of the isle in the ship's boats; rowed deep into Fiddler's Hole, sounding as we went; and having taken stock of all possible accommodation, pitched on the northern inlet as the scene of operations. For it was no accident that had brought the lighthouse steamer to anchor in the Bay of Earraid. Fifteen miles away to seaward, a certain black rock stood environed by the Atlantic rollers, the outpost of the Torran reefs. Here was a tower to be built, and a star lighted, for the conduct of seamen. But as the rock was small, and hard of access, and far from land, the work would be one of years; and my father was now looking for a shore station, where the stones might be quarried and dressed, the men live, and the tender, with some degree of safety, lie at anchor.

I saw Earraid next from the stern thwart of an Iona lugger, Sam Bough and I sitting there cheek by jowl, with our feet upon our baggage, in a beautiful, clear, northern summer eve. And behold! there was now a pier of stone, there were rows of sheds, railways, travelling-cranes, a street of cottages, an iron house for the resident engineer, wooden bothies for the men, a stage where the courses of the tower were put together experimentally, and behind the settlement a great gash in the hillside where granite was quarried. In the bay, the steamer lay at her moorings. All day long there hung about the place the music of chinking tools; and even in the dead of night, the watchman carried his lantern to and fro in the dark settlement and could light the pipe of any midnight muser. It was, above all, strange to see Earraid on the Sunday, when the sound of the tools ceased and there fell a crystal quiet. All about the green compound men would be sauntering in their Sunday's best, walking with those lax joints of the reposing toiler, thoughtfully smoking, talking small, as if in honour of the stillness, or hearkening to the wailing of the gulls. And it was strange to see our Sabbath services, held, as they were, in one of the bothies, with Mr. Brebner reading at a table, and the congregation perched about in the double tier of sleeping bunks; and to hear the singing of the psalms, "the chapters," the inevitable Spurgeon's sermon, and the old, eloquent lighthouse prayer.

In fine weather, when by the spy-glass on the hill the sea was observed to run low upon the reef, there would be a sound of preparation in the very early morning; and before the sun had risen from behind Ben More, the tender would steam out of the bay. Over fifteen sea-miles of the great blue Atlantic rollers she ploughed her way, trailing at her tail a brace of wallowing stone-lighters. The open ocean widened upon either board, and the hills of the mainland began to go down on the horizon, before she came to her unhomely destination, and lay-to at last where the rock clapped its black head above the swell, with the tall iron barrack on its spider legs, and the truncated tower, and the cranes waving their arms, and the smoke of the engine-fire rising in the mid-sea. An ugly reef is this of the Dhu Heartach; no pleasant assemblage of shelves, and pools, and creeks, about which a child might play for a whole summer without weariness, like the Bell Rock or the Skerryvore, but one oval nodule of black-trap, sparsely bedabbled with an inconspicuous fucus, and alive in every crevice with a dingy insect between a slater and a bug. No other life was there but that of sea-birds, and of the sea itself, that here ran like a mill-race, and growled about the outer reef for ever, and ever and again, in the calmest weather, roared and spouted on the rock itself. Times were different upon Dhu-Heartach when it blew, and the night fell dark, and the neighbour lights of Skerryvore and Rhu-val were quenched in fog, and the men sat prisoned high up in their iron drum, that then resounded with the lashing of the sprays. Fear sat with them in their sea-beleaguered dwelling; and the colour changed in anxious faces when some greater billow struck the barrack, and its pillars quivered and sprang under the blow. It was then that the foreman builder, Mr. Goodwillie, whom I see before me still in his rock-habit of undecipherable rags, would get his fiddle down and strike up human minstrelsy amid the music of the storm. But it was in sunshine only that I saw Dhu-Heartach; and it was in sunshine, or the yet lovelier summer afterglow, that the steamer would return to Earraid, ploughing an enchanted sea; the obedient lighters, relieved of their deck cargo, riding in her wake more quietly; and the steersman upon each, as she rose on the long swell, standing tall and dark against the shining west.

But it was in Earraid itself that I delighted chiefly. The lighthouse settlement scarce encroached beyond its fences; over the top of the first brae the ground was all virgin, the world all shut out, the face of things unchanged by any of man's doings. Here was no living presence, save for the limpets on the rocks, for some old, gray, rain-beaten ram that I might rouse out of a ferny den betwixt two boulders, or for the haunting and the piping of the gulls. It was older than man; it was found so by incoming Celts, and seafaring Norsemen, and Columba's priests. The earthy savour of the bog-plants, the rude disorder of the boulders, the inimitable seaside brightness of the air, the brine and the iodine, the lap of the billows among the weedy reefs, the sudden springing up of a great run of dashing surf along the sea-front of the isle, all that I saw and felt my predecessors must have seen and felt with scarce a difference. I steeped myself in open air and in past ages.

> "Delightful would it be to me to be in Uchd Ailiun
>
> On the pinnacle of a rock,
>
> That I might often see
>
> The face of the ocean;
>
> That I might hear the song of the wonderful birds,
>
> Source of happiness;

That I might hear the thunder of the crowding waves

 Upon the rocks:

At times at work without compulsion—

 This would be delightful;

At times plucking dulse from the rocks

 At times at fishing."

So, about the next island of Iona, sang Columba himself twelve hundred years before. And so might I have sung of Earraid.

And all the while I was aware that this life of sea-bathing and sun-burning was for me but a holiday. In that year cannon were roaring for days together on French battlefields; and I would sit in my isle (I call it mine, after the use of lovers) and think upon the war, and the loudness of these far-away battles, and the pain of the men's wounds, and the weariness of their marching. And I would think too of that other war which is as old as mankind, and is indeed the life of man: the unsparing war, the grinding slavery of competition; the toil of seventy years, dear-bought bread, precarious honour, the perils and pitfalls, and the poor rewards. It was a long look forward; the future summoned me as with trumpet calls, it warned me back as with a voice of weeping and beseeching; and I thrilled and trembled on the brink of life, like a childish bather on the beach.

There was another young man on Earraid in these days, and we were much together, bathing, clambering on the boulders, trying to sail a boat and spinning round instead in the oily whirlpools of the roost. But the most part of the time we spoke of the great uncharted desert of our futures; wondering together what should there befall us; hearing with surprise the sound of our own voices in the empty vestibule of youth. As far, and as hard, as it seemed then to look forward to the grave, so far it seems now to look backward upon these emotions; so hard to recall justly that loath submission, as of the sacrificial bull, with which we stooped our necks under the yoke of destiny. I met my old companion but the other day; I cannot tell of course what he was thinking; but, upon my part, I was wondering to see us both so much at home, and so composed and sedentary in the world; and how much we had gained, and how much we had lost, to attain to that composure; and which had been upon the whole our best estate: when we sat there prating sensibly like men of some experience, or when we shared our timorous and hopeful counsels in a western islet.

CHAPTER IX. THOMAS STEVENSON—CIVIL ENGINEER

The death of Thomas Stevenson will mean not very much to the general reader. His service to mankind took on forms of which the public knows little and understands less. He came seldom to London, and then only as a task, remaining always a stranger and a convinced provincial; putting up for years at the same hotel where his father had gone before him; faithful for long to the same restaurant, the same church, and the same theatre, chosen simply for propinquity; steadfastly refusing to dine out. He had a circle of his own, indeed, at home; few men were more beloved in Edinburgh, where he breathed an air that pleased him; and wherever he went, in railway carriages or hotel smoking-rooms, his strange, humorous vein of talk, and his transparent honesty, raised him up friends and admirers. But to the general public and the world of London, except about the parliamentary committee-rooms, he remained unknown. All the time, his lights were in every part of the world, guiding the mariner; his firm were consulting engineers to the Indian, the New Zealand, and the Japanese Lighthouse Boards, so that Edinburgh was a world centre for that branch of applied science; in Germany, he had been called "the Nestor of lighthouse illumination"; even in France, where his claims were long denied, he was at last, on the occasion of the late Exposition, recognised and medalled. And to show by one instance the inverted nature of his reputation, comparatively small at home, yet filling the world, a friend of mine was this winter on a visit to the Spanish main, and was asked by a Peruvian if he "knew Mr. Stevenson the author, because his works were much esteemed in Peru?" My friend supposed the reference was to the writer of tales; but the Peruvian had never heard of Dr. Jekyll; what he had in his eye, what was esteemed in Peru, where the volumes of the engineer.

Thomas Stevenson was born at Edinburgh in the year 1818, the grandson of Thomas Smith, first engineer to the Board of Northern Lights, son of Robert Stevenson, brother of Alan and David; so that his nephew, David Alan Stevenson, joined with him at the time of his death in the engineership, is the sixth of the family who has held, successively or conjointly, that office. The

Bell Rock, his father's great triumph, was finished before he was born; but he served under his brother Alan in the building of Skerryvore, the noblest of all extant deep-sea lights; and, in conjunction with his brother David, he added two—the Chickens and Dhu Heartach—to that small number of man's extreme outposts in the ocean. Of shore lights, the two brothers last named erected no fewer than twenty-seven; of beacons, [84] about twenty-five. Many harbours were successfully carried out: one, the harbour of Wick, the chief disaster of my father's life, was a failure; the sea proved too strong for man's arts; and after expedients hitherto unthought of, and on a scale hyper-cyclopean, the work must be deserted, and now stands a ruin in that bleak, God-forsaken bay, ten miles from John-o'-Groat's. In the improvement of rivers the brothers were likewise in a large way of practice over both England and Scotland, nor had any British engineer anything approaching their experience.

It was about this nucleus of his professional labours that all my father's scientific inquiries and inventions centred; these proceeded from, and acted back upon, his daily business. Thus it was as a harbour engineer that he became interested in the propagation and reduction of waves; a difficult subject in regard to which he has left behind him much suggestive matter and some valuable approximate results. Storms were his sworn adversaries, and it was through the study of storms that he approached that of meteorology at large. Many who knew him not otherwise, knew—perhaps have in their gardens—his louvre-boarded screen for instruments. But the great achievement of his life was, of course, in optics as applied to lighthouse illumination. Fresnel had done much; Fresnel had settled the fixed light apparatus on a principle that still seems unimprovable; and when Thomas Stevenson stepped in and brought to a comparable perfection the revolving light, a not unnatural jealousy and much painful controversy rose in France. It had its hour; and, as I have told already, even in France it has blown by. Had it not, it would have mattered the less, since all through his life my father continued to justify his claim by fresh advances. New apparatus for lights in new situations was continually being designed with the same unwearied search after perfection, the same nice ingenuity of means; and though the holophotal revolving light perhaps still remains his most elegant contrivance, it is difficult to give it the palm over the much later condensing system, with its thousand possible modifications. The number and the value of these improvements entitle their author to the name of one of mankind's benefactors. In all parts of the world a safer landfall awaits the mariner. Two things must be said: and, first, that Thomas Stevenson was no mathematician. Natural shrewdness, a sentiment of optical laws, and a great intensity of consideration led him to just conclusions; but to calculate the necessary formulæ for the instruments he had conceived was often beyond him, and he must fall back on the help of others, notably on that of his cousin and lifelong intimate friend, emeritus Professor Swan, of St. Andrews, and his later friend, Professor P. G. Tait. It is a curious enough circumstance, and a great encouragement to others, that a man so ill equipped should have succeeded in one of the most abstract and arduous walks of applied science. The second remark is one that applies to the whole family, and only particularly to Thomas Stevenson from the great number and importance of his inventions: holding as the Stevensons did a Government appointment they regarded their original work as something due already to the nation, and none of them has ever taken out a patent. It is another cause of the comparative obscurity of the name: for a patent not only brings in money, it infallibly spreads reputation; and my father's instruments enter anonymously into a hundred light-rooms, and are passed anonymously over in a hundred reports, where the least considerable patent would stand out and tell its author's story.

But the life-work of Thomas Stevenson remains; what we have lost, what we now rather try to recall, is the friend and companion. He was a man of a somewhat antique strain: with a blended sternness and softness that was wholly Scottish and at first somewhat bewildering; with a profound essential melancholy of disposition and (what often accompanies it) the most humorous geniality in company; shrewd and childish; passionately attached, passionately prejudiced; a man of many extremes, many faults of temper, and no very stable foothold for himself among life's troubles. Yet he was a wise adviser; many men, and these not inconsiderable, took counsel with him habitually. "I sat at his feet," writes one of these, "when I asked his advice, and when the broad brow was set in thought and the firm mouth said his say, I always knew that no man could add to the worth of the conclusion." He had excellent taste, though whimsical and partial; collected old furniture and delighted specially in sunflowers long before the days of Mr. Wilde; took a lasting pleasure in prints and pictures; was a devout admirer of Thomson of Duddingston at a time when few shared the taste; and though he read little, was constant to his favourite books. He had never any Greek; Latin he happily re-taught himself after he had left school, where he was a mere consistent idler: happily, I say, for Lactantius, Vossius, and Cardinal Bona were his chief authors. The first he must have read for twenty years uninterruptedly, keeping it near him in his study, and carrying it in his bag on journeys. Another old theologian, Brown of Wamphray, was often in his hands. When he was indisposed, he had two books, Guy Mannering and The Parent's Assistant, of which he never wearied. He was a strong Conservative, or, as he preferred to call himself, a Tory; except in so far as his views were modified by a hot-headed chivalrous sentiment for women. He was actually in favour of a marriage law under which any woman might have a divorce for the asking, and no man on any ground whatever; and the same sentiment found another expression in a Magdalen Mission in Edinburgh, founded and largely supported by himself. This was but one of the many channels of his public generosity; his private was equally unstrained. The Church of Scotland, of which he held the doctrines (though in a sense of his own) and to which he bore a clansman's loyalty, profited often by his time and money; and though, from a morbid sense of his own unworthiness, he would never consent to be an office-bearer, his advice was often sought, and he served the Church on many committees. What he perhaps valued highest in his work were his contributions to the defence of Christianity; one of which, in particular, was praised by Hutchinson Stirling and reprinted at the request of Professor Crawford.

His sense of his own unworthiness I have called morbid; morbid, too, were his sense of the fleetingness of life and his concern for death. He had never accepted the conditions of man's life or his own character; and his inmost thoughts were ever tinged with the Celtic melancholy. Cases of conscience were sometimes grievous to him, and that delicate employment of a scientific witness cost him many qualms. But he found respite from these troublesome humours in his work, in his lifelong study of natural science, in the society of those he loved, and in his daily walks, which now would carry him far into the country with some congenial friend, and now keep him dangling about the town from one old book-shop to another, and scraping romantic acquaintance with every dog that passed. His talk, compounded of so much sterling sense and so much freakish humour, and clothed in language so apt, droll, and emphatic, was a perpetual delight to all who knew him before the clouds began to settle on his mind. His use of language was both just and picturesque; and when at the beginning of his illness he began to feel the ebbing of this power, it was strange and painful to hear him reject one word after another as inadequate, and at length desist from the search and leave his phrase unfinished rather than finish it without propriety. It was perhaps another Celtic trait that his affections and emotions, passionate as these were, and liable to passionate ups and downs, found the most eloquent expression both in words and gestures. Love, anger, and indignation shone through him and broke forth in imagery, like what we read of Southern races. For all these emotional extremes, and in spite of the melancholy ground of his character, he had upon the whole a happy life; nor was he less fortunate in his death, which at the last came to him unaware.

CHAPTER X. TALK AND TALKERS

Sir, we had a good talk.—Johnson.

As we must account for every idle word, so we must for every idle silence.—Franklin.

There can be no fairer ambition than to excel in talk; to be affable, gay, ready, clear and welcome; to have a fact, a thought, or an illustration, pat to every subject; and not only to cheer the flight of time among our intimates, but bear our part in that great international congress, always sitting, where public wrongs are first declared, public errors first corrected, and the course of public opinion shaped, day by day, a little nearer to the right. No measure comes before Parliament but it has been long ago prepared by the grand jury of the talkers; no book is written that has not been largely composed by their assistance. Literature in many of its branches is no other than the shadow of good talk; but the imitation falls far short of the original in life, freedom and effect. There are always two to a talk, giving and taking, comparing experience and according conclusions. Talk is fluid, tentative, continually "in further search and progress"; while written words remain fixed, become idols even to the writer, found wooden dogmatisms, and preserve flies of obvious error in the amber of the truth. Last and chief, while literature, gagged with linsey-woolsey, can only deal with a fraction of the life of man, talk goes fancy free and may call a spade a spade. Talk has none of the freezing immunities of the pulpit. It cannot, even if it would, become merely æsthetic or merely classical like literature. A jest intervenes, the solemn humbug is dissolved in laughter, and speech runs forth out of the contemporary groove into the open fields of nature, cheery and cheering, like schoolboys out of school. And it is in talk alone that we can learn our period and ourselves. In short, the first duty of a man is to speak; that is his chief business in this world; and talk, which is the harmonious speech of two or more, is by far the most accessible of pleasures. It costs nothing in money; it is all profit; it completes our education, founds and fosters our friendships, and can be enjoyed at any age and in almost any state of health.

The spice of life is battle; the friendliest relations are still a kind of contest; and if we would not forego all that is valuable in our lot, we must continually face some other person, eye to eye, and wrestle a fall whether in love or enmity. It is still by force of body, or power of character or intellect, that we attain to worthy pleasures. Men and women contend for each other in the lists of love, like rival mesmerists; the active and adroit decide their challenges in the sports of the body; and the sedentary sit down to chess or conversation. All sluggish and pacific pleasures are, to the same degree, solitary and selfish; and every durable bond between human beings is founded in or heightened by some element of competition. Now, the relation that has the least root in matter is undoubtedly that airy one of friendship; and hence, I suppose, it is that good talk most commonly arises among friends. Talk is, indeed, both the scene and instrument of friendship. It is in talk alone that the friends can measure strength, and enjoy that amicable counter-assertion of personality which is the gauge of relations and the sport of life.

A good talk is not to be had for the asking. Humours must first be accorded in a kind of overture or prologue; hour, company and circumstance be suited; and then, at a fit juncture, the subject, the quarry of two heated minds, spring up like a deer out of the wood. Not that the talker has any of the hunter's pride, though he has all and more than all his ardour. The genuine artist follows the stream of conversation as an angler follows the windings of a brook, not dallying where he fails to "kill." He trusts implicitly to hazard; and he is rewarded by continual variety, continual pleasure, and those changing prospects of the truth that are the best of education. There is nothing in a subject, so called, that we should regard it as an idol, or follow it beyond the promptings of desire. Indeed, there are few subjects; and so far as they are truly talkable, more than the half of them may be reduced to three: that I am I, that you are you, and that there are other people dimly understood to be not quite the same as either. Wherever talk may range, it still runs half the time on these eternal lines. The theme being set, each plays on himself as on an instrument; asserts and justifies himself; ransacks his brain for instances and opinions, and brings them forth new-minted, to his own surprise and the admiration of his adversary. All natural talk is a festival of ostentation; and by the laws of the game each accepts and fans the vanity of the other. It is from that reason that we venture to lay ourselves so open, that we dare to be so warmly eloquent, and that we swell in each other's eyes to such a vast proportion. For talkers, once launched, begin to overflow the limits of their ordinary selves, tower up to the height of their secret pretensions, and give themselves out for the heroes, brave, pious, musical and wise, that in their most shining moments they aspire to be. So they weave for themselves with words and for a while inhabit a palace of delights, temple at once and theatre, where they fill the round of the world's dignities, and feast with the gods, exulting in Kudos. And when the talk is over, each goes his way, still flushed with vanity and admiration, still trailing clouds of glory; each declines from the height of his ideal orgie, not in a moment, but by slow declension. I remember, in the entr'acte of an afternoon performance, coming forth into the sunshine, in a beautiful green, gardened corner of a romantic city; and as I sat and smoked, the music moving in my blood, I seemed to sit there and evaporate The Flying Dutchman (for it was that I had been hearing) with a wonderful sense of life, warmth, well-being and pride; and the noises of the city, voices, bells and marching feet, fell together in my ears like a symphonious orchestra. In the same way, the excitement of a good talk lives for a long while after in the blood, the heart still hot within you, the brain still simmering, and the physical earth swimming around you with the colours of the sunset.

Natural talk, like ploughing, should turn up a large surface of life, rather than dig mines into geological strata. Masses of experience, anecdote, incident, cross-lights, quotation, historical instances, the whole flotsam and jetsam of two minds forced in and in upon the matter in hand from every point of the compass, and from every degree of mental elevation and abasement—these are the material with which talk is fortified, the food on which the talkers thrive. Such argument as is proper to the exercise should still be brief and seizing. Talk should proceed by instances; by the apposite, not the expository. It should keep close along the lines of humanity, near the bosoms and businesses of men, at the level where history, fiction and experience intersect and illuminate each other. I am I, and You are You, with all my heart; but conceive how these lean propositions change and brighten when, instead of words, the actual you and I sit cheek by jowl, the spirit housed in the live body, and the very clothes uttering voices to corroborate the story in the face. Not less surprising is the change when we leave off to speak of generalities—the bad, the good, the miser, and all the characters of Theophrastus—and call up other men, by anecdote or instance, in their very trick and feature; or trading on a common knowledge, toss each other famous names, still glowing with the hues of life. Communication is no longer by words, but by the instancing of whole biographies, epics, systems of philosophy, and epochs of history, in bulk. That which is understood excels that which is spoken in quantity and quality alike; ideas thus figured and personified, change hands, as we may say, like coin; and the speakers imply without effort the most obscure and intricate thoughts. Strangers who have a large common ground of reading will, for this reason, come the sooner to the grapple of genuine converse. If they know Othello and Napoleon, Consuelo and Clarissa Harlowe, Vautrin and Steenie Steenson, they can leave generalities and begin at once to speak by figures.

Conduct and art are the two subjects that arise most frequently and that embrace the widest range of facts. A few pleasures bear discussion for their own sake, but only those which are most social or most radically human; and even these can only be discussed among their devotees. A technicality is always welcome to the expert, whether in athletics, art or law; I have heard the best kind of talk on technicalities from such rare and happy persons as both know and love their business. No human being ever spoke of scenery for above two minutes at a time, which makes me suspect we hear too much of it in literature. The weather is regarded as the very nadir and scoff of conversational topics. And yet the weather, the dramatic element in scenery, is far more tractable in language, and far more human both in import and suggestion than the stable features of the landscape. Sailors and shepherds, and the people generally of coast and mountain, talk well of it; and it is often excitingly presented in literature. But the tendency of all living talk draws it back and back into the common focus of humanity. Talk is a creature of the street and market-place, feeding on gossip; and its last resort is still in a discussion on morals. That is the heroic form of gossip; heroic in virtue of its high pretensions; but still gossip, because it turns on personalities. You can keep no men long, nor Scotchmen at all, off moral or theological discussion. These are to all the world what law is to lawyers; they are everybody's technicalities; the medium through which all consider life, and the dialect in which they express their judgments. I knew three young men who walked together daily for some two months in a solemn and beautiful forest and in cloudless summer weather; daily they talked with unabated zest, and yet scarce wandered that whole time beyond two subjects—theology and love. And perhaps neither a court of love nor an assembly of divines would have granted their premises or welcomed their conclusions.

Conclusions, indeed, are not often reached by talk any more than by private thinking. That is not the profit. The profit is in the exercise, and above all in the experience; for when we reason at large on any subject, we review our state and history in life. From time to time, however, and specially, I think, in talking art, talk becomes effective, conquering like war, widening the boundaries of knowledge like an exploration. A point arises; the question takes a problematical, a baffling, yet a likely air; the talkers begin to feel lively presentiments of some conclusion near at hand; towards this they strive with emulous ardour, each by his own path, and struggling for first utterance; and then one leaps upon the summit of that matter with a shout, and almost at the same moment the other is beside him; and behold they are agreed. Like enough, the progress is illusory, a mere cat's cradle having been wound and unwound out of words. But the sense of joint discovery is none the less giddy and inspiriting. And in the life of the talker such triumphs, though imaginary, are neither few nor far apart; they are attained with speed and pleasure, in the hour of mirth; and by the nature of the process, they are always worthily shared.

There is a certain attitude, combative at once and deferential, eager to fight yet most averse to quarrel, which marks out at once the talkable man. It is not eloquence, not fairness, not obstinacy, but a certain proportion of all of these that I love to encounter in my amicable adversaries. They must not be pontiffs holding doctrine, but huntsmen questing after elements of truth. Neither must they be boys to be instructed, but fellow-teachers with whom I may wrangle and agree on equal terms. We must reach some solution, some shadow of consent; for without that, eager talk becomes a torture. But we do not wish to reach it cheaply, or quickly, or without the tussle and effort wherein pleasure lies.

The very best talker, with me, is one whom I shall call Spring-Heel'd Jack. I say so, because I never knew any one who mingled so largely the possible ingredients of converse. In the Spanish proverb, the fourth man necessary to compound a salad, is a madman to mix it: Jack is that madman. I know not which is more remarkable; the insane lucidity of his conclusions the humorous eloquence of his language, or his power of method, bringing the whole of life into the focus of the subject treated, mixing the conversational salad like a drunken god. He doubles like the serpent, changes and flashes like the shaken kaleidoscope, transmigrates bodily into the views of others, and so, in the twinkling of an eye and with a heady rapture, turns questions inside out and flings them empty before you on the ground, like a triumphant conjuror. It is my common practice when a piece of conduct puzzles me, to attack it in the presence of Jack with such grossness, such partiality and such wearing iteration, as at length shall spur him up in its defence. In a moment he transmigrates, dons the required character, and with moonstruck philosophy justifies the act in question. I can fancy nothing to compare with the vim of these impersonations, the strange scale of language, flying from Shakespeare to Kant, and from Kant to Major Dyngwell—

"As fast as a musician scatters sounds

Out of an instrument"

the sudden, sweeping generalisations, the absurd irrelevant particularities, the wit, wisdom, folly, humour, eloquence and bathos, each startling in its kind, and yet all luminous in the admired disorder of their combination. A talker of a different calibre, though belonging to the same school, is Burly. Burly is a man of a great presence; he commands a larger atmosphere, gives the impression of a grosser mass of character than most men. It has been said of him that his presence could be felt in a room you entered blindfold; and the same, I think, has been said of other powerful constitutions condemned to much physical inaction. There is something boisterous and piratic in Burly's manner of talk which suits well enough with this impression. He will roar you down, he will bury his face in his hands, he will undergo passions of revolt and agony; and meanwhile his attitude of mind is really both conciliatory and receptive; and after Pistol has been out Pistol'd, and the welkin rung for hours, you begin to perceive a certain subsidence in these spring torrents, points of agreement issue, and you end arm-in-arm, and in a glow of mutual admiration. The outcry only serves to make your final union the more unexpected and precious. Throughout there has been perfect sincerity, perfect intelligence, a desire to hear although not always to listen, and an unaffected eagerness to meet concessions. You have, with Burly, none of the dangers that attend debate with Spring-Heel'd Jack; who may at any moment turn his powers of transmigration on yourself, create for you a view you never held, and then furiously fall on you for holding it. These, at least, are my two favourites, and both are loud, copious, intolerant talkers. This argues that I myself am in the same category; for if we love talking at all, we love a bright, fierce adversary, who will hold his ground, foot by foot, in much our own manner, sell his attention dearly, and give us our full measure of the dust and exertion of battle. Both these men can be beat from a position, but it takes six hours to do it; a high and hard adventure, worth attempting. With both you can pass days in an enchanted country of the mind, with people, scenery and manners of its own; live a life apart, more arduous, active and glowing than any real existence; and come forth again when the talk is over, as out of a theatre or a dream, to find the east wind still blowing and the chimney-pots of the old battered city still around you. Jack has the far finer mind, Burly the far more honest; Jack gives us the animated poetry, Burly the romantic prose, of similar themes; the one glances high like a meteor and makes a light in darkness; the other, with many changing hues of fire, burns at the sea-level, like a conflagration; but both have the same humour and artistic interests, the same unquenched ardour in pursuit, the same gusts of talk and thunderclaps of contradiction.

Cockshot [100] is a different article, but vastly entertaining, and has been meat and drink to me for many a long evening. His manner is dry, brisk and pertinacious, and the choice of words not much. The point about him is his extraordinary readiness and spirit. You can propound nothing but he has either a theory about it ready-made, or will have one instantly on the stocks, and proceed to lay its timbers and launch it in your presence. "Let me see," he will say. "Give me a moment. I should have some theory for that." A blither spectacle than the vigour with which he sets about the task, it were hard to fancy. He is possessed by a demoniac energy, welding the elements for his life, and bending ideas, as an athlete bends a horse-shoe, with a visible and lively effort. He has, in theorising, a compass, an art; what I would call the synthetic gusto; something of a Herbert Spencer, who should see the fun of the thing. You are not bound, and no more is he, to place your faith in these brand-new opinions. But some of them are right enough, durable even for life; and the poorest serve for a cock shy—as when idle people, after picnics, float a bottle on a pond and have an hour's diversion ere it sinks. Whichever they are, serious opinions or humours of the moment, he still defends his ventures with indefatigable wit and spirit, hitting savagely himself, but taking punishment like a man. He knows and never forgets that people talk, first of all, for the sake of talking; conducts himself in the ring, to use the old slang, like a thorough "glutton," and honestly enjoys a telling facer from his adversary. Cockshot is bottled effervescency, the sworn foe of sleep. Three-in-the-morning Cockshot, says a victim. His talk is like the driest of all imaginable dry champagnes. Sleight of hand and inimitable quickness are the qualities by which he lives. Athelred, on the other hand, presents you with the spectacle of a sincere and somewhat slow nature thinking aloud. He is the most unready man I ever knew to shine in conversation. You may see him sometimes wrestle with a refractory jest for a minute or two together, and perhaps fail to throw it in the end. And there is something singularly engaging, often instructive, in the simplicity with which he thus exposes the process as well as the result, the works as well as the dial of the clock. Withal he has his hours of inspiration Apt words come to him as if by accident, and, coming from deeper down, they smack the more personally, they have the more of fine old crusted humanity, rich in sediment and humour. There are sayings of his in which he has stamped himself into the very grain of the language; you would think he must have worn the words next his skin and slept with them. Yet it is not as a sayer of particular good things that Athelred is most to be regarded, rather as the stalwart woodman of thought. I have pulled on a light cord often enough, while he has been wielding the broad-axe; and between us, on this unequal division, many a specious fallacy has fallen. I have known him to battle the same question night after night for years, keeping it in the reign of talk, constantly applying it and re-applying it to life with humorous or grave intention, and all the while, never hurrying, nor flagging, nor taking an unfair advantage of the facts. Jack at a given moment, when arising, as it were, from the tripod, can be more radiantly just to those from whom he differs; but then the tenor of his thoughts is even calumnious; while Athelred, slower to forge excuses, is yet slower to condemn, and sits over the welter of the world, vacillating but still judicial, and still faithfully contending with his doubts.

Both the last talkers deal much in points of conduct and religion studied in the "dry light" of prose. Indirectly and as if against his will the same elements from time to time appear in the troubled and poetic talk of Opalstein. His various and exotic knowledge, complete although unready sympathies, and fine, full, discriminative flow of language, fit him out to be the best of talkers; so perhaps he is with some, not quite with me—proxime accessit, I should say. He sings the praises of the earth and the arts, flowers and jewels, wine and music, in a moonlight, serenading manner, as to the light guitar; even wisdom comes from his tongue like singing; no one is, indeed, more tuneful in the upper notes. But even while he sings the song of the Sirens, he still hearkens to the barking of the Sphinx. Jarring Byronic notes interrupt the flow of his Horatian humours. His mirth has something of the tragedy of the world for its perpetual background; and he feasts like Don Giovanni to a double orchestra, one lightly sounding for the dance, one pealing Beethoven in the distance. He is not truly reconciled either with life or with himself; and this instant war in his members sometimes divides the man's attention. He does not always, perhaps not often, frankly surrender himself in conversation. He brings into the talk other thoughts than those which he expresses; you are conscious that he keeps an eye on something else, that he does not shake off the world, nor quite forget himself. Hence arise occasional disappointments; even an occasional unfairness for his companions, who find themselves one day giving too much, and the next, when they are wary out of season, giving perhaps too little. Purcel is in another class from any I have mentioned. He is no debater, but appears in conversation, as occasion rises, in two distinct characters, one of which I admire and fear, and the other love. In the first, he is radiantly civil and rather silent, sits on a high, courtly hilltop, and from that vantage-ground drops you his remarks like favours. He seems not to share in our sublunary contentions; he wears no sign of interest; when on a sudden there falls in a crystal of wit, so polished that the dull do not perceive it, but so right that the sensitive are silenced. True talk should have more body and blood, should be louder, vainer and more declaratory of the man; the true talker should not hold so steady an advantage over whom he speaks with; and that is one reason out of a score why I prefer my Purcel in his second character, when he unbends into a strain of graceful gossip, singing like the fireside kettle. In these moods he has an elegant homeliness that rings of the true Queen Anne. I know another person who attains, in his moments, to the insolence of a Restoration comedy, speaking, I declare, as Congreve wrote; but that is a sport of nature, and scarce falls under the rubric, for there is none, alas! to give him answer.

One last remark occurs: It is the mark of genuine conversation that the sayings can scarce be quoted with their full effect beyond the circle of common friends. To have their proper weight they should appear in a biography, and with the portrait of the speaker. Good talk is dramatic; it is like an impromptu piece of acting where each should represent himself to the greatest advantage; and that is the best kind of talk where each speaker is most fully and candidly himself, and where, if you were to shift the speeches round from one to another, there would be the greatest loss in significance and perspicuity. It is for this reason that talk depends so wholly on our company. We should like to introduce Falstaff and Mercutio, or Falstaff and Sir Toby; but Falstaff in talk with Cordelia seems even painful. Most of us, by the Protean quality of man, can talk to some degree with all; but the true talk, that strikes out all the slumbering best of us, comes only with the peculiar brethren of our spirits, is founded as deep as love in the constitution of our being, and is a thing to relish with all our energy, while yet we have it, and to be grateful for forever.

CHAPTER XI. TALK AND TALKERS [105]

II

In the last paper there was perhaps too much about mere debate; and there was nothing said at all about that kind of talk which is merely luminous and restful, a higher power of silence, the quiet of the evening shared by ruminating friends. There is something, aside from personal preference, to be alleged in support of this omission. Those who are no chimney-cornerers, who rejoice in the social thunderstorm, have a ground in reason for their choice. They get little rest indeed; but restfulness is a quality for cattle; the virtues are all active, life is alert, and it is in repose that men prepare themselves for evil. On the other hand, they are bruised into a knowledge of themselves and others; they have in a high degree the fencer's pleasure in dexterity displayed and proved; what they get they get upon life's terms, paying for it as they go; and once the talk is launched, they are assured of honest dealing from an adversary eager like themselves. The aboriginal man within us, the cave-dweller, still lusty as when he fought tooth and nail for roots and berries, scents this kind of equal battle from afar; it is like his old primæval days upon the crags, a return to the sincerity of savage life from the comfortable fictions of the civilised. And if it be delightful to the Old Man, it is none the less profitable to his younger brother, the conscientious gentleman I feel never quite sure of your urbane and smiling coteries; I fear they indulge a man's vanities in silence, suffer him to encroach, encourage him on to be an ass, and send him forth again, not merely contemned for the moment, but radically more contemptible than when he entered. But if I have a flushed, blustering fellow for my opposite, bent on carrying a point, my vanity is sure to have its ears rubbed, once at least, in the course of the debate. He will not spare me when we differ; he will not fear to demonstrate my folly to my face.

For many natures there is not much charm in the still, chambered society, the circle of bland countenances, the digestive silence, the admired remark, the flutter of affectionate approval. They demand more atmosphere and exercise; "a gale upon their spirits," as our pious ancestors would phrase it;

to have their wits well breathed in an uproarious Valhalla. And I suspect that the choice, given their character and faults, is one to be defended. The purely wise are silenced by facts; they talk in a clear atmosphere, problems lying around them like a view in nature; if they can be shown to be somewhat in the wrong, they digest the reproof like a thrashing, and make better intellectual blood. They stand corrected by a whisper; a word or a glance reminds them of the great eternal law. But it is not so with all. Others in conversation seek rather contact with their fellow-men than increase of knowledge or clarity of thought. The drama, not the philosophy, of life is the sphere of their intellectual activity. Even when they pursue truth, they desire as much as possible of what we may call human scenery along the road they follow. They dwell in the heart of life; the blood sounding in their ears, their eyes laying hold of what delights them with a brutal avidity that makes them blind to all besides, their interest riveted on people, living, loving, talking, tangible people. To a man of this description, the sphere of argument seems very pale and ghostly. By a strong expression, a perturbed countenance, floods of tears, an insult which his conscience obliges him to swallow, he is brought round to knowledge which no syllogism would have conveyed to him. His own experience is so vivid, he is so superlatively conscious of himself, that if, day after day, he is allowed to hector and hear nothing but approving echoes, he will lose his hold on the soberness of things and take himself in earnest for a god. Talk might be to such an one the very way of moral ruin; the school where he might learn to be at once intolerable and ridiculous.

This character is perhaps commoner than philosophers suppose. And for persons of that stamp to learn much by conversation, they must speak with their superiors, not in intellect, for that is a superiority that must be proved, but in station. If they cannot find a friend to bully them for their good, they must find either an old man, a woman, or some one so far below them in the artificial order of society, that courtesy may be particularly exercised.

The best teachers are the aged. To the old our mouths are always partly closed; we must swallow our obvious retorts and listen. They sit above our heads, on life's raised dais, and appeal at once to our respect and pity. A flavour of the old school, a touch of something different in their manner—

which is freer and rounder, if they come of what is called a good family, and often more timid and precise if they are of the middle class—serves, in these days, to accentuate the difference of age and add a distinction to gray hairs. But their superiority is founded more deeply than by outward marks or gestures. They are before us in the march of man; they have more or less solved the irking problem; they have battled through the equinox of life; in good and evil they have held their course; and now, without open shame, they near the crown and harbour. It may be we have been struck with one of fortune's darts; we can scarce be civil, so cruelly is our spirit tossed. Yet long before we were so much as thought upon, the like calamity befell the old man or woman that now, with pleasant humour, rallies us upon our inattention, sitting composed in the holy evening of man's life, in the clear shining after rain. We grow ashamed of our distresses, new and hot and coarse, like villainous roadside brandy; we see life in aerial perspective, under the heavens of faith; and out of the worst, in the mere presence of contented elders, look forward and take patience. Fear shrinks before them "like a thing reproved," not the flitting and ineffectual fear of death, but the instant, dwelling terror of the responsibilities and revenges of life. Their speech, indeed, is timid; they report lions in the path; they counsel a meticulous footing; but their serene, marred faces are more eloquent and tell another story. Where they have gone, we will go also, not very greatly fearing; what they have endured unbroken, we also, God helping us, will make a shift to bear.

Not only is the presence of the aged in itself remedial, but their minds are stored with antidotes, wisdom's simples, plain considerations overlooked by youth. They have matter to communicate, be they never so stupid. Their talk is not merely literature, it is great literature; classic in virtue of the speaker's detachment, studded, like a book of travel, with things we should not otherwise have learnt. In virtue, I have said, of the speaker's detachment,— and this is why, of two old men, the one who is not your father speaks to you with the more sensible authority; for in the paternal relation the oldest have lively interests and remain still young. Thus I have known two young men great friends; each swore by the other's father; the father of each swore by the other lad; and yet each pair of parent and child were perpetually by the ears. This is typical: it reads like the germ of some kindly comedy.

The old appear in conversation in two characters: the critically silent and the garrulous anecdotic. The last is perhaps what we look for; it is perhaps the more instructive. An old gentleman, well on in years, sits handsomely and naturally in the bow-window of his age, scanning experience with reverted eye; and chirping and smiling, communicates the accidents and reads the lesson of his long career. Opinions are strengthened, indeed, but they are also weeded out in the course of years. What remains steadily present to the eye of the retired veteran in his hermitage, what still ministers to his content, what still quickens his old honest heart—these are "the real long-lived things" that Whitman tells us to prefer. Where youth agrees with age, not where they differ, wisdom lies; and it is when the young disciple finds his heart to beat in tune with his gray-bearded teacher's that a lesson may be learned. I have known one old gentleman, whom I may name, for he is now gathered to his stock—Robert Hunter, Sheriff of Dumbarton, and author of an excellent law-book still re-edited and republished. Whether he was originally big or little is more than I can guess. When I knew him he was all fallen away and fallen in; crooked and shrunken; buckled into a stiff waistcoat for support; troubled by ailments, which kept him hobbling in and out of the room; one foot gouty; a wig for decency, not for deception, on his head; close shaved, except under his chin—and for that he never failed to apologise, for it went sore against the traditions of his life. You can imagine how he would fare in a novel by Miss Mather; yet this rag of a Chelsea veteran lived to his last year in the plenitude of all that is best in man, brimming with human kindness, and staunch as a Roman soldier under his manifold infirmities. You could not say that he had lost his memory, for he would repeat Shakespeare and Webster and Jeremy Taylor and Burke by the page together; but the parchment was filled up, there was no room for fresh inscriptions, and he was capable of repeating the same anecdote on many successive visits. His voice survived in its full power, and he took a pride in using it. On his last voyage as Commissioner of lighthouses, he hailed a ship at sea and made himself clearly audible without a speaking trumpet, ruffling the while with a proper vanity in his achievement. He had a habit of eking out his words with interrogative hems, which was puzzling and a little wearisome, suited ill with his appearance, and seemed a survival from some former stage of bodily portliness. Of yore, when he was a great pedestrian and no enemy to good claret, he may have pointed with these minute guns his allocutions to the bench. His humour was perfectly equable, set beyond the reach of fate; gout, rheumatism, stone and gravel might have combined their forces against that frail tabernacle, but when I came round on Sunday evening, he would lay aside Jeremy Taylor's Life of Christ and greet me with the same open brow, the same kind formality of manner. His opinions and sympathies dated the man almost to a decade. He had begun life, under his mother's influence, as an admirer of Junius, but on maturer knowledge had transferred his admiration to Burke. He cautioned me, with entire gravity, to be punctilious in writing English; never to forget that I was a Scotchman, that English was a foreign tongue, and that if I attempted the colloquial, I should certainly, be shamed: the remark was apposite, I suppose, in the days of David Hume. Scott was too new for him; he had known the author—known him, too, for a Tory; and to the genuine classic a contemporary is always something of a trouble. He had the old, serious love of the play; had even, as he was proud to tell, played a certain part in the history of Shakespearian revivals, for he had successfully pressed on Murray, of the old Edinburgh Theatre, the idea of producing Shakespeare's fairy pieces with great scenic display. A moderate in religion, he was much struck in the last years of his life by a conversation with two young lads, revivalists "H'm," he would say—"new to me. I have had—h'm—no such experience." It struck him, not with pain, rather with a solemn philosophic interest, that he, a Christian as he hoped, and a Christian of so old a standing, should hear these young fellows talking of his own subject, his own weapons that he had fought the battle of life with,—"and—h'm—not understand." In this wise and graceful attitude he did justice to himself and others, reposed unshaken in his old beliefs, and recognised their limits without anger or alarm. His last recorded remark, on the last night of his life, was after he had been arguing against Calvinism with his minister and was interrupted by an intolerable pang. "After all," he said, "of all the 'isms, I know none so bad as rheumatism." My own last sight of him was some time before, when we dined together at an inn; he had been on circuit, for he stuck to his duties like a chief part of his existence; and I remember it as the only occasion on which he ever soiled his lips with slang—a thing he loathed. We were both Roberts;

and as we took our places at table, he addressed me with a twinkle: "We are just what you would call two bob." He offered me port, I remember, as the proper milk of youth; spoke of "twenty-shilling notes"; and throughout the meal was full of old-world pleasantry and quaintness, like an ancient boy on a holiday. But what I recall chiefly was his confession that he had never read Othello to an end. Shakespeare was his continual study. He loved nothing better than to display his knowledge and memory by adducing parallel passages from Shakespeare, passages where the same word was employed, or the same idea differently treated. But Othello had beaten him. "That noble gentleman and that noble lady—h'm—too painful for me." The same night the hoardings were covered with posters, "Burlesque of Othello," and the contrast blazed up in my mind like a bonfire. An unforgettable look it gave me into that kind man's soul. His acquaintance was indeed a liberal and pious education. All the humanities were taught in that bare dining-room beside his gouty footstool. He was a piece of good advice; he was himself the instance that pointed and adorned his various talk. Nor could a young man have found elsewhere a place so set apart from envy, fear, discontent, or any of the passions that debase; a life so honest and composed; a soul like an ancient violin, so subdued to harmony, responding to a touch in music—as in that dining-room, with Mr. Hunter chatting at the eleventh hour, under the shadow of eternity, fearless and gentle.

The second class of old people are not anecdotic; they are rather hearers than talkers, listening to the young with an amused and critical attention. To have this sort of intercourse to perfection, I think we must go to old ladies. Women are better hearers than men, to begin with; they learn, I fear in anguish, to bear with the tedious and infantile vanity of the other sex; and we will take more from a woman than even from the oldest man in the way of biting comment. Biting comment is the chief part, whether for profit or amusement, in this business. The old lady that I have in my eye is a very caustic speaker, her tongue, after years of practice, in absolute command, whether for silence or attack. If she chance to dislike you, you will be tempted to curse the malignity of age. But if you chance to please even slightly, you will be listened to with a particular laughing grace of sympathy, and from time to time chastised, as if in play, with a parasol as heavy as a pole-axe. It requires a singular art, as well as the vantage-ground of age, to deal these stunning corrections among the coxcombs of the young. The pill is disguised in sugar of wit; it is administered as a compliment—if you had not pleased, you would not have been censured; it is a personal affair—a hyphen, a trait d'union, between you and your censor; age's philandering, for her pleasure and your good. Incontestably the young man feels very much of a fool; but he must be a perfect Malvolio, sick with self-love, if he cannot take an open buffet and still smile. The correction of silence is what kills; when you know you have transgressed, and your friend says nothing and avoids your eye. If a man were made of gutta-percha, his heart would quail at such a moment. But when the word is out, the worst is over; and a fellow with any good-humour at all may pass through a perfect hail of witty criticism, every bare place on his soul hit to the quick with a shrewd missile, and reappear, as if after a dive, tingling with a fine moral reaction, and ready, with a shrinking readiness, one-third loath, for a repetition of the discipline.

There are few women, not well sunned and ripened, and perhaps toughened, who can thus stand apart from a man and say the true thing with a kind of genial cruelty. Still there are some—and I doubt if there be any man who can return the compliment. The class of man represented by Vernon Whitford in The Egoist says, indeed, the true thing, but he says it stockishly. Vernon is a noble fellow, and makes, by the way, a noble and instructive contrast to Daniel Deronda; his conduct is the conduct of a man of honour; but we agree with him, against our consciences, when he remorsefully considers "its astonishing dryness." He is the best of men, but the best of women manage to combine all that and something more. Their very faults assist them; they are helped even by the falseness of their position in life. They can retire into the fortified camp of the proprieties. They can touch a subject and suppress it. The most adroit employ a somewhat elaborate reserve as a means to be frank, much as they wear gloves when they shake hands. But a man has the full responsibility of his freedom, cannot evade a question, can scarce be silent without rudeness, must answer for his words upon the moment, and is not seldom left face to face with a damning choice, between the more or less dishonourable wriggling of Deronda and the downright woodenness of Vernon Whitford.

But the superiority of women is perpetually menaced; they do not sit throned on infirmities like the old; they are suitors as well as sovereigns; their vanity is engaged, their affections are too apt to follow; and hence much of the talk between the sexes degenerates into something unworthy of the name. The desire to please, to shine with a certain softness of lustre and to draw a fascinating picture of oneself, banishes from conversation all that is sterling and most of what is humorous. As soon as a strong current of mutual admiration begins to flow, the human interest triumphs entirely over the intellectual, and the commerce of words, consciously or not, becomes secondary to the commercing of eyes. But even where this ridiculous danger is avoided, and a man and woman converse equally and honestly, something in their nature or their education falsifies the strain. An instinct prompts them to agree; and where that is impossible, to agree to differ. Should they neglect the warning, at the first suspicion of an argument, they find themselves in different hemispheres. About any point of business or conduct, any actual affair demanding settlement, a woman will speak and listen, hear and answer arguments, not only with natural wisdom, but with candour and logical honesty. But if the subject of debate be something in the air, an abstraction, an excuse for talk, a logical Aunt Sally, then may the male debater instantly abandon hope; he may employ reason, adduce facts, be supple, be smiling, be angry, all shall avail him nothing; what the woman said first, that (unless she has forgotten it) she will repeat at the end. Hence, at the very junctures when a talk between men grows brighter and quicker and begins to promise to bear fruit, talk between the sexes is menaced with dissolution. The point of difference, the point of interest, is evaded by the brilliant woman, under a shower of irrelevant conversational rockets; it is bridged by the discreet woman with a rustle of silk, as she passes smoothly forward to the nearest point of safety. And this sort of prestidigitation, juggling the dangerous topic out of sight until it can be reintroduced with safety in an altered shape, is a piece of tactics among the true drawing-room queens.

The drawing-room is, indeed, an artificial place; it is so by our choice and for our sins. The subjection of women; the ideal imposed upon them from the cradle, and worn, like a hair-shirt, with so much constancy; their motherly, superior tenderness to man's vanity and self-importance; their managing arts—the arts of a civilised slave among good-natured barbarians—are all painful ingredients and all help to falsify relations. It is not till we get clear of that amusing artificial scene that genuine relations are founded, or ideas honestly compared. In the garden, on the road or the hillside, or tête-à-tête and apart from interruptions, occasions arise when we may learn much from any single woman; and nowhere more often than in married life. Marriage is one long conversation, chequered by disputes. The disputes are valueless; they but ingrain the difference; the heroic heart of woman prompting her at once to nail her colours to the mast. But in the intervals, almost unconsciously and with no desire to shine, the whole material of life is turned over and over, ideas are struck out and shared, the two persons more and more adapt their notions one to suit the other, and in process of time, without sound of trumpet, they conduct each other into new worlds of thought.

CHAPTER XII. THE CHARACTER OF DOGS

The civilisation, the manners, and the morals of dog-kind are to a great extent subordinated to those of his ancestral master, man. This animal, in many ways so superior, has accepted a position of inferiority, shares the domestic life, and humours the caprices of the tyrant. But the potentate, like the British in India, pays small regard to the character of his willing client, judges him with listless glances, and condemns him in a byword. Listless have been the looks of his admirers, who have exhausted idle terms of praise, and buried the poor soul below exaggerations. And yet more idle and, if possible, more unintelligent has been the attitude of his express detractors; those who are very fond of dogs "but in their proper place"; who say "poo' fellow, poo' fellow," and are themselves far poorer; who whet the knife of the vivisectionist or heat his oven; who are not ashamed to admire "the creature's instinct"; and flying far beyond folly, have dared to resuscitate the theory of animal machines. The "dog's instinct" and the "automaton-dog," in this age of psychology and science, sound like strange anachronisms. An automaton he certainly is; a machine working independently of his control, the heart, like the mill-wheel, keeping all in motion, and the consciousness, like a person shut in the mill garret, enjoying the view out of the window and shaken by the thunder of the stones; an automaton in one corner of which a living spirit is confined: an automaton like man. Instinct again he certainly possesses. Inherited aptitudes are his, inherited frailties. Some things he at once views and understands, as though he were awakened from a sleep, as though he came "trailing clouds of glory." But with him, as with man, the field of instinct is limited; its utterances are obscure and occasional; and about the far larger part of life both the dog and his master must conduct their steps by deduction and observation.

The leading distinction between dog and man, after and perhaps before the different duration of their lives, is that the one can speak and that the other cannot. The absence of the power of speech confines the dog in the development of his intellect. It hinders him from many speculations, for words are the beginning of meta-physic. At the same blow it saves him from many superstitions, and his silence has won for him a higher name for virtue than his conduct justifies. The faults of the dog are many. He is vainer than man, singularly greedy of notice, singularly intolerant of ridicule, suspicious like the deaf, jealous to the degree of frenzy, and radically devoid of truth. The day of an intelligent small dog is passed in the manufacture and the laborious communication of falsehood; he lies with his tail, he lies with his eye, he lies with his protesting paw; and when he rattles his dish or scratches at the door his purpose is other than appears. But he has some apology to offer for the vice. Many of the signs which form his dialect have come to bear an arbitrary meaning, clearly understood both by his master and himself; yet when a new want arises he must either invent a new vehicle of meaning or wrest an old one to a different purpose; and this necessity frequently recurring must tend to lessen his idea of the sanctity of symbols. Meanwhile the dog is clear in his own conscience, and draws, with a human nicety, the distinction between formal and essential truth. Of his punning perversions, his legitimate dexterity with symbols, he is even vain; but when he has told and been detected in a lie, there is not a hair upon his body but confesses guilt. To a dog of gentlemanly feeling theft and falsehood are disgraceful vices. The canine, like the human, gentleman demands in his misdemeanours Montaigne's "je ne sais quoi de généreux." He is never more than half ashamed of having barked or bitten; and for those faults into which he has been led by the desire to shine before a lady of his race, he retains, even under physical correction, a share of pride. But to be caught lying, if he understands it, instantly uncurls his fleece.

Just as among dull observers he preserves a name for truth, the dog has been credited with modesty. It is amazing how the use of language blunts the faculties of man—that because vain glory finds no vent in words, creatures supplied with eyes have been unable to detect a fault so gross and obvious. If a small spoiled dog were suddenly to be endowed with speech, he would prate interminably, and still about himself; when we had friends, we should be forced to lock him in a garret; and what with his whining jealousies and his foible for falsehood, in a year's time he would have gone far to weary out our love. I was about to compare him to Sir Willoughby Patterne, but the

Patternes have a manlier sense of their own merits; and the parallel, besides, is ready. Hans Christian Andersen, as we behold him in his startling memoirs, thrilling from top to toe with an excruciating vanity, and scouting even along the street for shadows of offence—here was the talking dog.

It is just this rage for consideration that has betrayed the dog into his satellite position as the friend of man. The cat, an animal of franker appetites, preserves his independence. But the dog, with one eye ever on the audience, has been wheedled into slavery, and praised and patted into the renunciation of his nature. Once he ceased hunting and became man's plate-licker, the Rubicon was crossed. Thenceforth he was a gentleman of leisure; and except the few whom we keep working, the whole race grew more and more self-conscious, mannered and affected. The number of things that a small dog does naturally is strangely small. Enjoying better spirits and not crushed under material cares, he is far more theatrical than average man. His whole life, if he be a dog of any pretension to gallantry, is spent in a vain show, and in the hot pursuit of admiration. Take out your puppy for a walk, and you will find the little ball of fur clumsy, stupid, bewildered, but natural. Let but a few months pass, and when you repeat the process you will find nature buried in convention. He will do nothing plainly; but the simplest processes of our material life will all be bent into the forms of an elaborate and mysterious etiquette. Instinct, says the fool, has awakened. But it is not so. Some dogs—some, at the very least—if they be kept separate from others, remain quite natural; and these, when at length they meet with a companion of experience, and have the game explained to them, distinguish themselves by the severity of their devotion to its rules. I wish I were allowed to tell a story which would radiantly illuminate the point; but men, like dogs, have an elaborate and mysterious etiquette. It is their bond of sympathy that both are the children of convention.

The person, man or dog, who has a conscience is eternally condemned to some degree of humbug; the sense of the law in their members fatally precipitates either towards a frozen and affected bearing. And the converse is true; and in the elaborate and conscious manners of the dog, moral opinions and the love of the ideal stand confessed. To follow for ten minutes in the street some swaggering, canine cavalier, is to receive a lesson in dramatic art and the cultured conduct of the body; in every act and gesture you see him true to a refined conception; and the dullest cur, beholding him, pricks up his ear and proceeds to imitate and parody that charming ease. For to be a high-mannered and high-minded gentleman, careless, affable, and gay, is the inborn pretension of the dog. The large dog, so much lazier, so much more weighed upon with matter, so majestic in repose, so beautiful in effort, is born with the dramatic means to wholly represent the part. And it is more pathetic and perhaps more instructive to consider the small dog in his conscientious and imperfect efforts to outdo Sir Philip Sidney. For the ideal of the dog is feudal and religious; the ever-present polytheism, the whip-bearing Olympus of mankind, rules them on the one hand; on the other, their singular difference of size and strength among themselves effectually prevents the appearance of the democratic notion. Or we might more exactly compare their society to the curious spectacle presented by a school—ushers, monitors, and big and little boys—qualified by one circumstance, the introduction of the other sex. In each, we should observe a somewhat similar tension of manner, and somewhat similar points of honour. In each the larger animal keeps a contemptuous good humour; in each the smaller annoys him with wasp-like impudence, certain of practical immunity; in each we shall find a double life producing double characters, and an excursive and noisy heroism combined with a fair amount of practical timidity. I have known dogs, and I have known school heroes that, set aside the fur, could hardly have been told apart; and if we desire to understand the chivalry of old, we must turn to the school playfields or the dungheap where the dogs are trooping.

Woman, with the dog, has been long enfranchised. Incessant massacre of female innocents has changed the proportions of the sexes and perverted their relations. Thus, when we regard the manners of the dog, we see a romantic and monogamous animal, once perhaps as delicate as the cat, at war with impossible conditions. Man has much to answer for; and the part he plays is yet more damnable and parlous than Corin's in the eyes of Touchstone. But his intervention has at least created an imperial situation for the rare surviving ladies. In that society they reign without a rival: conscious queens; and in the only instance of a canine wife-beater that has ever fallen under my notice, the criminal was somewhat excused by the circumstances of his story. He is a little, very alert, well-bred, intelligent Skye, as black as a hat, with a wet bramble for a nose and two cairngorms for eyes. To the human observer, he is decidedly well-looking; but to the ladies of his race he seems abhorrent. A thorough elaborate gentleman, of the plume and sword-knot order, he was born with a nice sense of gallantry to women. He took at their hands the most outrageous treatment; I have heard him bleating like a sheep, I have seen him streaming blood, and his ear tattered like a regimental banner; and yet he would scorn to make reprisals. Nay more, when a human lady upraised the contumelious whip against the very dame who had been so cruelly misusing him, my little great-heart gave but one hoarse cry and fell upon the tyrant tooth and nail. This is the tale of a soul's tragedy. After three years of unavailing chivalry, he suddenly, in one hour, threw off the yoke of obligation; had he been Shakespeare he would then have written Troilus and Cressida to brand the offending sex; but being only a little dog, he began to bite them. The surprise of the ladies whom he attacked indicated the monstrosity of his offence; but he had fairly beaten off his better angel, fairly committed moral suicide; for almost in the same hour, throwing aside the last rags of decency, he proceeded to attack the aged also. The fact is worth remark, showing, as it does, that ethical laws are common both to dogs and men; and that with both a single deliberate violation of the conscience loosens all. "But while the lamp holds on to burn," says the paraphrase, "the greatest sinner may return." I have been cheered to see symptoms of effectual penitence in my sweet ruffian; and by the handling that he accepted uncomplainingly the other day from an indignant fair one, I begin to hope the period of Sturm und Drang is closed.

All these little gentlemen are subtle casuists. The duty to the female dog is plain; but where competing duties rise, down they will sit and study them out, like Jesuit confessors. I knew another little Skye, somewhat plain in manner and appearance, but a creature compact of amiability and solid wisdom. His family going abroad for a winter, he was received for that period by an uncle in the same city. The winter over, his own family home again, and his own house (of which he was very proud) reopened, he found himself in a dilemma between two conflicting duties of loyalty and gratitude. His old friends were not to be neglected, but it seemed hardly decent to desert the new. This was how he solved the problem. Every morning, as soon as the door was opened, off posted Coolin to his uncle's, visited the children in the nursery, saluted the whole family, and was back at home in time for breakfast and his bit of fish. Nor was this done without a sacrifice on his part, sharply felt; for he had to forego the particular honour and jewel of his day—his morning's walk with my father. And, perhaps from this cause, he gradually wearied of and relaxed the practice, and at length returned entirely to his ancient habits. But the same decision served him in another and more distressing case of divided duty, which happened not long after. He was not at all a kitchen dog, but the cook had nursed him with unusual kindness during the distemper; and though he did not adore her as he adored my father—although (born snob) he was critically conscious of her position as "only a servant"—he still cherished for her a special gratitude. Well, the cook left, and retired some streets away to lodgings of her own; and there was Coolin in precisely the same situation with any young gentleman who has had the inestimable benefit of a faithful nurse. The canine conscience did not solve the problem with a pound of tea at Christmas. No longer content to pay a flying visit, it was the whole forenoon that he dedicated to his solitary friend. And so, day by day, he continued to comfort her solitude until (for some reason which I could never understand and cannot approve) he was kept locked up to break him of the graceful habit. Here, it is not the similarity, it is the difference, that is worthy of remark; the clearly marked degrees of gratitude and the proportional duration of his visits. Anything further removed from instinct it were hard to fancy; and one is even stirred to a certain impatience with a character so destitute of spontaneity, so passionless in justice, and so priggishly obedient to the voice of reason.

There are not many dogs like this good Coolin, and not many people. But the type is one well marked, both in the human and the canine family. Gallantry was not his aim, but a solid and somewhat oppressive respectability. He was a sworn foe to the unusual and the conspicuous, a praiser of the golden mean, a kind of city uncle modified by Cheeryble. And as he was precise and conscientious in all the steps of his own blameless course, he looked for the same precision and an even greater gravity in the bearing of his deity, my father. It was no sinecure to be Coolin's idol: he was exacting like a rigid parent; and at every sign of levity in the man whom he respected, he announced loudly the death of virtue and the proximate fall of the pillars of the earth.

I have called him a snob; but all dogs are so, though in varying degrees. It is hard to follow their snobbery among themselves; for though I think we can perceive distinctions of rank, we cannot grasp what is the criterion. Thus in Edinburgh, in a good part of the town, there were several distinct societies or clubs that met in the morning to—the phrase is technical—to "rake the backets" in a troop. A friend of mine, the master of three dogs, was one day surprised to observe that they had left one club and joined another; but whether it was a rise or a fall, and the result of an invitation or an expulsion, was more than he could guess. And this illustrates pointedly our ignorance of the real life of dogs, their social ambitions and their social hierarchies. At least, in their dealings with men they are not only conscious of sex, but of the difference of station. And that in the most snobbish manner; for the poor man's dog is not offended by the notice of the rich, and keeps all his ugly feeling for those poorer or more ragged than his master. And again, for every station they have an ideal of behaviour, to which the master, under pain of derogation, will do wisely to conform. How often has not a cold glance of an eye informed me that my dog was disappointed; and how much more gladly would he not have taken a beating than to be thus wounded in the seat of piety!

I knew one disrespectable dog. He was far liker a cat; cared little or nothing for men, with whom he merely coexisted as we do with cattle, and was entirely devoted to the art of poaching. A house would not hold him, and to live in a town was what he refused. He led, I believe, a life of troubled but genuine pleasure, and perished beyond all question in a trap. But this was an exception, a marked reversion to the ancestral type; like the hairy human infant. The true dog of the nineteenth century, to judge by the remainder of my fairly large acquaintance, is in love with respectability. A street-dog was once adopted by a lady. While still an Arab, he had done as Arabs do, gambolling in the mud, charging into butchers' stalls, a cat-hunter, a sturdy beggar, a common rogue and vagabond; but with his rise into society he laid aside these inconsistent pleasures. He stole no more, he hunted no more cats; and conscious of his collar, he ignored his old companions. Yet the canine upper class was never brought to recognise the upstart, and from that hour, except for human countenance, he was alone. Friendless, shorn of his sports and the habits of a lifetime, he still lived in a glory of happiness, content with his acquired respectability, and with no care but to support it solemnly. Are we to condemn or praise this self-made dog? We praise his human brother. And thus to conquer vicious habits is as rare with dogs as with men. With the more part, for all their scruple-mongering and moral thought, the vices that are born with them remain invincible throughout; and they live all their years, glorying in their virtues, but still the slaves of their defects. Thus the sage Coolin was a thief to the last; among a thousand peccadilloes, a whole goose and a whole cold leg of mutton lay upon his conscience; but Woggs, [128] whose soul's shipwreck in the matter of gallantry I have recounted above, has only twice been known to steal, and has often nobly conquered the temptation. The eighth is his favourite commandment. There is something painfully human in these unequal virtues and mortal frailties of the best. Still more painful is the bearing of those "stammering professors" in the house of sickness and under the terror of death. It is beyond a doubt to me that, somehow or other, the dog connects together, or confounds, the uneasiness of sickness and the consciousness of guilt. To the pains of the body he often adds the tortures of the conscience; and at these times his haggard protestations form, in regard to the human deathbed, a dreadful parody or parallel.

I once supposed that I had found an inverse relation between the double etiquette which dogs obey; and that those who were most addicted to the showy street life among other dogs were less careful in the practice of home virtues for the tyrant man. But the female dog, that mass of carneying affections, shines equally in either sphere; rules her rough posse of attendant swains with unwearying tact and gusto; and with her master and mistress pushes the arts of insinuation to their crowning point. The attention of man and the regard of other dogs flatter (it would thus appear) the same sensibility; but perhaps, if we could read the canine heart, they would be found to flatter it in very different degrees. Dogs live with man as courtiers round a monarch, steeped in the flattery of his notice and enriched with sinecures. To push their favour in this world of pickings and caresses is, perhaps, the business of their lives; and their joys may lie outside. I am in despair at our persistent ignorance. I read in the lives of our companions the same processes of reason, the same antique and fatal conflicts of the right against the wrong, and of unbitted nature with too rigid custom; I see them with our weaknesses, vain, false, inconstant against appetite, and with our one stalk of virtue, devoted to the dream of an ideal; and yet, as they hurry by me on the street with tail in air, or come singly to solicit my regard, I must own the secret purport of their lives is still inscrutable to man. Is man the friend, or is he the patron only? Have they indeed forgotten nature's voice? or are those moments snatched from courtiership when they touch noses with the tinker's mongrel, the brief reward and pleasure of their artificial lives? Doubtless, when man shares with his dog the toils of a profession and the pleasures of an art, as with the shepherd or the poacher, the affection warms and strengthens till it fills the soul. But doubtless, also, the masters are, in many cases, the object of a merely interested cultus, sitting aloft like Louis Quatorze, giving and receiving flattery and favour; and the dogs, like the majority of men, have but foregone their true existence and become the dupes of their ambition.

CHAPTER XIII. A PENNY PLAIN AND TWOPENCE COLOURED

These words will be familiar to all students of Skelt's Juvenile Drama. That national monument, after having changed its name to Park's, to Webb's, to Redington's, and last of all to Pollock's, has now become, for the most part, a memory. Some of its pillars, like Stonehenge, are still afoot, the rest clean vanished. It may be the Museum numbers a full set; and Mr. Ionides perhaps, or else her gracious Majesty, may boast their great collections; but to the plain private person they are become, like Raphaels, unattainable. I have, at different times, possessed Aladdin, The Red Rover, The Blind Boy, The Old Oak Chest, The Wood Dæmon, Jack Sheppard, The Miller and his Men, Der Freischütz, The Smuggler, The Forest of Bondy, Robin Hood, The Waterman, Richard I., My Poll and my Partner Joe, The Inchcape Bell (imperfect), and Three-Fingered Jack, The Terror of Jamaica; and I have assisted others in the illumination of Maid of the Inn and The Battle of Waterloo. In this roll-call of stirring names you read the evidences of a happy childhood; and though not half of them are still to be procured of any living stationer, in the mind of their once happy owner all survive, kaleidoscopes of changing pictures, echoes of the past.

There stands, I fancy, to this day (but now how fallen!) a certain stationer's shop at a corner of the wide thoroughfare that joins the city of my childhood with the sea. When, upon any Saturday, we made a party to behold the ships, we passed that corner; and since in those days I loved a ship as a man loves Burgundy or daybreak, this of itself had been enough to hallow it. But there was more than that. In the Leith Walk window, all the year round, there stood displayed a theatre in working order, with a "forest set," a "combat," and a few "robbers carousing" in the slides; and below and about, dearer tenfold to me! the plays themselves, those budgets of romance, lay tumbled one upon another. Long and often have I lingered there with empty pockets. One figure, we shall say, was visible in the first plate of characters, bearded, pistol in hand, or drawing to his ear the clothyard arrow; I would spell the name: was it Macaire, or Long Tom Coffin, or Grindoff, 2d dress? O, how

I would long to see the rest! how—if the name by chance were hidden—I would wonder in what play he figured, and what immortal legend justified his attitude and strange apparel! And then to go within, to announce yourself as an intending purchaser, and, closely watched, be suffered to undo those bundles and breathlessly devour those pages of gesticulating villains, epileptic combats, bosky forests, palaces and war-ships, frowning fortresses and prison vaults—it was a giddy joy. That shop, which was dark and smelt of Bibles, was a loadstone rock for all that bore the name of boy. They could not pass it by, nor, having entered, leave it. It was a place besieged; the shopmen, like the Jews rebuilding Salem, had a double task. They kept us at the stick's end, frowned us down, snatched each play out of our hand ere we were trusted with another, and, incredible as it may sound, used to demand of us upon our entrance, like banditti, if we came with money or with empty hand. Old Mr. Smith himself, worn out with my eternal vacillation, once swept the treasures from before me, with the cry: "I do not believe, child, that you are an intending purchaser at all!" These were the dragons of the garden; but for such joys of paradise we could have faced the Terror of Jamaica himself. Every sheet we fingered was another lightning glance into obscure, delicious story; it was like wallowing in the raw stuff of story-books. I know nothing to compare with it save now and then in dreams, when I am privileged to read in certain unwrit stories of adventure, from which I awake to find the world all vanity. The crux of Buridan's donkey was as nothing to the uncertainty of the boy as he handled and lingered and doated on these bundles of delight; there was a physical pleasure in the sight and touch of them which he would jealously prolong; and when at length the deed was done, the play selected, and the impatient shopman had brushed the rest into the gray portfolio, and the boy was forth again, a little late for dinner, the lamps springing into light in the blue winter's even, and The Miller, or The Rover, or some kindred drama clutched against his side—on what gay feet he ran, and how he laughed aloud in exultation! I can hear that laughter still. Out of all the years of my life, I can recall but one home-coming to compare with these, and that was on the night when I brought back with me the Arabian Entertainments in the fat, old, double-columned volume with the prints. I was just well into the story of the Hunchback, I remember, when my clergyman-grandfather (a man we counted pretty stiff) came in behind me. I grew blind with terror. But instead of ordering the book away, he said he envied me. Ah, well he might!

The purchase and the first half-hour at home, that was the summit. Thenceforth the interest declined by little and little. The fable, as set forth in the play-book, proved to be not worthy of the scenes and characters: what fable would not? Such passages as: "Scene 6. The Hermitage. Night set scene. Place back of scene 1, No. 2, at back of stage and hermitage, Fig. 2, out of set piece, R. H. in a slanting direction"—such passages, I say, though very practical, are hardly to be called good reading. Indeed, as literature, these dramas did not much appeal to me. I forget the very outline of the plots. Of The Blind Boy, beyond the fact that he was a most injured prince and once, I think, abducted, I know nothing. And The Old Oak Chest, what was it all about? that proscript (1st dress), that prodigious number of banditti, that old woman with the broom, and the magnificent kitchen in the third act (was it in the third?)—they are all fallen in a deliquium, swim faintly in my brain, and mix and vanish.

I cannot deny that joy attended the illumination; nor can I quite forget that child who, wilfully foregoing pleasure, stoops to "twopence coloured." With crimson lake (hark to the sound of it—crimson lake!—the horns of elf-land are not richer on the ear)—with crimson lake and Prussian blue a certain purple is to be compounded which, for cloaks especially, Titian could not equal. The latter colour with gamboge, a hated name although an exquisite pigment, supplied a green of such a savoury greenness that to-day my heart regrets it. Nor can I recall without a tender weakness the very aspect of the water where I dipped my brush. Yes, there was pleasure in the painting. But when all was painted, it is needless to deny it, all was spoiled. You might, indeed, set up a scene or two to look at; but to cut the figures out was simply sacrilege; nor could any child twice court the tedium, the worry, and the long-drawn disenchantment of an actual performance. Two days after the purchase the honey had been sucked. Parents used to complain; they thought I wearied of my play. It was not so: no more than a person can be said to have wearied of his dinner when he leaves the bones and dishes; I had got the marrow of it and said grace.

Then was the time to turn to the back of the play-book and to study that enticing double file of names, where poetry, for the true child of Skelt, reigned happy and glorious like her Majesty the Queen. Much as I have travelled in these realms of gold, I have yet seen, upon that map or abstract, names of El Dorados that still haunt the ear of memory, and are still but names. The Floating Beacon—why was that denied me? or The Wreck Ashore? Sixteen-String Jack whom I did not even guess to be a highwayman, troubled me awake and haunted my slumbers; and there is one sequence of three from that enchanted calender that I still at times recall, like a loved verse of poetry: Lodoiska, Silver Palace, Echo of Westminster Bridge. Names, bare names, are surely more to children than we poor, grown-up, obliterated fools remember.

The name of Skelt itself has always seemed a part and parcel of the charm of his productions. It may be different with the rose, but the attraction of this paper drama sensibly declined when Webb had crept into the rubric: a poor cuckoo, flaunting in Skelt's nest. And now we have reached Pollock, sounding deeper gulfs. Indeed, this name of Skelt appears so stagey and piratic, that I will adopt it boldly to design these qualities. Skeltery, then, is a quality of much art. It is even to be found, with reverence be it said, among the works of nature. The stagey is its generic name; but it is an old, insular, home-bred staginess; not French, domestically British; not of to-day, but smacking of O. Smith, Fitzball, and the great age of melodrama: a peculiar fragrance haunting it; uttering its unimportant message in a tone of voice that has the charm of fresh antiquity. I will not insist upon the art of Skelt's purveyors. These wonderful characters that once so thrilled our soul with their bold attitude, array of deadly engines and incomparable costume, to-day look somewhat pallidly; the extreme hard favour of the heroine strikes me, I had almost said with pain; the villain's scowl no longer thrills me like a trumpet; and the scenes themselves, those once unparalleled landscapes, seem the efforts of a prentice hand. So much of fault we find; but on the other side the impartial critic rejoices to remark the presence of a great unity of gusto; of those direct clap-trap appeals, which a man is dead and buriable when he fails to answer; of the footlight glamour, the ready-made, bare-faced, transpontine picturesque, a thing not one with cold reality, but how much dearer to the mind!

The scenery of Skeltdom—or, shall we say, the kingdom of Transpontus?—had a prevailing character. Whether it set forth Poland as in The Blind Boy, or Bohemia with The Miller and his Men, or Italy with The Old Oak Chest, still it was Transpontus. A botanist could tell it by the plants. The hollyhock was all pervasive, running wild in deserts; the dock was common, and the bending reed; and overshadowing these were poplar, palm, potato tree, and Quercus Skeltica—brave growths. The caves were all embowelled in the Surreyside formation; the soil was all betrodden by the light pump of T. P. Cooke. Skelt, to be sure, had yet another, an oriental string: he held the gorgeous east in fee; and in the new quarter of Hyères, say, in the garden of the Hotel des Iles d'Or, you may behold these blessed visions realised. But on these I will not dwell; they were an outwork; it was in the occidental scenery that Skelt was all himself. It had a strong flavour of England; it was a sort of indigestion of England and drop-scenes, and I am bound to say was charming. How the roads wander, how the castle sits upon the hill, how the sun eradiates from behind the cloud, and how the congregated clouds themselves up-roll, as stiff as bolsters! Here is the cottage interior, the usual first flat, with the cloak upon the nail, the rosaries of onions, the gun and powder-horn and corner-cupboard; here is the inn (this drama must be nautical, I foresee Captain Luff and Bold Bob Bowsprit) with the red curtain, pipes, spittoons, and eight-day clock; and there again is that impressive dungeon with the chains, which was so dull to colour. England, the hedgerow elms, the thin brick houses, windmills, glimpses of the navigable Thames—England, when at last I came to visit it, was only Skelt made evident: to cross the border was, for the Scotsman, to come home to Skelt; there was the inn-sign and there the horse-trough, all foreshadowed in the faithful Skelt. If, at the ripe age of fourteen years, I bought a certain cudgel, got a friend to load it, and thenceforward walked the tame ways of the earth my own ideal, radiating pure romance—still I was but a puppet in the hand of Skelt; the original of that regretted bludgeon, and surely the antitype of all the bludgeon kind, greatly improved from Cruikshank, had adorned the hand of Jonathan Wild, pl. i. "This is mastering me," as Whitman cries, upon some lesser provocation. What am I? what are life, art, letters, the world, but what my Skelt has made them? He stamped himself upon my immaturity.

The world was plain before I knew him, a poor penny world; but soon it was all coloured with romance. If I go to the theatre to see a good old melodrama, 'tis but Skelt a little faded. If I visit a bold scene in nature, Skelt would have been bolder; there had been certainly a castle on that mountain, and the hollow tree—that set piece—I seem to miss it in the foreground. Indeed, out of this cut-and-dry, dull, swaggering, obtrusive, and infantile art, I seem to have learned the very spirit of my life's enjoyment; met there the shadows of the characters I was to read about and love in a late future; got the romance of Der Freischütz long ere I was to hear of Weber or the mighty Formes; acquired a gallery of scenes and characters with which, in the silent theatre of the brain, I might enact all novels and romances; and took from these rude cuts an enduring and transforming pleasure. Reader—and yourself?

A word of moral: it appears that B. Pollock, late J. Redington, No. 73 Hoxton Street, not only publishes twenty-three of these old stage favourites, but owns the necessary plates and displays a modest readiness to issue other thirty-three. If you love art, folly, or the bright eyes of children, speed to Pollock's, or to Clarke's of Garrick Street. In Pollock's list of publicanda I perceive a pair of my ancient aspirations: Wreck Ashore and Sixteen-String Jack; and I cherish the belief that when these shall see once more the light of day, B. Pollock will remember this apologist. But, indeed, I have a dream at times that is not all a dream. I seem to myself to wander in a ghostly street—E. W., I think, the postal district—close below the fool's-cap of St. Paul's, and yet within easy hearing of the echo of the Abbey bridge. There in a dim shop, low in the roof and smelling strong of glue and footlights, I find myself in quaking treaty with great Skelt himself, the aboriginal all dusty from the tomb. I buy, with what a choking heart—I buy them all, all but the pantomimes; I pay my mental money, and go forth; and lo! the packets are dust.

CHAPTER XIV. A GOSSIP ON A NOVEL OF DUMAS'S

The books that we re-read the oftenest are not always those that we admire the most; we choose and we re-visit them for many and various reasons, as we choose and revisit human friends. One or two of Scott's novels, Shakespeare, Molière, Montaigne, The Egoist, and the Vicomte de Bragelonne, form the inner circle of my intimates. Behind these comes a good troop of dear acquaintances; The Pilgrim's Progress in the front rank, The Bible in Spain not far behind. There are besides a certain number that look at me with reproach as I pass them by on my shelves: books that I once thumbed and studied: houses which were once like home to me, but where I now rarely visit. I am on these sad terms (and blush to confess it) with Wordsworth, Horace, Burns and Hazlitt. Last of all, there is the class of book that has its hour of brilliancy—glows, sings, charms, and then fades again into insignificance until the fit return. Chief of those who thus smile and frown on me by turns, I must name Virgil and Herrick, who, were they but

"Their sometime selves the same throughout the year,"

must have stood in the first company with the six names of my continual literary intimates. To these six, incongruous as they seem, I have long been faithful, and hope to be faithful to the day of death. I have never read the whole of Montaigne, but I do not like to be long without reading some of him, and my delight in what I do read never lessens. Of Shakespeare I have read all but Richard III., Henry VI., Titus Andronicus, and All's Well that Ends Well; and these, having already made all suitable endeavour, I now know that I shall never read—to make up for which unfaithfulness I could read much of the rest for ever. Of Molière—surely the next greatest name of Christendom—I could tell a very similar story; but in a little corner of a little essay these princes are too much out of place, and I prefer to pay my fealty and pass on. How often I have read Guy Mannering, Rob Roy, or Redgauntlet, I have no means of guessing, having begun young. But it is either four or five times that I have read The Egoist, and either five or six that

I have read the Vicomte de Bragelonne.

Some, who would accept the others, may wonder that I should have spent so much of this brief life of ours over a work so little famous as the last. And, indeed, I am surprised myself; not at my own devotion, but the coldness of the world. My acquaintance with the Vicomte began, somewhat indirectly, in the year of grace 1863, when I had the advantage of studying certain illustrated dessert plates in a hotel at Nice. The name of d'Artagnan in the legends I already saluted like an old friend, for I had met it the year before in a work of Miss Yonge's. My first perusal was in one of those pirated editions that swarmed at that time out of Brussels, and ran to such a troop of neat and dwarfish volumes. I understood but little of the merits of the book; my strongest memory is of the execution of d'Eyméric and Lyodot—a strange testimony to the dulness of a boy, who could enjoy the rough-and-tumble in the Place de Grêve, and forget d'Artagnan's visits to the two financiers. My next reading was in winter-time, when I lived alone upon the Pentlands. I would return in the early night from one of my patrols with the shepherd; a friendly face would meet me in the door, a friendly retriever scurry upstairs to fetch my slippers; and I would sit down with the Vicomte for a long, silent, solitary lamp-light evening by the fire. And yet I know not why I call it silent, when it was enlivened with such a clatter of horse-shoes, and such a rattle of musketry, and such a stir of talk; or why I call those evenings solitary in which I gained so many friends. I would rise from my book and pull the blind aside, and see the snow and the glittering hollies chequer a Scotch garden, and the winter moonlight brighten the white hills. Thence I would turn again to that crowded and sunny field of life in which it was so easy to forget myself, my cares, and my surroundings: a place busy as a city, bright as a theatre, thronged with memorable faces, and sounding with delightful speech. I carried the thread of that epic into my slumbers, I woke with it unbroken, I rejoiced to plunge into the book again at breakfast, it was with a pang that I must lay it down and turn to my own labours; for no part of the world has ever seemed to me so charming as these pages, and not even my friends are quite so real, perhaps quite so dear, as d'Artagnan.

Since then I have been going to and fro at very brief intervals in my favourite book; and I have now just risen from my last (let me call it my fifth) perusal, having liked it better and admired it more seriously than ever. Perhaps I have a sense of ownership, being so well known in these six volumes. Perhaps I think that d'Artagnan delights to have me read of him, and Louis Quatorze is gratified, and Fouquet throws me a look, and Aramis, although he knows I do not love him, yet plays to me with his best graces, as to an old patron of the show. Perhaps, if I am not careful, something may befall me like what befell George IV. about the battle of Waterloo, and I may come to fancy the Vicomte one of the first, and Heaven knows the best, of my own works. At least, I avow myself a partisan; and when I compare the popularity of the Vicomte with that of Monte Cristo, or its own elder brother, the Trois Mousquetaires, I confess I am both pained and puzzled.

To those who have already made acquaintance with the titular hero in the pages of Vingt Ans Après, perhaps the name may act as a deterrent. A man might, well stand back if he supposed he were to follow, for six volumes, so well-conducted, so fine-spoken, and withal so dreary a cavalier as Bragelonne. But the fear is idle. I may be said to have passed the best years of my life in these six volumes, and my acquaintance with Raoul has never gone beyond a bow; and when he, who has so long pretended to be alive, is at last suffered to pretend to be dead, I am sometimes reminded of a saying in an earlier volume: "Enfin, dit Miss Stewart,"—and it was of Bragelonne she spoke— "enfin il a fait quelquechose: c'est, ma foi! bien heureux." I am reminded of it, as I say; and the next moment, when Athos dies of his death, and my dear d'Artagnan bursts into his storm of sobbing, I can but deplore my flippancy.

Or perhaps it is La Vallière that the reader of Vingt Ans Après is inclined to flee. Well, he is right there too, though not so right. Louise is no success. Her creator has spared no pains; she is well-meant, not ill-designed, sometimes has a word that rings out true; sometimes, if only for a breath, she may even engage our sympathies. But I have never envied the King his triumph. And so far from pitying Bragelonne for his defeat, I could wish him no worse (not for lack of malice, but imagination) than to be wedded to that lady. Madame enchants me; I can forgive that royal minx her most serious offences; I can thrill and soften with the King on that memorable occasion when he goes to upbraid and remains to flirt; and when it comes to the "Allons, aimez-moi donc," it is my heart that melts in the bosom of de Guiche. Not so with Louise. Readers cannot fail to have remarked that what an author tells us of the beauty or the charm of his creatures goes for nought; that we know instantly better; that the heroine cannot open her mouth but what, all in a moment, the fine phrases of preparation fall from round her like the robes from Cinderella, and she stands before us, self-betrayed, as a poor, ugly, sickly wench, or perhaps a strapping market-woman. Authors, at least, know it well; a heroine will too often start the trick of "getting ugly;" and no disease is more difficult to cure. I said authors; but indeed I had a side eye to one author in particular, with whose works I am very well acquainted, though I cannot read them, and who has spent many vigils in this cause, sitting beside his ailing puppets and (like a magician) wearying his art to restore them to youth and beauty. There are others who ride too high for these misfortunes. Who doubts the loveliness of Rosalind? Arden itself was not more lovely. Who ever questioned the perennial charm of Rose Jocelyn, Lucy Desborough, or Clara Middleton? fair women with fair names, the daughters of George Meredith. Elizabeth Bennet has but to speak, and I am at her knees. Ah! these are the creators of desirable women. They would never have fallen in the mud with Dumas and poor La Vallière. It is my only consolation that not one of all of them, except the first, could have plucked at the moustache of d'Artagnan.

Or perhaps, again, a proportion of readers stumble at the threshold. In so vast a mansion there were sure to be back stairs and kitchen offices where no one would delight to linger; but it was at least unhappy that the vestibule should be so badly lighted; and until, in the seventeenth chapter, d'Artagnan sets off to seek his friends, I must confess, the book goes heavily enough. But, from thenceforward, what a feast is spread! Monk kidnapped; d'Artagnan enriched; Mazarin's death; the ever delectable adventure of Belle Isle, wherein Aramis outwits d'Artagnan, with its epilogue (vol. v. chap. xxviii.), where d'Artagnan regains the moral superiority; the love adventures at Fontainebleau, with St. Aignan's story of the dryad and the business of de Guiche, de Wardes, and Manicamp; Aramis made general of the Jesuits; Aramis at the bastille; the night talk in the forest of Sénart; Belle Isle again, with the death of Porthos; and last, but not least, the taming of d'Artagnan the untamable, under the lash of the young King. What other novel has such epic variety and nobility of incident? often, if you will, impossible; often of the order of an Arabian story; and yet all based in human nature. For if you come to that, what novel has more human nature? not studied with the microscope, but seen largely, in plain daylight, with the natural eye? What novel has more good sense, and gaiety, and wit, and unflagging, admirable literary skill? Good souls, I suppose, must sometimes read it in the blackguard travesty of a translation. But there is no style so untranslatable; light as a whipped trifle, strong as silk; wordy like a village tale; pat like a general's despatch; with every fault, yet never tedious; with no merit, yet inimitably right. And, once more, to make an end of commendations, what novel is inspired with a more unstrained or a more wholesome morality?

Yes; in spite of Miss Yonge, who introduced me to the name of d'Artagnan only to dissuade me from a nearer knowledge of the man, I have to add morality. There is no quite good book without a good morality; but the world is wide, and so are morals. Out of two people who have dipped into Sir Richard Burton's Thousand and One Nights, one shall have been offended by the animal details; another to whom these were harmless, perhaps even pleasing, shall yet have been shocked in his turn by the rascality and cruelty of all the characters. Of two readers, again, one shall have been pained by the morality of a religious memoir, one by that of the Vicomte de Bragelonne. And the point is that neither need be wrong. We shall always shock each other both in life and art; we cannot get the sun into our pictures, nor the abstract right (if there be such a thing) into our books; enough if, in the one, there glimmer some hint of the great light that blinds us from heaven; enough if, in the other, there shine, even upon foul details, a spirit of magnanimity. I would scarce send to the Vicomte a reader who was in quest of what we may call puritan morality. The ventripotent mulatto, the great eater, worker, earner and waster, the man of much and witty laughter, the man of the great heart and alas! of the doubtful honesty, is a figure not yet clearly set before the world; he still awaits a sober and yet genial portrait; but with whatever art that may be touched, and whatever indulgence, it will not be the portrait of a precisian. Dumas was certainly not thinking of himself, but of Planchet, when he put into the mouth of d'Artagnan's old servant this excellent profession: "Monsieur, j'étais une de ces bonnes pâtes d'hommes que Dieu a fait pour s'animer pendant un certain temps et pour trouver bonnes toutes choses qui accompagnent leur séjour sur la terre." He was thinking, as I say, of Planchet, to whom the words are aptly fitted; but they were fitted also to Planchet's creator; and perhaps this struck him as he wrote, for observe what follows: "D'Artagnan s'assit alors près de la fenêtre, et, cette philosophie de Planchet lui ayant paru solide, il y rêva." In a man who finds all things good, you will scarce expect much zeal for negative virtues: the active alone will have a charm for him; abstinence, however wise, however kind, will always seem to such a judge entirely mean and partly impious. So with Dumas. Chastity is not near his heart; nor yet, to his own sore cost, that virtue of frugality which is the armour of the artist. Now, in the Vicomte, he had much to do with the contest of Fouquet and Colbert. Historic justice should be all upon the side of Colbert, of official honesty, and fiscal competence. And Dumas knew it well: three times at least he shows his knowledge; once it is but flashed upon us and received with the laughter of Fouquet himself, in the jesting controversy in the gardens of Saint Mandé; once it is touched on by Aramis in the forest of Sénart; in the end, it is set before us clearly in one dignified speech of the triumphant Colbert. But in Fouquet, the waster, the lover of good cheer and wit and art, the swift transactor of much business, "l'homme de bruit, l'homme de plaisir, l'homme qui n'est que parceque les autres sont," Dumas saw something of himself and drew the figure the more tenderly. It is to me even touching to see how he insists on Fouquet's honour; not seeing, you might think, that unflawed honour is impossible to spendthrifts; but rather, perhaps, in the light of his own life, seeing it too well, and clinging the more to what was left. Honour can survive a wound; it can live and thrive without a member. The man rebounds from his disgrace; he begins fresh foundations on the ruins of the old; and when his sword is broken, he will do valiantly with his dagger. So it is with Fouquet in the book; so it was with Dumas on the battlefield of life.

To cling to what is left of any damaged quality is virtue in the man; but perhaps to sing its praises is scarcely to be called morality in the writer. And it is elsewhere, it is in the character of d'Artagnan, that we must look for that spirit of morality, which is one of the chief merits of the book, makes one of the main joys of its perusal, and sets it high above more popular rivals. Athos, with the coming of years, has declined too much into the preacher, and the preacher of a sapless creed; but d'Artagnan has mellowed into a man so witty, rough, kind and upright, that he takes the heart by storm. There is nothing of the copy-book about his virtues, nothing of the drawing-room in his fine, natural civility; he will sail near the wind; he is no district visitor—no Wesley or Robespierre; his conscience is void of all refinement whether for good or evil; but the whole man rings true like a good sovereign. Readers who have approached the Vicomte, not across country, but by the legitimate, five-volumed avenue of the Mousquetaires and Vingt Ans Après, will not have forgotten d'Artagnan's ungentlemanly and perfectly improbable trick upon Milady. What a pleasure it is, then, what a reward, and how agreeable a lesson, to see the old captain humble himself to the son of the man whom he had personated! Here, and throughout, if I am to choose virtues for myself or my friends, let me choose the virtues of d'Artagnan. I do not say there is no character as well drawn in Shakespeare; I do say there is none that I love so wholly. There are many spiritual eyes that seem to spy upon our actions—eyes of the dead and the absent, whom we imagine to behold us in our most private hours, and whom we fear and scruple to offend: our witnesses and judges. And among these, even if you should think me childish, I must count my d'Artagnan—not d'Artagnan of the memoirs whom Thackeray pretended to prefer—a preference, I take the freedom of saying, in which he stands alone; not the d'Artagnan of flesh and blood, but him of the ink and paper; not Nature's, but Dumas's. And this is the particular crown and triumph of the artist—not to be true merely, but to be lovable; not simply to convince, but to enchant.

There is yet another point in the Vicomte which I find incomparable. I can recall no other work of the imagination in which the end of life is represented with so nice a tact. I was asked the other day if Dumas made me laugh or cry. Well in this my late fifth reading of the Vicomte, I did laugh once at the small Coquelin de Volière business, and was perhaps a thought surprised at having done so: to make up for it, I smiled continually. But for tears, I do not know. If you put a pistol to my throat, I must own the tale trips upon a very airy foot—within a measurable distance of unreality; and for those who like the big guns to be discharged and the great passions to appear authentically, it may even seem inadequate from first to last. Not so to me; I cannot count that a poor dinner, or a poor book, where I meet with those I love; and, above all, in this last volume, I find a singular charm of spirit. It breathes a pleasant and a tonic sadness, always brave, never hysterical. Upon the crowded, noisy life of this long tale, evening gradually falls; and the lights are extinguished, and the heroes pass away one by one. One by one they go, and not a regret embitters their departure; the young succeed them in their places, Louis Quatorze is swelling larger and shining broader, another generation and another France dawn on the horizon; but for us and these old men whom we have loved so long, the inevitable end draws near and is welcome. To read this well is to anticipate experience. Ah, if only when these hours of the long shadows fall for us in reality and not in figure, we may hope to face them with a mind as quiet!

But my paper is running out; the siege guns are firing on the Dutch frontier; and I must say adieu for the fifth time to my old comrade fallen on the field of glory. Adieu—rather au revoir! Yet a sixth time, dearest d'Artagnan, we shall kidnap Monk and take horse together for Belle Isle.

CHAPTER XV. A GOSSIP ON ROMANCE

In anything fit to be called by the name of reading, the process itself should be absorbing and voluptuous; we should gloat over a book, be rapt clean out of ourselves, and rise from the perusal, our mind filled with the busiest, kaleidoscopic dance of images, incapable of sleep or of continuous thought. The words, if the book be eloquent, should run thenceforward in our ears like the noise of breakers, and the story, if it be a story, repeat itself in a thousand coloured pictures to the eye. It was for this last pleasure that we read so closely, and loved our books so dearly, in the bright, troubled period of boyhood. Eloquence and thought, character and conversation, were but obstacles to brush aside as we dug blithely after a certain sort of incident, like a pig for truffles. For my part, I liked a story to begin with an old wayside inn where, "towards the close of the year 17--," several gentlemen in three-cocked hats were playing bowls. A friend of mine preferred the Malabar coast in a storm, with a ship beating to windward, and a scowling fellow of Herculean proportions striding along the beach; he, to be sure, was a pirate. This was further afield than my home-keeping fancy loved to travel, and designed altogether for a larger canvas than the tales that I affected. Give me a highwayman and I was full to the brim; a Jacobite would do, but the highwayman was my favourite dish. I can still hear that merry clatter of the hoofs along the moonlit lane; night and the coming of day are still related in my mind with the doings of John Rann or Jerry Abershaw; and the words "post-chaise," the "great North road," "ostler," and "nag" still sound in my ears like poetry. One and all, at least, and each with his particular fancy, we read story-books in childhood, not for eloquence or character or thought, but for some quality of the brute incident. That quality was not mere bloodshed or wonder. Although each of these was welcome in its place, the charm for the sake of which we read depended on something different from either. My elders used to read novels aloud; and I can still remember four different passages which I heard, before I was ten, with the same keen and lasting pleasure. One I discovered long afterwards to be the admirable opening of

What will he Do with It: it was no wonder I was pleased with that. The other three still remain unidentified. One is a little vague; it was about a dark, tall house at night, and people groping on the stairs by the light that escaped from the open door of a sickroom. In another, a lover left a ball, and went walking in a cool, dewy park, whence he could watch the lighted windows and the figures of the dancers as they moved. This was the most sentimental impression I think I had yet received, for a child is somewhat deaf to the sentimental. In the last, a poet, who had been tragically wrangling with his wife, walked forth on the sea-beach on a tempestuous night and witnessed the horrors of a wreck. [153] Different as they are, all these early favourites have a common note—they have all a touch of the romantic.

Drama is the poetry of conduct, romance the poetry of circumstance. The pleasure that we take in life is of two sorts—the active and the passive. Now we are conscious of a great command over our destiny; anon we are lifted up by circumstance, as by a breaking wave, and dashed we know not how into the future. Now we are pleased by our conduct, anon merely pleased by our surroundings. It would be hard to say which of these modes of satisfaction is the more effective, but the latter is surely the more constant. Conduct is three parts of life, they say; but I think they put it high. There is a vast deal in life and letters both which is not immoral, but simply a-moral; which either does not regard the human will at all, or deals with it in obvious and healthy relations; where the interest turns, not upon what a man shall choose to do, but on how he manages to do it; not on the passionate slips and hesitations of the conscience, but on the problems of the body and of the practical intelligence, in clean, open-air adventure, the shock of arms or the diplomacy of life. With such material as this it is impossible to build a play, for the serious theatre exists solely on moral grounds, and is a standing proof of the dissemination of the human conscience. But it is possible to build, upon this ground, the most joyous of verses, and the most lively, beautiful, and buoyant tales.

One thing in life calls for another; there is a fitness in events and places. The sight of a pleasant arbour puts it in our mind to sit there. One place suggests work, another idleness, a third early rising and long rambles in the dew. The effect of night, of any flowing water, of lighted cities, of the peep of day, of ships, of the open ocean, calls up in the mind an army of anonymous desires and pleasures. Something, we feel, should happen; we know not what, yet we proceed in quest of it. And many of the happiest hours of life fleet by us in this vain attendance on the genius of the place and moment. It is thus that tracts of young fir, and low rocks that reach into deep soundings, particularly torture and delight me. Something must have happened in such places, and perhaps ages back, to members of my race; and when I was a child I tried in vain to invent appropriate games for them, as I still try, just as vainly, to fit them with the proper story. Some places speak distinctly. Certain dank gardens cry aloud for a murder; certain old houses demand to be haunted; certain coasts are set apart for shipwreck. Other spots again seem to abide their destiny, suggestive and impenetrable, "miching mallecho." The inn at Burford Bridge, with its arbours and green garden and silent, eddying river—though it is known already as the place where Keats wrote some of his Endymion and Nelson parted from his Emma—still seems to wait the coming of the appropriate legend. Within these ivied walls, behind these old green shutters, some further business smoulders, waiting for its hour. The old Hawes Inn at the Queen's Ferry makes a similar call upon my fancy. There it stands, apart from the town, beside the pier, in a climate of its own, half inland, half marine—in front, the ferry bubbling with the tide and the guardship swinging to her anchor; behind, the old garden with the trees. Americans seek it already for the sake of Lovel and Oldbuck, who dined there at the beginning of the Antiquary. But you need not tell me—that is not all; there is some story, unrecorded or not yet complete, which must express the meaning of that inn more fully. So it is with names and faces; so it is with incidents that are idle and inconclusive in themselves, and yet seem like the beginning of some quaint romance, which the all-careless author leaves untold. How many of these romances have we not seen determine at their birth; how many people have met us with a look of meaning in their eye, and sunk at once into trivial acquaintances; to how many places have we not drawn near, with express intimations—"here my destiny awaits me"—and we have but dined there and passed on! I have lived both at the Hawes and Burford in a perpetual flutter, on the heels, as it seemed, of some adventure that should justify the place; but though the feeling had me to bed at night and called me again at morning in one unbroken round of pleasure and suspense, nothing befell me in either worth remark. The man or the hour had not yet come; but some day, I think, a boat shall put off from the Queen's Ferry, fraught with a dear cargo, and some frosty night a horseman, on a tragic errand, rattle with his whip upon the green shutters of the inn at Burford. [155]

Now, this is one of the natural appetites with which any lively literature has to count. The desire for knowledge, I had almost added the desire for meat, is not more deeply seated than this demand for fit and striking incident. The dullest of clowns tells, or tries to tell, himself a story, as the feeblest of children uses invention in his play; and even as the imaginative grown person, joining in the game, at once enriches it with many delightful circumstances, the great creative writer shows us the realisation and the apotheosis of the day-dreams of common men. His stories may be nourished with the realities of life, but their true mark is to satisfy the nameless longings of the reader, and to obey the ideal laws of the day-dream. The right kind of thing should fall out in the right kind of place; the right kind of thing should follow; and not only the characters talk aptly and think naturally, but all the circumstances in a tale answer one to another like notes in music. The threads of a story come from time to time together and make a picture in the web; the characters fall from time to time into some attitude to each other or to nature, which stamps the story home like an illustration. Crusoe recoiling from the footprint, Achilles shouting over against the Trojans, Ulysses bending the great bow, Christian running with his fingers in his ears, these are each culminating moments in the legend, and each has been printed on the mind's eye for ever. Other things we may forget; we may forget the words, although they are beautiful; we may forget the author's comment, although perhaps it was ingenious and true; but these epoch-making scenes, which put the last mark of truth upon a story and fill up, at one blow, our capacity for sympathetic pleasure, we so adopt into the very bosom of our mind that neither time nor tide can efface or weaken the impression. This, then, is the plastic part of literature: to embody character, thought, or emotion in some act or attitude that shall be remarkably striking to the mind's eye. This is the highest and hardest thing to do in words; the thing which, once accomplished, equally delights the schoolboy and the sage, and makes, in its own right, the quality of epics. Compared with this, all other purposes in literature, except the purely lyrical or the purely philosophic, are bastard in nature, facile of execution, and feeble in result. It is one thing to write about the inn at Burford, or to describe scenery with the word-painters; it is quite another to seize on the heart of the suggestion and make a country famous with a legend. It is one thing to remark and to dissect, with the most cutting logic, the complications of life, and of the human spirit; it is quite another to give them body and blood in the story of Ajax or of Hamlet. The first is literature, but the second is something besides, for it is likewise art.

English people of the present day [157] are apt, I know not why, to look somewhat down on incident, and reserve their admiration for the clink of teaspoons and the accents of the curate. It is thought clever to write a novel with no story at all, or at least with a very dull one. Reduced even to the lowest terms, a certain interest can be communicated by the art of narrative; a sense of human kinship stirred; and a kind of monotonous fitness, comparable to the words and air of Sandy's Mull, preserved among the infinitesimal occurrences recorded. Some people work, in this manner, with even a strong touch. Mr. Trollope's inimitable clergymen naturally arise to the mind in this connection. But even Mr. Trollope does not confine himself to chronicling small beer. Mr. Crawley's collision with the Bishop's wife, Mr. Melnotte dallying in the deserted banquet-room, are typical incidents, epically conceived, fitly embodying a crisis. Or again look at Thackeray. If Rawdon Crawley's blow were not delivered, Vanity Fair would cease to be a work of art. That scene is the chief ganglion of the tale; and the discharge of energy from Rawdon's fist is the reward and consolation of the reader. The end of Esmond is a yet wider excursion from the author's customary fields; the scene at Castlewood is pure Dumas; the great and wily English borrower has here borrowed from the great, unblushing French thief; as usual, he has borrowed admirably well, and the breaking of the sword rounds off the best of all his books with a manly, martial note. But perhaps nothing can more strongly illustrate the necessity for marking incident than to compare the living fame of Robinson Crusoe with the discredit of Clarissa Harlowe. Clarissa is a book of a far more startling import, worked out, on a great canvas, with inimitable courage and unflagging art. It contains wit, character, passion, plot, conversations full of spirit and insight, letters sparkling with unstrained humanity; and if the death of the heroine be somewhat frigid and artificial, the last days of the hero strike the only note of what we now call Byronism, between the Elizabethans and Byron himself. And yet a little story of a shipwrecked sailor, with not a tenth part of the style nor a thousandth part of the wisdom, exploring none of the arcana of humanity and deprived of the perennial interest of love, goes on from edition to edition, ever young, while Clarissa lies upon the shelves unread. A friend of mine, a Welsh blacksmith, was twenty-five years old and could neither read nor write, when he heard a chapter of Robinson read aloud in a farm kitchen. Up to that moment he had sat content, huddled in his ignorance, but he left that farm another man. There were day-dreams, it appeared, divine day-dreams, written and printed and bound, and to be bought for money and enjoyed at pleasure. Down he sat that day, painfully learned to read Welsh, and returned to borrow the book. It had been lost, nor could he find another copy but one that was in English. Down he sat once more, learned English, and at length, and with entire delight, read Robinson. It is like the story of a love-chase. If he had heard a letter from Clarissa, would he have been fired with the same chivalrous ardour? I wonder. Yet Clarissa has every quality that can be shown in prose, one alone excepted—pictorial or picture-making romance. While Robinson depends, for the most part and with the overwhelming majority of its readers, on the charm of circumstance.

In the highest achievements of the art of words, the dramatic and the pictorial, the moral and romantic interest, rise and fall together by a common and organic law. Situation is animated with passion, passion clothed upon with situation. Neither exists for itself, but each inheres indissolubly with the other. This is high art; and not only the highest art possible in words, but the highest art of all, since it combines the greatest mass and diversity of the elements of truth and pleasure. Such are epics, and the few prose tales that have the epic weight. But as from a school of works, aping the creative, incident and romance are ruthlessly discarded, so may character and drama be omitted or subordinated to romance. There is one book, for example, more generally loved than Shakespeare, that captivates in childhood, and still delights in age—I mean the Arabian Nights—where you shall look in vain for moral or for intellectual interest. No human face or voice greets us among that wooden crowd of kings and genies, sorcerers and beggarmen. Adventure, on the most naked terms, furnishes forth the entertainment and is found enough. Dumas approaches perhaps nearest of any modern to these Arabian authors in the purely material charm of some of his romances. The early part of Monte Cristo, down to the finding of the treasure, is a piece of perfect story-telling; the man never breathed who shared these moving incidents without a tremor; and yet Faria is a thing of packthread and Dantès little more than a name. The sequel is one long-drawn error, gloomy, bloody, unnatural and dull; but as for these early chapters, I do not believe there is another volume extant where you can breathe the same unmingled atmosphere of romance. It is very thin and light to be sure, as on a high mountain; but it is brisk and clear and sunny in proportion. I saw the other day, with envy, an old and a very clever lady setting forth on a second or third voyage into Monte Cristo. Here are stories which powerfully affect the reader, which can be reperused at any age, and where the characters are no more than puppets. The bony fist of the showman visibly propels them; their springs are an open secret; their faces are of wood, their bellies filled with bran; and yet we thrillingly partake of their adventures. And the point may be illustrated still further. The last interview between Lucy and Richard Feveril is pure drama; more than that, it is the strongest scene, since Shakespeare, in the English tongue. Their first meeting by the river, on the other hand, is pure romance; it has nothing to do with character; it might happen to any other boy or maiden, and be none the less delightful for the change. And yet I think he would be a bold man who should choose between these passages. Thus, in the same book, we may have two scenes, each capital in its order: in the one, human passion, deep calling unto deep, shall utter its genuine voice; in the second, according circumstances, like instruments in tune, shall build up a trivial but desirable incident, such as we love to prefigure for ourselves; and in the end, in spite of the critics, we may hesitate to give the preference to either. The one may ask more genius—I do not say it does; but at least the other dwells as clearly in the memory.

True romantic art, again, makes a romance of all things. It reaches into the highest abstraction of the ideal; it does not refuse the most pedestrian realism. Robinson Crusoe is as realistic as it is romantic; both qualities are pushed to an extreme, and neither suffers. Nor does romance depend upon the material importance of the incidents. To deal with strong and deadly elements, banditti, pirates, war and murder, is to conjure with great names, and, in the event of failure, to double the disgrace. The arrival of Haydn and Consuelo at the Canon's villa is a very trifling incident; yet we may read a dozen boisterous stories from beginning to end, and not receive so fresh and stirring an impression of adventure. It was the scene of Crusoe at the wreck, if I remember rightly, that so bewitched my blacksmith. Nor is the fact surprising. Every single article the castaway recovers from the hulk is "a joy for ever" to the man who reads of them. They are the things that should be found, and the bare enumeration stirs the blood. I found a glimmer of the same interest the other day in a new book, The Sailor's Sweetheart, by Mr. Clark Russell. The whole business of the brig Morning Star is very rightly felt and spiritedly written; but the clothes, the books and the money satisfy the reader's mind like things to eat. We are dealing here with the old cut-and-dry, legitimate interest of treasure trove. But even treasure trove can be made dull. There are few people who have not groaned under the plethora of goods that fell to the lot of the Swiss Family Robinson, that dreary family. They found article after article, creature after creature, from milk kine to pieces of ordnance, a whole consignment; but no informing taste had presided over the selection, there was no smack or relish in the invoice; and these riches left the fancy cold. The box of goods in Verne's Mysterious Island is another case in point: there was no gusto and no glamour about that; it might have come from a shop. But the two hundred and seventy-eight Australian sovereigns on board the Morning Star fell upon me like a surprise that I had expected; whole vistas of secondary stories, besides the one in hand, radiated forth from that discovery, as they radiate from a striking particular in life; and I was made for the moment as happy as a reader has the right to be.

To come at all at the nature of this quality of romance, we must bear in mind the peculiarity of our attitude to any art. No art produces illusion; in the theatre we never forget that we are in the theatre; and while we read a story, we sit wavering between two minds, now merely clapping our hands at the merit of the performance, now condescending to take an active part in fancy with the characters. This last is the triumph of romantic story-telling: when the reader consciously plays at being the hero, the scene is a good scene. Now in character-studies the pleasure that we take is critical; we watch, we approve, we smile at incongruities, we are moved to sudden heats of sympathy with courage, suffering or virtue. But the characters are still themselves, they are not us; the more clearly they are depicted, the more widely do they stand away from us, the more imperiously do they thrust us back into our place as a spectator. I cannot identify myself with Rawdon Crawley or with Eugène de Rastignac, for I have scarce a hope or fear in common with them. It is not character but incident that woos us out of our reserve. Something happens as we desire to have it happen to ourselves; some situation, that we have long dallied with in fancy, is realised in the story with enticing and appropriate details. Then we forget the characters; then we push the hero aside; then we plunge into the tale in our own person and bathe in fresh experience; and then, and then only, do we say we have been reading a romance. It is not only pleasurable things that we imagine in our day-dreams; there are lights in which we are willing to contemplate even the idea of our own death; ways in which it seems as if it would amuse us to be cheated, wounded or calumniated. It is thus possible to construct a story, even of tragic import, in which every incident, detail and trick of circumstance shall be welcome to the reader's thoughts. Fiction is to the grown man what play is to the child; it is there that he changes the atmosphere and tenor of his life; and when the game so chimes with his fancy that he can join in it with all his heart, when it pleases him with every turn, when he loves to recall it and dwells upon its recollection with entire delight, fiction is called romance.

Walter Scott is out and away the king of the romantics. The Lady of the Lake has no indisputable claim to be a poem beyond the inherent fitness and desirability of the tale. It is just such a story as a man would make up for himself, walking, in the best health and temper, through just such scenes as it is laid in. Hence it is that a charm dwells undefinable among these slovenly verses, as the unseen cuckoo fills the mountains with his note; hence, even after we have flung the book aside, the scenery and adventures remain present to the mind, a new and green possession, not unworthy of that beautiful name, The Lady of the Lake, or that direct, romantic opening—one of the most spirited and poetical in literature—"The stag at eve had drunk his fill." The same strength and the same weaknesses adorn and disfigure the novels. In that ill-written, ragged book, The Pirate, the figure of Cleveland—cast up by the sea on the resounding foreland of Dunrossness—moving, with the blood on his hands and the Spanish words on his tongue, among the simple islanders—singing a serenade under the window of his Shetland mistress—is conceived in the very highest manner of romantic invention. The words of his song, "Through groves of palm," sung in such a scene and by such a lover, clench, as in a nutshell, the emphatic contrast upon which the tale is built. In Guy Mannering, again, every incident is delightful to the imagination; and the scene when Harry Bertram lands at Ellangowan is a model instance of romantic method.

"'I remember the tune well,' he says, 'though I cannot guess what should at present so strongly recall it to my memory.'" He took his flageolet from his pocket and played a simple melody. Apparently the tune awoke the corresponding associations of a damsel. She immediately took up the song—

"'Are these the links of Forth, she said;

Or are they the crooks of Dee,

Or the bonny woods of Warroch Head

That I so fain would see?'

"'By heaven!' said Bertram, 'it is the very ballad.'"

On this quotation two remarks fall to be made. First, as an instance of modern feeling for romance, this famous touch of the flageolet and the old song is selected by Miss Braddon for omission. Miss Braddon's idea of a story, like Mrs Todgers's idea of a wooden leg, were something strange to have expounded. As a matter of personal experience, Meg's appearance to old Mr. Bertram on the road, the ruins of Derncleugh, the scene of the flageolet, and the Dominie's recognition of Harry, are the four strong notes that continue to ring in the mind after the book is laid aside. The second point is still more curious. The reader will observe a mark of excision in the passage as quoted by me. Well, here is how it runs in the original: "a damsel, who, close behind a fine spring about half-way down the descent, and which had once supplied the castle with water, was engaged in bleaching linen." A man who gave in such copy would be discharged from the staff of a daily paper. Scott has forgotten to prepare the reader for the presence of the "damsel"; he has forgotten to mention the spring and its relation to the ruin; and now, face to face with his omission, instead of trying back and starting fair, crams all this matter, tail foremost, into a single shambling sentence. It is not merely bad English, or bad style; it is abominably bad narrative besides.

Certainly the contrast is remarkable; and it is one that throws a strong light upon the subject of this paper. For here we have a man of the finest creative instinct touching with perfect certainty and charm the romantic junctures of his story; and we find him utterly careless, almost, it would seem, incapable, in the technical matter of style, and not only frequently weak, but frequently wrong in points of drama. In character parts, indeed, and particularly in the Scotch, he was delicate, strong and truthful; but the trite, obliterated features of too many of his heroes have already wearied two generations of readers. At times his characters will speak with something far beyond propriety with a true heroic note; but on the next page they will be wading wearily forward with an ungrammatical and undramatic rigmarole of words. The man who could conceive and write the character of Elspeth of the Craigburnfoot, as Scott has conceived and written it, had not only splendid romantic, but splendid tragic gifts. How comes it, then, that he could so often fob us off with languid, inarticulate twaddle?

It seems to me that the explanation is to be found in the very quality of his surprising merits. As his books are play to the reader, so were they play to him. He conjured up the romantic with delight, but he had hardly patience to describe it. He was a great day-dreamer, a seer of fit and beautiful and humorous visions, but hardly a great artist; hardly, in the manful sense, an artist at all. He pleased himself, and so he pleases us. Of the pleasures of his art he tasted fully; but of its toils and vigils and distresses never man knew less. A great romantic—an idle child.

CHAPTER XVI. A HUMBLE REMONSTRANCE [168a]

We have recently [168b] enjoyed a quite peculiar pleasure: hearing, in some detail, the opinions, about the art they practise, of Mr. Walter Besant and Mr. Henry James; two men certainly of very different calibre: Mr. James so precise of outline, so cunning of fence, so scrupulous of finish, and Mr. Besant so genial, so friendly, with so persuasive and humorous a vein of whim: Mr. James the very type of the deliberate artist, Mr. Besant the impersonation of good nature. That such doctors should differ will excite no great surprise; but one point in which they seem to agree fills me, I confess, with wonder. For they are both content to talk about the "art of fiction"; and Mr. Besant, waxing exceedingly bold, goes on to oppose this so-called "art of fiction" to the "art of poetry." By the art of poetry he can mean nothing but the art of verse, an art of handicraft, and only comparable with the art of prose. For that heat and height of sane emotion which we agree to call by the name of poetry, is but a libertine and vagrant quality; present, at times, in any art, more often absent from them all; too seldom present in the prose novel, too frequently absent from the ode and epic. Fiction is the same case; it is no substantive art, but an element which enters largely into all the arts but architecture. Homer, Wordsworth, Phidias, Hogarth, and Salvini, all deal in fiction; and yet I do not suppose that either Hogarth or Salvini, to mention but these two, entered in any degree into the scope of Mr. Besant's interesting lecture or Mr. James's charming essay. The art of fiction, then, regarded as a definition, is both too ample and too scanty. Let me suggest another; let me suggest that what both Mr. James and Mr. Besant had in view was neither more nor less than the art of narrative.

But Mr. Besant is anxious to speak solely of "the modern English novel," the stay and bread-winner of Mr. Mudie; and in the author of the most pleasing novel on that roll, All Sorts and Conditions of Men, the desire is natural enough. I can conceive, then, that he would hasten to propose two additions, and read thus: the art of fictitious narrative in prose.

Now the fact of the existence of the modern English novel is not to be denied; materially, with its three volumes, leaded type, and gilded lettering, it is easily distinguishable from other forms of literature; but to talk at all fruitfully of any branch of art, it is needful to build our definitions on some more fundamental ground then binding. Why, then, are we to add "in prose"? The Odyssey appears to me the best of romances; The Lady of the Lake to stand high in the second order; and Chaucer's tales and prologues to contain more of the matter and art of the modern English novel than the whole treasury of Mr. Mudie. Whether a narrative be written in blank verse or the Spenserian stanza, in the long period of Gibbon or the chipped phrase of Charles Reade, the principles of the art of narrative must be equally observed. The choice of a noble and swelling style in prose affects the problem of narration in the same way, if not to the same degree, as the choice of measured verse; for both imply a closer synthesis of events, a higher key of dialogue, and a more picked and stately strain of words. If you are to refuse Don Juan, it is hard to see why you should include Zanoni or (to bracket works of very different value) The Scarlet Letter; and by what discrimination are you to open your doors to The Pilgrim's Progress and close them on The Faery Queen? To bring things closer home, I will here propound to Mr. Besant a conundrum. A narrative called Paradise Lost was written in English verse by one John Milton; what was it then? It was next translated by Chateaubriand into French prose; and what was it then? Lastly, the French translation was, by some inspired compatriot of George Gilfillan (and of mine) turned bodily into an English novel; and, in the name of clearness, what was it then?

But, once more, why should we add "fictitious"? The reason why is obvious. The reason why not, if something more recondite, does not want for weight. The art of narrative, in fact, is the same, whether it is applied to the selection and illustration of a real series of events or of an imaginary series. Boswell's Life of Johnson (a work of cunning and inimitable art) owes its success to the same technical manœuvres as (let us say) Tom Jones: the clear conception of certain characters of man, the choice and presentation of certain incidents out of a great number that offered, and the invention (yes, invention) and preservation of a certain key in dialogue. In which these things are done with the more art—in which with the greater air of nature—readers will differently judge. Boswell's is, indeed, a very special case, and almost a generic; but it is not only in Boswell, it is in every biography with any salt of life, it is in every history where events and men, rather than ideas, are presented—in Tacitus, in Carlyle, in Michelet, in Macaulay—that the novelist will find many of his own methods most conspicuously and adroitly handled. He will find besides that he, who is free—who has the right to invent or steal a missing incident, who has the right, more precious still, of wholesale omission—is frequently defeated, and, with all his advantages, leaves a less strong impression of reality and passion. Mr. James utters his mind with a becoming fervour on the sanctity of truth to the novelist; on a more careful examination truth will seem a word of very debateable propriety, not only for the labours of the novelist, but for those of the historian. No art—to use the daring phrase of Mr. James—can successfully "compete with life"; and the art that seeks to do so is condemned to perish montibus aviis. Life goes before us, infinite in complication; attended by the most various and surprising meteors; appealing at once to the eye, to the ear, to the mind—the seat of wonder, to the touch—so thrillingly delicate, and to the belly—so imperious when starved. It combines and employs in its manifestation the method and material, not of one art only, but of all the arts, Music is but an arbitrary trifling with a few of life's majestic chords; painting is but a shadow of its pageantry of light and colour; literature does but drily indicate that wealth of incident, of moral obligation, of virtue, vice, action, rapture and agony, with which it teems. To "compete with life," whose sun we cannot look upon, whose passions and diseases waste and slay us—to compete with the flavour of wine, the beauty of the dawn, the scorching of fire, the bitterness of death and separation—here is, indeed, a projected escalade of heaven; here are, indeed, labours for a Hercules in a dress coat, armed with a pen and a dictionary to depict the passions, armed with a tube of superior flake-white to paint the portrait of the insufferable sun. No art is true in this sense: none can "compete with life": not even history, built indeed of indisputable facts, but these facts robbed of their vivacity and sting; so that even when we read of the sack of a city or the fall of an empire, we are surprised, and justly commend the author's talent, if our pulse be quickened. And mark, for a last differentia, that this quickening of the pulse is, in almost every case, purely agreeable; that these phantom reproductions of experience, even at their most acute, convey decided pleasure; while experience itself, in the cockpit of life, can torture and slay.

What, then, is the object, what the method, of an art, and what the source of its power? The whole secret is that no art does "compete with life." Man's one method, whether he reasons or creates, is to half-shut his eyes against the dazzle and confusion of reality. The arts, like arithmetic and geometry, turn away their eyes from the gross, coloured and mobile nature at our feet, and regard instead a certain figmentary abstraction. Geometry will tell us of a circle, a thing never seen in nature; asked about a green circle or an iron circle, it lays its hand upon its mouth. So with the arts. Painting, ruefully comparing sunshine and flake-white, gives up truth of colour, as it had already given up relief and movement; and instead of vying with nature, arranges a scheme of harmonious tints. Literature, above all in its most typical mood, the mood of narrative, similarly flees the direct challenge and pursues instead an independent and creative aim. So far as it imitates at all, it imitates not life but speech: not the facts of human destiny, but the emphasis and the suppressions with which the human actor tells of them. The real art that dealt with life directly was that of the first men who told their stories round the savage camp-fire. Our art is occupied, and bound to be occupied, not so much in making stories true as in making them typical; not so much in capturing the lineaments of each fact, as in marshalling all of them towards a common end. For the welter of impressions, all forcible but all discreet, which life presents, it substitutes a certain artificial series of impressions, all indeed most feebly represented, but all aiming at the same effect, all eloquent of the same idea, all chiming together like consonant notes in music or like the graduated tints in a good picture. From all its chapters, from all its pages, from all its sentences, the well-written novel echoes and re-echoes its one creative and controlling thought; to this must every incident and character contribute; the style must have been pitched in unison with this; and if there is anywhere a word that looks another way, the book would be stronger, clearer, and (I had almost said) fuller without it. Life is monstrous, infinite, illogical, abrupt and poignant; a work of art, in comparison, is neat, finite, self-contained, rational, flowing and emasculate. Life imposes by brute energy, like inarticulate thunder; art catches the ear, among the far louder noises of experience, like an air artificially made by a discreet musician. A proposition of geometry does not compete with life; and a proposition of geometry is a fair and luminous parallel for a work of art. Both are reasonable, both untrue to the crude fact; both inhere in nature, neither represents it. The novel, which is a work of art, exists, not by its resemblances to life, which are forced and material, as a shoe must still consist of leather, but by its immeasurable difference from life, which is designed and significant, and is both the method and the meaning of the work.

The life of man is not the subject of novels, but the inexhaustible magazine from which subjects are to be selected; the name of these is legion; and with each new subject—for here again I must differ by the whole width of heaven from Mr. James—the true artist will vary his method and change the point of attack. That which was in one case an excellence, will become a defect in another; what was the making of one book, will in the next be impertinent or dull. First each novel, and then each class of novels, exists by and for itself. I will take, for instance, three main classes, which are fairly distinct: first, the novel of adventure, which appeals to certain almost sensual and quite illogical tendencies in man; second, the novel of character, which appeals to our intellectual appreciation of man's foibles and mingled and inconstant motives; and third, the dramatic novel, which deals with the same stuff as the serious theatre, and appeals to our emotional nature and moral judgment.

And first for the novel of adventure. Mr. James refers, with singular generosity of praise, to a little book about a quest for hidden treasure; but he lets fall, by the way, some rather startling words. In this book he misses what he calls the "immense luxury" of being able to quarrel with his author. The luxury, to most of us, is to lay by our judgment, to be submerged by the tale as by a billow, and only to awake, and begin to distinguish and find fault, when the piece is over and the volume laid aside. Still more remarkable is Mr. James's reason. He cannot criticise the author, as he goes, "because," says he, comparing it with another work, "I have been a child, but I have never been on a quest for buried treasure." Here is, indeed, a wilful paradox; for if he has never been on a quest for buried treasure, it can be demonstrated that he has never been a child. There never was a child (unless Master James) but has hunted gold, and been a pirate, and a military commander, and a bandit of the mountains; but has fought, and suffered shipwreck and prison, and imbrued its little hands in gore, and gallantly retrieved the lost battle, and triumphantly protected innocence and beauty. Elsewhere in his essay Mr. James has protested with excellent reason against too narrow a conception of experience; for the born artist, he contends, the "faintest hints of life" are converted into revelations; and it will be found true, I believe, in a majority of cases, that the artist writes with more gusto and effect of those things which he has only wished to do, than of those which he has done. Desire is a wonderful telescope, and Pisgah the best observatory. Now, while it is true that neither Mr. James nor the author of the work in question has ever, in the fleshly sense, gone questing after gold, it is probable that both have ardently desired and fondly imagined the details of such a life in youthful day-dreams; and the author, counting upon that, and well aware (cunning and low-minded man!) that this class of interest, having been frequently treated, finds a readily accessible and beaten road to the sympathies of the reader, addressed himself throughout to the building up and circumstantiation of this boyish dream. Character to the boy is a sealed book; for him, a pirate is a beard, a pair of wide trousers and a liberal complement of pistols. The author, for the sake of circumstantiation and because he was himself more or less grown up, admitted character, within certain limits, into his design; but only within certain limits. Had the same puppets figured in a scheme of another sort, they had been drawn to very different purpose; for in this elementary novel of adventure, the characters need to be presented with but one class of qualities—the warlike and formidable. So as they appear insidious in deceit and fatal in the combat, they have served their end. Danger is the matter with which this class of novel deals; fear, the passion with which it idly trifles; and the characters are portrayed only so far as they realise the sense of danger and provoke the sympathy of fear. To add more traits, to be too clever, to start the hare of moral or intellectual interest while we are running the fox of material interest, is not to enrich but to stultify your tale. The stupid reader will only be offended, and the clever reader lose the scent.

The novel of character has this difference from all others: that it requires no coherency of plot, and for this reason, as in the case of Gil Blas, it is sometimes called the novel of adventure. It turns on the humours of the persons represented; these are, to be sure, embodied in incidents, but the incidents themselves, being tributary, need not march in a progression; and the characters may be statically shown. As they enter, so they may go out; they must be consistent, but they need not grow. Here Mr. James will recognise the note of much of his own work: he treats, for the most part, the statics of character, studying it at rest or only gently moved; and, with his usual delicate and just artistic instinct, he avoids those stronger passions which would deform the attitudes he loves to study, and change his sitters from the humorists of ordinary life to the brute forces and bare types of more emotional moments. In his recent Author of Beltraffio, so just in conception, so nimble and neat in workmanship, strong passion is indeed employed; but observe that it is not displayed. Even in the heroine the working of the passion is suppressed; and the great struggle, the true tragedy, the scène-à-faire passes unseen behind the panels of a locked door. The delectable invention of the young visitor is introduced, consciously or not, to this end: that Mr. James, true to his method, might avoid the scene of passion. I trust no reader will suppose me guilty of undervaluing this little masterpiece. I mean merely that it belongs to one marked class of novel, and that it would have been very differently conceived and treated had it belonged to that other marked class, of which I now proceed to speak.

I take pleasure in calling the dramatic novel by that name, because it enables me to point out by the way a strange and peculiarly English misconception. It is sometimes supposed that the drama consists of incident. It consists of passion, which gives the actor his opportunity; and that passion must progressively increase, or the actor, as the piece proceeded, would be unable to carry the audience from a lower to a higher pitch of interest and emotion. A good serious play must therefore be founded on one of the passionate cruces of life, where duty and inclination come nobly to the grapple; and the same is true of what I call, for that reason, the dramatic novel. I will instance a few worthy specimens, all of our own day and language; Meredith's Rhoda Fleming, that wonderful and painful book, long out of print, [178] and hunted for at bookstalls like an Aldine; Hardy's Pair of Blue

Eyes; and two of Charles Reade's, Griffith Gaunt and the Double Marriage, originally called White Lies, and founded (by an accident quaintly favourable to my nomenclature) on a play by Maquet, the partner of the great Dumas. In this kind of novel the closed door of The Author of Beltraffio must be broken open; passion must appear upon the scene and utter its last word; passion is the be-all and the end-all, the plot and the solution, the protagonist and the deus ex machinâ in one. The characters may come anyhow upon the stage: we do not care; the point is, that, before they leave it, they shall become transfigured and raised out of themselves by passion. It may be part of the design to draw them with detail; to depict a full-length character, and then behold it melt and change in the furnace of emotion. But there is no obligation of the sort; nice portraiture is not required; and we are content to accept mere abstract types, so they be strongly and sincerely moved. A novel of this class may be even great, and yet contain no individual figure; it may be great, because it displays the workings of the perturbed heart and the impersonal utterance of passion; and with an artist of the second class it is, indeed, even more likely to be great, when the issue has thus been narrowed and the whole force of the writer's mind directed to passion alone. Cleverness again, which has its fair field in the novel of character, is debarred all entry upon this more solemn theatre. A far-fetched motive, an ingenious evasion of the issue, a witty instead of a passionate turn, offend us like an insincerity. All should be plain, all straightforward to the end. Hence it is that, in Rhoda Fleming, Mrs. Lovell raises such resentment in the reader; her motives are too flimsy, her ways are too equivocal, for the weight and strength of her surroundings. Hence the hot indignation of the reader when Balzac, after having begun the Duchesse de Langeais in terms of strong if somewhat swollen passion, cuts the knot by the derangement of the hero's clock. Such personages and incidents belong to the novel of character; they are out of place in the high society of the passions; when the passions are introduced in art at their full height, we look to see them, not baffled and impotently striving, as in life, but towering above circumstance and acting substitutes for fate.

And here I can imagine Mr. James, with his lucid sense, to intervene. To much of what I have said he would apparently demur; in much he would, somewhat impatiently, acquiesce. It may be true; but it is not what he desired to say or to hear said. He spoke of the finished picture and its worth when done; I, of the brushes, the palette, and the north light. He uttered his views in the tone and for the ear of good society; I, with the emphasis and technicalities of the obtrusive student. But the point, I may reply, is not merely to amuse the public, but to offer helpful advice to the young writer. And the young writer will not so much be helped by genial pictures of what an art may aspire to at its highest, as by a true idea of what it must be on the lowest terms. The best that we can say to him is this: Let him choose a motive, whether of character or passion; carefully construct his plot so that every incident is an illustration of the motive, and every property employed shall bear to it a near relation of congruity or contrast; avoid a sub-plot, unless, as sometimes in Shakespeare, the sub-plot be a reversion or complement of the main intrigue; suffer not his style to flag below the level of the argument; pitch the key of conversation, not with any thought of how men talk in parlours, but with a single eye to the degree of passion he may be called on to express; and allow neither himself in the narrative nor any character in the course of the dialogue, to utter one sentence that is not part and parcel of the business of the story or the discussion of the problem involved. Let him not regret if this shortens his book; it will be better so; for to add irrelevant matter is not to lengthen but to bury. Let him not mind if he miss a thousand qualities, so that he keeps unflaggingly in pursuit of the one he has chosen. Let him not care particularly if he miss the tone of conversation, the pungent material detail of the day's manners, the reproduction of the atmosphere and the environment. These elements are not essential: a novel may be excellent, and yet have none of them; a passion or a character is so much the better depicted as it rises clearer from material circumstance. In this age of the particular, let him remember the ages of the abstract, the great books of the past, the brave men that lived before Shakespeare and before Balzac. And as the root of the whole matter, let him bear in mind that his novel is not a transcript of life, to be judged by its exactitude; but a simplification of some side or point of life, to stand or fall by its significant simplicity. For although, in great men, working upon great motives, what we observe and admire is often their complexity, yet underneath appearances the truth remains unchanged: that simplification was their method, and that simplicity is their excellence.

II

Since the above was written another novelist has entered repeatedly the lists of theory: one well worthy of mention, Mr. W. D. Howells; and none ever couched a lance with narrower convictions. His own work and those of his pupils and masters singly occupy his mind; he is the bondslave, the zealot of his school; he dreams of an advance in art like what there is in science; he thinks of past things as radically dead; he thinks a form can be outlived: a strange immersion in his own history; a strange forgetfulness of the history of the race! Meanwhile, by a glance at his own works (could he see them with the eager eyes of his readers) much of this illusion would be dispelled. For while he holds all the poor little orthodoxies of the day—no poorer and no smaller than those of yesterday or to-morrow, poor and small, indeed, only so far as they are exclusive—the living quality of much that he has done is of a contrary, I had almost said of a heretical, complexion. A man, as I read him, of an originally strong romantic bent—a certain glow of romance still resides in many of his books, and lends them their distinction. As by accident he runs out and revels in the exceptional; and it is then, as often as not, that his reader rejoices—justly, as I contend. For in all this excessive eagerness to be centrally human, is there not one central human thing that Mr. Howells is too often tempted to neglect: I mean himself? A poet, a finished artist, a man in love with the appearances of life, a cunning reader of the mind, he has other passions and aspirations than those he loves to draw. And why should he suppress himself and do such reverence to the Lemuel Barkers? The obvious is not of necessity the normal; fashion rules and deforms; the majority fall tamely into the contemporary shape, and thus attain, in the eyes of the true observer, only a higher power of insignificance; and the danger is lest, in seeking to draw the normal, a man should draw the null, and write the novel of society instead of the romance of man.

Footnotes:

[1] 1881.

[15] Written for the "Book" of the Edinburgh University Union Fancy Fair.

[17] Professor Tait's laboratory assistant.

[84] In Dr. Murray's admirable new dictionary, I have remarked a flaw sub voce Beacon. In its express, technical sense, a beacon may be defined as "a founded, artificial sea-mark, not lighted."

[100] The late Fleeming Jenkin.

[105] This sequel was called forth by an excellent article in The Spectator.

[128] Waiter, Watty, Woggy, Woggs, Wogg, and lastly Bogue; under which last name he fell in battle some twelve months ago. Glory was his aim and he attained it; for his icon, by the hand of Caldecott, now lies among the treasures of the nation.

[153] Since traced by many obliging correspondents to the gallery of Charles Kingsley.

[155] Since the above was written I have tried to launch the boat with my own hands in Kidnapped. Some day, perhaps, I may try a rattle at the shutters.

[157] 1882.

[168a] This paper, which does not otherwise fit the present volume, is reprinted here as the proper continuation of the last.

[168b] 1884

[178] Now no longer so, thank Heaven!

About Author

Childhood and youth

Stevenson was born at 8 Howard Place, Edinburgh, Scotland on 13 November 1850 to Thomas Stevenson (1818–87), a leading lighthouse engineer, and his wife Margaret Isabella (born Balfour, 1829–97). He was christened Robert Lewis Balfour Stevenson. At about age 18, he changed the spelling of "Lewis" to "Louis", and he dropped "Balfour" in 1873.

Lighthouse design was the family's profession; Thomas's father (Robert's grandfather) was civil engineer Robert Stevenson, and Thomas's brothers (Robert's uncles) Alan and David were in the same field. Thomas's maternal grandfather Thomas Smith had been in the same profession. However, Robert's mother's family were gentry, tracing their lineage back to Alexander Balfour who had held the lands of Inchyra in Fife in the fifteenth century. His mother's father Lewis Balfour (1777–1860) was a minister of the Church of Scotland at nearby Colinton, and her siblings included physician George William Balfour and marine engineer James Balfour. Stevenson spent the greater part of his boyhood holidays in his maternal grandfather's house. "Now I often wonder what I inherited from this old minister," Stevenson wrote. "I must suppose, indeed, that he was fond of preaching sermons, and so am I, though I never heard it maintained that either of us loved to hear them."

Lewis Balfour and his daughter both had weak chests, so they often needed to stay in warmer climates for their health. Stevenson inherited a tendency to coughs and fevers, exacerbated when the family moved to a damp, chilly house at 1 Inverleith Terrace in 1851. The family moved again to the sunnier 17 Heriot Row when Stevenson was six years old, but the tendency to extreme sickness in winter remained with him until he was 11. Illness was a recurrent feature of his adult life and left him extraordinarily thin. Contemporaneous views were that he had tuberculosis, but more recent views are that it was bronchiectasis or even sarcoidosis.

Stevenson's parents were both devout Presbyterians, but the household was not strict in its adherence to Calvinist principles. His nurse Alison Cunningham (known as Cummy) was more fervently religious. Her mix of Calvinism and folk beliefs were an early source of nightmares for the child, and he showed a precocious concern for religion. But she also cared for him tenderly in illness, reading to him from John Bunyan and the Bible as he lay sick in bed and telling tales of the Covenanters. Stevenson recalled this time of sickness in "The Land of Counterpane" in A Child's Garden of Verses (1885), dedicating the book to his nurse.

Stevenson was an only child, both strange-looking and eccentric, and he found it hard to fit in when he was sent to a nearby school at age 6, a problem repeated at age 11 when he went on to the Edinburgh Academy; but he mixed well in lively games with his cousins in summer holidays at Colinton. His frequent illnesses often kept him away from his first school, so he was taught for long stretches by private tutors. He was a late reader, learning at age 7 or 8, but even before this he dictated stories to his mother and nurse, and he compulsively wrote stories throughout his childhood. His father was proud of this interest; he had also written stories in his spare time until his own father found them and told him to "give up such nonsense and mind your business." He paid for the printing of Robert's first publication at 16, entitled The Pentland Rising: A Page of History, 1666. It was an account of the Covenanters' rebellion which was published in 1866, the 200th anniversary of the event.

Education

In September 1857, Stevenson went to Mr Henderson's School in India Street, Edinburgh, but because of poor health stayed only a few weeks and did not return until October 1859. During his many absences he was taught by private tutors. In October 1861, he went to Edinburgh Academy, an independent school for boys, and stayed there sporadically for about fifteen months. In the autumn of 1863, he spent one term at an English boarding school at Spring Grove in Isleworth in Middlesex (now an urban area of West London). In October 1864, following an improvement to his health, he was sent to Robert Thomson's private school in Frederick Street, Edinburgh, where he remained until he went to university. In November 1867, Stevenson entered the University of Edinburgh to study engineering. He showed from the start no enthusiasm for his studies and devoted much energy to avoiding lectures. This time was more important for the friendships he made with other students in the Speculative Society (an exclusive debating club), particularly with Charles Baxter, who would become Stevenson's financial agent, and with a professor, Fleeming Jenkin, whose house staged amateur drama in which Stevenson took part, and whose biography he would later write. Perhaps most important at this point in his life was a cousin, Robert Alan Mowbray Stevenson (known as "Bob"), a lively and light-hearted young man who, instead of the family profession, had chosen to study art. Each year during vacations, Stevenson travelled to inspect the family's engineering works—to Anstruther and Wick in 1868, with his father on his official tour of Orkney and Shetland islands lighthouses in 1869, and for three weeks to the island of Erraid in 1870. He enjoyed the travels more for the material they gave for his writing than for any engineering interest. The voyage with his father pleased him because a similar journey of Walter Scott with Robert Stevenson had provided the inspiration for Scott's 1822 novel The Pirate. In April 1871, Stevenson notified his father of his decision to pursue a life of letters. Though the elder Stevenson was naturally disappointed, the surprise cannot have been great, and Stevenson's mother reported that he was "wonderfully resigned" to his son's choice. To provide some security, it was agreed that Stevenson should read Law (again at Edinburgh University) and be called to the Scottish bar. In his 1887 poetry collection Underwoods, Stevenson muses on his having turned from the family profession:

Say not of me that weakly I declined

The labours of my sires, and fled the sea,

The towers we founded and the lamps we lit,

To play at home with paper like a child.

But rather say: In the afternoon of time

A strenuous family dusted from its hands

The sand of granite, and beholding far

Along the sounding coast its pyramids

And tall memorials catch the dying sun,

Smiled well content, and to this childish task

Around the fire addressed its evening hours.

In other respects too, Stevenson was moving away from his upbringing. His dress became more Bohemian; he already wore his hair long, but he now took to wearing a velveteen jacket and rarely attended parties in conventional evening dress. Within the limits of a strict allowance, he visited cheap pubs and brothels. More importantly, he had come to reject Christianity and declared himself an atheist. In January 1873, his father came across the constitution of the LJR (Liberty, Justice, Reverence) Club, of which Stevenson and his cousin Bob were members, which began: "Disregard everything our parents have taught us". Questioning his son about his beliefs, he discovered the truth, leading to a long period of dissension with both parents:

What a damned curse I am to my parents! As my father said "You have rendered my whole life a failure". As my mother said "This is the heaviest affliction that has ever befallen me". O Lord, what a pleasant thing it is to have damned the happiness of (probably) the only two people who care a damn about you in the world.

Early writing and travels

Stevenson was visiting a cousin in England in late 1873 when he met two people who became very important to him: Sidney Colvin and Fanny (Frances Jane) Sitwell. Sitwell was a 34-year-old woman with a son, who was separated from her husband. She attracted the devotion of many who met her, including Colvin, who married her in 1901. Stevenson was also drawn to her, and they kept up a warm correspondence over several years in which he wavered between the role of a suitor and a son (he addressed her as "Madonna"). Colvin became Stevenson's literary adviser and was the first editor of his letters after his death. He placed Stevenson's first paid contribution in The Portfolio, an essay entitled "Roads".

Stevenson was soon active in London literary life, becoming acquainted with many of the writers of the time, including Andrew Lang, Edmund Gosse, and Leslie Stephen, the editor of the Cornhill Magazine who took an interest in Stevenson's work. Stephen took Stevenson to visit a patient at the Edinburgh Infirmary named William Ernest Henley, an energetic and talkative man with a wooden leg. Henley became a close friend and occasional literary collaborator, until a quarrel broke up the friendship in 1888, and he is often considered to be the model for Long John Silver in Treasure Island.

Stevenson was sent to Menton on the French Riviera in November 1873 to recuperate after his health failed. He returned in better health in April 1874 and settled down to his studies, but he returned to France several times after that. He made long and frequent trips to the neighborhood of the Forest of Fontainebleau, staying at Barbizon, Grez-sur-Loing, and Nemours and becoming a member of the artists' colonies there. He also traveled to Paris to visit galleries and the theatres. He qualified for the Scottish bar in July 1875, and his father added a brass plate to the Heriot Row house reading "R.L. Stevenson, Advocate". His law studies did influence his books, but he never practised law; all his energies were spent in travel and writing. One of his journeys was a canoe voyage in Belgium and France with Sir Walter Simpson, a friend from the Speculative Society, a frequent travel companion, and the author of The Art of Golf (1887). This trip was the basis of his first travel book An Inland Voyage (1878).

Marriage

The canoe voyage with Simpson brought Stevenson to Grez in September 1876 where he met Fanny Van de Grift Osbourne (1840–1914), born in Indianapolis. She had married at age 17 and moved to Nevada to rejoin husband Samuel after his participation in the American Civil War. Their children were Isobel (or "Belle"), Lloyd, and Hervey (who died in 1875). But anger over her husband's infidelities led to a number of separations. In 1875, she had taken her children to France where she and Isobel studied art.

Stevenson returned to Britain shortly after this first meeting, but Fanny apparently remained in his thoughts, and he wrote the essay "On falling in love" for the Cornhill Magazine. They met again early in 1877 and became lovers. Stevenson spent much of the following year with her and her children in France. In August 1878, she returned to San Francisco and Stevenson remained in Europe, making the walking trip that formed the basis for Travels with a Donkey in the Cévennes (1879). But he set off to join her in August 1879, against the advice of his friends and without notifying his parents. He took second-class passage on the steamship Devonia, in part to save money but also to learn how others traveled and to increase the adventure of the journey. He then traveled overland by train from New York City to California. He later wrote about the experience in The Amateur Emigrant. It was good experience for his writing, but it broke his health.

He was near death when he arrived in Monterey, California, where some local ranchers nursed him back to health. He stayed for a time at the French Hotel located at 530 Houston Street, now a museum dedicated to his memory called the "Stevenson House". While there, he often dined "on the cuff," as he said, at a nearby restaurant run by Frenchman Jules Simoneau which stood at what is now Simoneau Plaza; several years later, he sent Simoneau an inscribed copy of his novel Strange Case of Dr Jekyll and Mr Hyde (1886), writing that it would be a stranger case still if Robert Louis Stevenson ever forgot Jules Simoneau. While in Monterey, he wrote an evocative article about "the Old Pacific Capital" of Monterey.

By December 1879, Stevenson had recovered his health enough to continue to San Francisco where he struggled "all alone on forty-five cents a day, and sometimes less, with quantities of hard work and many heavy thoughts," in an effort to support himself through his writing. But by the end of the winter, his health was broken again and he found himself at death's door. Fanny was now divorced and recovered from her own illness, and she came to his bedside and nursed him to recovery. "After a while," he wrote, "my spirit got up again in a divine frenzy, and has since kicked and spurred my vile body forward with great emphasis and success." When his father heard of his condition, he cabled him money to help him through this period.

Fanny and Robert were married in May 1880, although he said that he was "a mere complication of cough and bones, much fitter for an emblem of mortality than a bridegroom." He travelled with his new wife and her son Lloyd north of San Francisco to Napa Valley and spent a summer honeymoon at an abandoned mining camp on Mount Saint Helena. He wrote about this experience in The Silverado Squatters. He met Charles Warren Stoddard, co-editor of the Overland Monthly and author of South Sea Idylls, who urged Stevenson to travel to the South Pacific, an idea which returned to him many years later. In August 1880, he sailed with Fanny and Lloyd from New York to Britain and found his parents and his friend Sidney Colvin on the wharf at Liverpool, happy to see him return home. Gradually, his wife was able to patch up differences between father and son and make herself a part of the family through her charm and wit.

Attempted settlement in Europe and the US

Stevenson searched in vain between 1880 and 1887 for a residence suitable to his health. He spent his summers at various places in Scotland and England, including Westbourne, Dorset, a residential area in Bournemouth. It was during his time in Bournemouth that he wrote the story Strange Case of Dr Jekyll and Mr Hyde, naming the character Mr. Poole after the town of Poole which is situated next to Bournemouth. In Westbourne, he named his house Skerryvore after the tallest lighthouse in Scotland, which his uncle Alan had built (1838–44). In the wintertime, Stevenson travelled to France and lived at Davos Platz and the Chalet de Solitude at Hyères, where he was very happy for a time. "I have so many things to make life sweet for me," he wrote, "it seems a pity I cannot have that other one thing—health. But though you will be angry to hear it, I believe, for myself at least, what is is best." In spite of his ill health, he produced the bulk of his best-known work during these years. Treasure Island was published under the pseudonym "Captain George North" and became his first widely popular book; he wrote it during this time, along with Kidnapped, Strange Case of Dr Jekyll and Mr Hyde (which established his wider reputation), The Black Arrow: A Tale of the Two Roses, A Child's Garden of Verses, and Underwoods. He gave a copy of Kidnapped to his friend and frequent Skerryvore visitor Henry James.

His father died in 1887 and Stevenson felt free to follow the advice of his physician to try a complete change of climate, so he headed for Colorado with his mother and family. But after landing in New York, they decided to spend the winter in the Adirondacks at a cure cottage now known as Stevenson Cottage at Saranac Lake, New York. During the intensely cold winter, Stevenson wrote some of his best essays, including Pulvis et Umbra. He also began The Master of Ballantrae and lightheartedly planned a cruise to the southern Pacific Ocean for the following summer.

Politics

Stevenson believed in Conservatism for most of his life. His cousin and biographer Sir Graham Balfour said that "he probably throughout life would, if compelled to vote, have always supported the Conservative candidate." In 1866, Stevenson voted for Benjamin Disraeli, future Conservative Prime Minister of the United Kingdom, over Thomas Carlyle for the Lord Rectorship of the University of Edinburgh. During his college years, he briefly identified himself as a "red-hot socialist". He wrote at age 26: "I look back to the time when I was a Socialist with something like regret.... Now I know that in thus turning Conservative with years, I am going through the normal cycle of change and travelling in the common orbit of men's opinions."

Journey to the Pacific

In June 1888, Stevenson chartered the yacht Casco and set sail with his family from San Francisco. The vessel "plowed her path of snow across the empty deep, far from all track of commerce, far from any hand of help." The sea air and thrill of adventure for a time restored his health, and for nearly three years he wandered the eastern and central Pacific, stopping for extended stays at the Hawaiian Islands where he became a good friend of King Kalākaua. He befriended the king's niece Princess Victoria Kaiulani, who also had Scottish heritage. He spent time at the Gilbert Islands, Tahiti, New Zealand, and the Samoan Islands. During this period, he completed The Master of Ballantrae, composed two ballads based on the legends of the islanders, and wrote The Bottle Imp. He preserved the experience of these years in his various letters and in his In the South Seas (which was published posthumously). He made a voyage in 1889 with Lloyd on the trading schooner Equator, visiting Butaritari, Mariki, Apaiang, and Abemama in the Gilbert Islands. They spent several months on Abemama with tyrant-chief Tem Binoka, whom Stevenson described in In the South Seas.

Stevenson left Sydney on the Janet Nicoll in April 1890 for his third and final voyage among the South Seas islands. He intended to produce another book of travel writing to follow his earlier book In the South Seas, but it was his wife who eventually published her journal of their third voyage. (Fanny misnames the ship in her account The Cruise of the Janet Nichol.) A fellow passenger was Jack Buckland, whose stories of life as an island trader became the inspiration for the character of Tommy Hadden in The Wrecker (1892), which Stevenson and Lloyd Osbourne wrote together. Buckland visited the Stevensons at Vailima in 1894.

Last years

In 1890, Stevenson purchased a tract of about 400 acres (1.6 km^2) in Upolu, an island in Samoa where he established himself on his estate in the village of Vailima after two aborted attempts to visit Scotland. He took the native name Tusitala (Samoan for "Teller of Tales"). His influence spread among the Samoans, who consulted him for advice, and he soon became involved in local politics. He was convinced that the European officials who had been appointed to rule the Samoans were incompetent, and he published A Footnote to History after many futile attempts to resolve the matter. This was such a stinging protest against existing conditions that it resulted in the recall of two officials, and Stevenson feared for a time that it would result in his own deportation. He wrote to Colvin, "I used to think meanly of the plumber; but how he shines beside the politician!"

He also found time to work at his writing, although he felt that "there was never any man had so many irons in the fire". He wrote The Beach of Falesa, Catriona (titled David Balfour in the US), The Ebb-Tide, and the Vailima Letters during this period.

Stevenson grew depressed and wondered if he had exhausted his creative vein, as he had been "overworked bitterly" and that the best he could write was "ditch-water". He even feared that he might again become a helpless invalid. He rebelled against this idea: "I wish to die in my boots; no more Land of Counterpane for me. To be drowned, to be shot, to be thrown from a horse — ay, to be hanged, rather than pass again through that slow dissolution." He then suddenly had a return of energy and he began work on Weir of Hermiston. "It's so good that it frightens me," he is reported to have exclaimed. He felt that this was the best work he had done.

On 3 December 1894, Stevenson was talking to his wife and straining to open a bottle of wine when he suddenly exclaimed, "What's that?", asked his wife "does my face look strange?", and collapsed. He died within a few hours, probably of a cerebral haemorrhage. He was 44 years old. The Samoans insisted on surrounding his body with a watch-guard during the night and on bearing him on their shoulders to nearby Mount Vaea, where they buried him on a spot overlooking the sea on land donated by British Acting Vice Consul Thomas Trood. Stevenson had always wanted his Requiem inscribed on his tomb:

> *Under the wide and starry sky,*
>
> *Dig the grave and let me lie.*
>
> *Glad did I live and gladly die,*
>
> *And I laid me down with a will.*
>
> *This be the verse you grave for me:*
>
> *Here he lies where he longed to be;*
>
> *Home is the sailor, home from sea,*
>
> *And the hunter home from the hill.*

Stevenson was loved by the Samoans, and his tombstone epigraph was translated to a Samoan song of grief. (Source: Wikipedia)

CPSIA information can be obtained
at www.ICGtesting.com
Printed in the USA
LVHW091555230620
658719LV00002B/282